THE WATERS OF THE SEA

THE WATERS
OF THE SEA

Dr. P. GROEN

Professor of Physical Oceanography and Meteorology
Free University, Amsterdam
and State University, Utrecht, Netherlands.

D. VAN NOSTRAND COMPANY LTD
LONDON

PRINCETON, NEW JERSEY   TORONTO

D. VAN NOSTRAND COMPANY LTD.
Windsor House, 46 Victoria Street, London, S.W.1

D. VAN NOSTRAND COMPANY INC.
120 Alexander Street, Princeton, New Jersey
24 West 40th Street, New York 18

D. VAN NOSTRAND COMPANY (CANADA) LTD.
25 Hollinger Road, Toronto 16

Library of Congress Catalog Card No. 66—19954

Printed in Great Britain by
Spottiswoode, Ballantyne & Company Ltd., London and Colchester

CONTENTS

PREFACE

THIS translation of the revised (1961) edition of my book *De Wateren van de Wereldzee* has a twofold purpose—it is intended for the general reader interested in the physical phenomena of the sea and for all those who have to make some general study of the science of the sea, including students of geography, marine geology and marine biology, and students in nautical schools. Besides being descriptive this text provides some account of the physical processes which are at work in the marine realm.

As a physicist, I have confined myself to a detailed account of the physical aspect of the subject, omitting any exposition of marine biology or marine geology.

The reader will discover that the major part of the book is devoted to the more 'classical' findings of oceanography, which still form the greater part of man's knowledge of the sea. It is, of course, necessary to correlate this corpus of classical marine science with more up-to-date developments, and due mention has therefore been made of important findings and techniques of modern research.

It is my particular pleasure to thank all those who have helped in the preparation of this book, especially Miss M. Hollander for her translation, Dr. J. N. Carruthers for critically reading most of it and checking the technical terms, and Dr. R. A. Cox and Mr. L. Draper for checking the section on the chemical content of sea-water and the chapter on waves respectively. I should also like to record my appreciation to the publishers, D. Van Nostrand Company Limited, London, and in particular to the house editors, for their thought and care in the editing of the manuscript.

P. GROEN
September, 1965.

INTRODUCTION

Let the sea roar, and the fulness thereof
(Psalm 96)

THIS is a book about the sea, with particular reference to its physics.
The word 'sea', without further definition, may conjure up very different pictures in the minds of different people. Some will immediately associate the sea with summer holidays, with basking in the sun on the beach, and gazing at the distant horizon. To others, it is the realm of wind and waves, in which they spend most of their lives and earn their livelihood. To countless others, however, 'the sea' is but a remote idea, conveying nothing tangible and appealing very little, if at all, to their imagination. The average native of East Turkestan, or Inner Mongolia, has no notion of what the sea, as we understand it, really is. He has never seen it himself, and knows nobody who has. Such people may tell each other that the river, which they do know, eventually runs into a stretch of water just as vast as all the land around them; but very few of them have ever seen that water.

True though it be that the inhabitants of this earth who have never set eyes on the sea exceed in numbers those who have, it is nevertheless a fact that to western culture—cradled mainly in that comparatively small area bounded by the Mediterranean Sea, the North Sea and the Baltic, but which has spread all over the world—the sea is something very real, and an idea of far-reaching significance.

The sea already plays a conspicuous part in Homer's tale of the wanderings of Ulysses who, after the fall of Troy, visited many cities and became acquainted with the peoples' way of life; but who also suffered many vicissitudes at sea. Besides referring to 'the sea' (pontos, thalassa), by which he means the Mediterranean, Homer also mentions the Okeanos (from which, of course, our word 'ocean' comes), that great river of the world (or its god) which encompasses everything and is the source of the whole of existence.

The sea holds a place all its own in Biblical imagery, notably in that of the Old Testament. The Israelites were not a seafaring nation like their neighbours the Phoenicians. To them, the sea was primarily not a trade-route, but the great, turbulent domain of primaeval forces, subject only to the might of the Creator. Their poets have one characteristic expression for it, the deep; 'And the earth was without form, and void; and darkness was upon the face of the deep. And the Spirit of God moved upon the face of the waters.' (Genesis 1). Elsewhere, 'Who laid the foundations of the earth, that it should not be removed for ever. Thou coveredst it with the deep as with a garment: the waters stood above the mountains. At thy rebuke they fled: at the voice of thy thunder they hasted away. They go up by the mountains; they go down by the valleys unto the place which thou hast founded for them. Thou hast set a bound that they may not pass over; that they turn not again to cover the earth.' (Psalm 104).

There certainly is this marked difference between the land and the sea; that Man can, to a very large extent, subject and shape the land, and bend it to his will, as he has already done; but he has never been able to hold sway over the sea; for in this sense too, 'mare liberum', the sea is free. How utterly ridiculous therefore was the action of Xerxes, king of the Persians, who, if Herodotus' account is to be credited, had his throne placed upon the beach, and watched while his slaves, at his command, flogged the sea with scourges, to punish it for having destroyed his fleet.

Man has never tamed the sea; yet, or perhaps for that very reason, it has done much to foster his cultural life; for it was precisely the *free* sea which enabled peoples and cultures to develop and to expand entirely along their own lines, lines which it would have been far more difficult to follow on land. The Mediterranean, that ancient ocean of the world, played a particularly important part in this. We have only to think of Greek culture, which developed on islands and peninsulas whence it spread far to east and west. How vividly we can imagine the thrilling sound of that shout, 'Thalassa, thalassa!' which the Greek soldiers sent up, when at long last they caught a glimpse of the sea, after their seemingly endless trek with Xenophon through the hinterland of Asia Minor.

Yes, it certainly must find an echo in our hearts, since so many of us have spent summer holidays by the sea. And, even if the average person is not as sea-minded as our history might suggest, yet to all of us the sea is a reality which appeals to the imagination even of those of us who have never sailed upon it. In western Europe, we may live in the heart of the country, yet the air we breathe is usually borne inland from the sea, and a strong wind blowing from the sea generally reaches us within a matter of hours. The sea is always there; it brings a thawing wind in winter and showers from the north-west in spring; it gives us cool days in summer and south-west storms in autumn.

That is how it is with many of us who, maybe, only know the sea as seen from a beach.

We must not underestimate the influence which the sea is liable to have even upon people who know it only in its seaside aspect. Countless thousands have experienced it in holiday mood as a liberation and relief from the stuffiness of their daily lives; have exclaimed with joy—though perhaps less vociferously than Xenophon's soldiers!—when suddenly coming upon it stretching from the never-resting surf to the far horizon, and have carried that image with them on returning home. The land is beautiful; the sea is—different.

We are also thinking of the impact of the sea upon the imagination of people who read about it, either in poetry or in tales of travel. Many of them, sitting in their armchairs, have mentally been sailing with explorers, with merchantmen, with pirates or, perhaps, with Jules Verne. How many, poring over an atlas, have not travelled, in thought, across those wide expanses of blue? So much blue—all of it water—miles upon miles of water and air, wind and waves.

There are other, less romantic, things to be said about the significance of the sea to people living in the country and in cities. Not least among them is the important part sea transport plays in our commerce and economy, and those of other countries.

During the Low Countries' fight for freedom in the sixteenth and seventeenth centuries, the sea became their ally and navigation brought prosperity to the Netherlands. On the other hand, however, that country, which was, so to speak, wrenched from the sea, has been besieged by it from time immemorial and yet has gone from strength to strength in her struggle against it. The people of the Netherlands cannot be expected to regard the sea as a good-hearted neighbour, and they were reminded, once again, on the night of 31st January/1st February 1953, that a people venturing to live behind dykes, in low-lying land, cannot afford to ignore the sea.

Be that as it may, the only people who really know the sea well are the *seafarers*, those who have *actively* sailed the seas, who have lived and worked on the seas, seen the sun rise out of the sea, seen it set into it and rise again; those in coastal trade, fishermen in the North Sea and the men on the big trade routes who have sailed the seven seas. Those who have stood day and night on the bridge, putting their trust in the stars and their compasses, under the tropical sun or the stormy clouds of high latitudes, under the Great Bear or the Southern Cross, on the long swell in the equatorial Pacific or tossed on the steep rollers of the North Atlantic or the roaring forties.

It is from their experiences and observations that we have derived much interesting information about the characteristics and physical properties of the seas and oceans. It was they who noticed the deep blue colour of the Gulf Stream, the green of the Labrador current and those brownish-red patches which they called 'blood sea'. They spoke of the strong Florida current and also of the Agulhas current, which sometimes runs at as much as a hundred miles in twenty-four hours along the east coast of South Africa. They reported waves travelling from a remote stormy region along great distances of comparatively calm seas; and they called such waves a swell. They have long known that this swell may precede a storm and thus forewarn a seaman who can read the signs. Another item of knowledge which we owe to them is that waves do not only break along the coastline and reefs, but also over shallows, whose presence they thus betray.

This is by no means all we have learned from them. They told of the pack-ice near the Newfoundland Bank, of the behaviour of the castle-shaped icebergs in the North Atlantic and of the great tabular icebergs in the South Polar Sea; of the 'dead water' (a phenomenon especially known from Scandinavian coastal waters in and off the mouths of the fjords) in which small craft can be trapped and their further progress severely hampered. And there is a great deal more, also, about the distribution of living organisms above and in the oceans.

Yes, it is the seafarers, indeed, who have really come to know the sea.

But do they know everything there is to know about it? The sea has yet another dimension, in the dark depths of which it is still the Great Unknown, even to those who have voyaged on its surface to every point of the compass. What about the submarine? *That* does not go down very far. And even Barton's diving sphere and Piccard's bathyscaphe do not alter the fact that, for the main part, the dark depths *below* the surface of the oceans are an unseen domain, of which less has been revealed to the human eye than of outer space.

This does not mean, of course, that human curiosity and endeavour have been confined to the surface of the sea. Seamen themselves have taken soundings, and so measured depths, in many places, especially in coastal waters, though naturally from motives of safety rather than curiosity.

Then, however, come the scientists who want to probe further into the depths of the seas and oceans, undaunted by the inaccessibility of the dark abysses beneath the waves. Armed with a variety of ingenious instruments, they have sailed away and lowered those instruments over the side. In this way they have obtained samples of water for analysis from every conceivable depth (down to eleven thousand metres) and have measured the temperatures at those depths, repeating the operation in many places, in many seas. They have charted currents down there, have hauled up a diversity of living organisms from the microscopically small to the very large—remarkable animals sometimes—and, lastly, they have been able to examine the floor of the oceans by means of samples brought to the surface by bottom-dredges, corers, or other devices. People have devoted their lives to this, impelled by the urge to know more about the empire of the seas.

Much still remains to be explored. There are vast stretches of the oceans about the internal nature of which we know comparatively little. A number of general questions still remain open; for man, not content with merely *knowing* more, yearns to have a better *understanding* of the mysterious ways of the sea. Why, he asks, is the water icy cold at very great depths in the oceans throughout the world, even in the tropics, where it is lukewarm at the surface? What keeps the Gulf Stream moving? How exactly does the action of the wind whip up the waves and why should there be impressive breakers on shores never exposed to storms? What makes life possible thousands of metres down, where no glimmer of light can penetrate and, therefore, no plants exist producing oxygen; why is it that the water there nevertheless always contains an appreciable amount of oxygen despite its uptake by animals?

Innumerable questions of this kind are challenging the intellect and ingenuity of those research workers whose special discipline is a branch of science called *oceanography* or *oceanology*. This comprises not only the description and study of the physical aspects of the oceans, known as physical oceanography, but also marine biology, which is the study of the living occupants of the sea, and includes the study of the sea bed; though this branch of science is considered, too, to belong to geology and is called 'marine geology'.

The subject matter of this book is, for the major part, *physical oceanography*, being concerned, as the words imply, with the physics of the oceans.

From the point of view of physics, the earth has three 'spheres', namely, the *atmosphere*, the solid earth, also called the *lithosphere* (stony sphere), and, in between, covering more than seven-tenths of the solid earth, the *hydrosphere*, i.e. the water-envelope of the earth, so, its seas and oceans, all of which are, in fact, interconnected, forming a whole.

Obviously, these three spheres are not discrete, insulated compartments; they act upon one another reciprocally. The atmosphere influences the seas and oceans in a variety of ways; the wind, for instance, raises the waves and keeps the currents moving. The sea, in turn, affects the atmosphere in many ways; we have only to think of its effect upon climate. Were there no other link, the sea and the land would still be associated by their common boundary. The sea affects the bottom in that it contributes to sedimentation (the laying down of deposits of solid matter) and induces microseisms, i.e. small vibrations which may be the result of standing waves in a storm area. Conversely, the bottom influences the behaviour of deep ocean currents and of tidal waves and also, in shallow waters, the course of swell and breakers.

It will be clear from the foregoing that 'physical oceanography' is likewise involved in the study of the other terrestrial spheres, the atmosphere and the lithosphere; in other words, in meteorology and geophysics in the narrower sense, i.e. the physics of the solid earth. In a broader sense, geophysics is also called the physics of the earth as a whole, hence comprising meteorology plus physical oceanography plus the physics of the solid earth.

As will become apparent from the ensuing chapters, the physics of the oceans are closely bound up with meteorology. It is therefore not surprising to find that oceanography and meteorology are often combined in the same institute.

Compared with other branches of physics, oceanology is a young science—about one hundred years old. There remains much to be investigated, primarily at sea, but also in the laboratory, the place where new measuring instruments are devised and designed and where small-scale experiments are carried out. But there is also, and above all, much thinking to be done; for insight, that is, not merely to know, but also to understand, is the ultimate goal of science.

Well then, you may ask, is it the oceanographers who fully know the sea? Alas, our knowledge is never exhaustive; we know only in part. The scientist of the sea knows a certain aspect of it. It always guards its innermost secret, which evades description and analysis. This is so of the whole of

Creation, of inanimate as well as animate nature, including the sea. Who can understand the *essence*, the purpose, of its never-ending movement? Which of us could express the *meaning* of its melody in words? Why does it roll on and on and on towards the shore, play gently with the sand, or batter and pound it, carefully lay out millions of shells along the water's edge and then, after a time, mercilessly smash them?

A Frenchman called the sea 'La grande triste'; and there certainly is a melancholy in the sound of it under grey skies, breaking on the shore day in, day out, as it has done for millions of years and will continue to do as long as this globe exists. It is like a bass accompaniment to the sighs of Creation. But it is also a voice in the *song* of Creation, which is a song of hope, of expectation. 'Let the heavens rejoice, and let the earth be glad; let the sea roar, and the fulness thereof . . .; for he cometh' (Psalm 96) who is the Maker of the heavens and the earth and of the sea.

Chapter One

EXPLORATION OF THE OCEANS

The fair breeze blew, the white foam flew,
The furrow followed free.
We were the first that ever burst
Into that silent sea.

(Samuel Taylor Coleridge,
The Rime of an Ancient Mariner.)

WHAT did people in earliest antiquity know about the seas? The Greeks were by no means the greatest seafarers of antiquity, but it was they who left behind them the bulk of the documentary evidence concerning knowledge of the sea in olden times; a knowledge which was based only to a very minor extent upon their own experiences.

In Homer's day—approximately 1000 B.C.—the civilized peoples living on the borders of the eastern part of the Mediterranean imagined the world to be a flat disc consisting of the countries around that sea. This region was 'the world' and encircling it was the all-embracing river Oceanus (Okeanus), the beginning and end of all things. 'The sea' as understood by Homer is the Mediterranean. The Homeric world-map is shown in Fig. 1.

The idea of an 'ocean' encircling the world appears to have stemmed from a yet older civilization. In Babylonian times the ocean, which encircled the land, was thought, itself, to be surrounded by The Dawn.

A modified version of this concept is discernible about 250 years after Homer, in the poems of Hesiod (*c.* 750 B.C.), who speaks of islands in that ocean, inhabited by the beings of Greek mythology. The existence of these islands found fairly general acceptance in the ancient world; and that fact was not without influence upon future voyages of discovery.

Meanwhile, many seafarers of antiquity, notably the Phoenicians and Carthaginians, undoubtedly knew about the Atlantic Ocean. They set forth long ago (perhaps earlier than 1000 B.C.) from the Mediterranean, passing between the Pillars of Hercules (as the Straits of Gibraltar were called) northward to the British Isles, and southward to the Canary Islands. They even appear to have sailed as far across the Atlantic as the Sargasso Sea, that region in the west which is known for the dark blue colour of the water and for the gulf weed, sargasso (*Sargassum*), masses of which float on the surface there. About 465 B.C., Hanno the Carthaginian sailed along the west coast of Africa, far southward, probably into the Gulf of Guinea.

Herodotus tells about Phoenician navigators who, on the orders of the Egyptian king Necho, sailed southward across the Red Sea, and how they returned to Egypt through the Pillars of Hercules three years later, having obviously sailed all round Africa! One interesting point in the account of the voyage, which Herodotus passes on with the comment that he finds it hard to credit, is that, after having sailed for a long time towards the south,

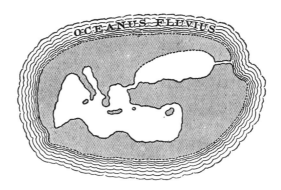

Fig. 1 The image of the world which was current in Homer's time, *c.* 1000 B.C.

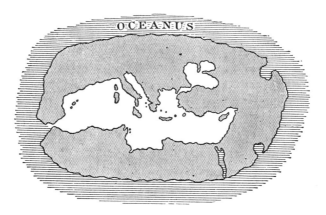

Fig. 2 The world as Hecataeus saw it, *c.* 500 B.C.

they no longer saw the sun rising on the left and setting on the right, but the other way round. It is an observation which makes the account all the more credible to us, proving, as it does, that they had crossed the Equator (for in the Southern Hemisphere the sun passes from east to west through the north instead of through the south). This voyage is said to have taken place about 600 B.C.

The map of the world as drawn by Herodotus (450 B.C.) presents a picture entirely different from the older ones. This Greek, to whom we are indebted for so much information, not only about everything he saw on his own travels, but also about what he heard from the mouths of others, no longer imagines the earth to be entirely encircled by an ocean. He leaves the land uncircumscribed to the north; but he knows that there is a sea to the west of the Pillars of Hercules, and he calls it the Atlantic Ocean; while he knows that Africa is surrounded by water, hence that the Atlantic merges with the Indian Ocean.

While on this subject we should also mention Plato and Aristotle, who came after Herodotus. It was Plato who mentioned the legend of Atlantis, the vanished island in the ocean to the west of the Pillars of Hercules. Even in those early days, Aristotle pictured the earth as a globe, with clearly distinguishable climatic zones. But he is vague and mistaken about the Atlantic Ocean, which he describes as muddy and shallow . . .

Then comes Pytheas (c. 300 B.C.), and with him the geographical horizon widens considerably. Born in Massilia, a Greek colony on the site of present-day Marseilles, he also sailed the seas on the other side of Gibraltar, and gave an account of his voyages in a book about the sea. Unfortunately, we do not possess that writing; all that we know about his travels has come down to us from other writers who quote him. However that may be, it was thanks to Pytheas that the ancient world at last became better acquainted with western Europe in general and with the British Isles in particular. He also referred to an island which he called Thule, which, he said, was six days' sailing north of Britain. This was, presumably, Iceland.

As far as we know, Pytheas was the first to connect the tides with the moon. It is assumed that this fact struck him during his visits to the British Isles, where the ranges of the tide are so much greater than in the Mediterranean. He must have been a good astronomer and navigator, as well as an adventurous, go-ahead explorer.

In the centuries immediately following Pytheas, no mention is made of further voyages of discovery to north-west Europe. Although Erastosthenes should be named, he was not so much an explorer, as a scholar who collected all the then available geographical facts and combined them into a single system. By astronomical calculations he arrived at a fair estimate of the circumference of the earth. He already drew meridians and latitude circles on his map, which, for the rest, represented the world as then known. He also expressed it as his opinion that it must be possible to sail round the globe and so, starting from Spain and keeping a steady westward course, to reach India, the only obstacle being, to his mind, the vast expanse of the Atlantic Ocean.

The Greek philosopher Posidonius, who lived about a hundred years before Christ, wrote a treatise on the sea. Again, this document has not been preserved, but we know something about it from other writers. Posidonius also travelled, and the first real deep-sea sounding is ascribed to him. He is alleged to have said that 'the greatest measured depth of any sea is that of the Sardinian Sea, being no less than a thousand fathoms'. How, we wonder, was this sounding taken?

We now come to Strabo and the times of the Roman Empire. His book *Geography* gives us an idea of the geographical knowledge which was more or less the common property of the Hellenistic world in those days. From the fact that he attached little value to Pytheas's reports, and flatly denied the existence of Thule, which Pytheas had mentioned, it is evident that that knowledge by no means comprehended every discovery of earlier navigators. That the Mediterranean should bear no other name than 'the Sea', or at best 'the Inner Sea' or 'Our Sea', even in Strabo's time, bears eloquent witness to the dominant part it played. The Phoenicians and Carthaginians, who were primarily *merchant* adventurers, kept most of what they knew to themselves, which is probably why comparatively little was generally known about their discoveries, made ages before the time of Strabo.

After referring to all these Greeks, it would be remiss on our part if we did not mention the Roman, Pliny, were it only on account of the following rather optimistic passage taken from his *Historia Naturalis* (a collection of writings in which, *inter alia*, he presents a list of one hundred and seventy-six sea animals—still four less than mentioned by Aristotle): 'By Hercules! Neither the sea nor the ocean, vast though this be, holds anything unknown to us; and—a remarkable fact indeed—we know most about those very things which nature keeps hidden in the depths . . .'!

In a sense, the Alexandrine astronomer, mathematician and geographer, Ptolemy, brings to a close the Greek and Hellenistic period in the history of the marine sciences. His book *Geographical Guide*, which appeared about the middle of the second century A.D., remained for more than twelve hundred years the most authoritative work on this subject, although comparatively little known for a long time in the Middle Ages, except to Arabian scholars. It was translated into Latin, without any changes, as late as 1410, because there was nothing better available.

Ptolemy also left us a map, the striking feature of which is the Indian Ocean, drawn as an entirely enclosed sea with a country to the south marked 'Terra Incognita', connecting Africa and China. Like those of others before him, Ptolemy's estimate of the circumference of the earth fell short of what it actually is, with the result that he greatly underestimated the distance from Spain westward to India. This mistake had considerable repercussions on later projects and attempts, notably those of Columbus, to reach India by crossing the Atlantic Ocean. Thus, in a way, it led to the discovery of America.

In subsequent medieval times then, the world as depicted in available documents did not go far beyond the limits outlined above. Only in the north and north-west did a somewhat larger region come within the field of vision (see Fig. 3), but owing to the almost total lack of communications, little, if anything, was generally known in those times of the principal discoveries, namely those of the Vikings (the 'Norsemen').

In about 750 A.D., Irish monks reached the Faroes, and they set foot on Iceland in approximately 790; a century later the great voyages of the Danes and Norsemen began. In about the middle of the ninth century, Other rounded the North Cape; by 861 the Vikings were in the Faroes, by 865 they were in Iceland, and by 982 in the south-western part of Greenland, where Eric the Red founded a settlement. It was from here, in the year 1000 or thereabouts, that one or two groups of Norsemen under his son Leif sailed towards the west and reached both Labrador and those parts now known as New Brunswick, or even further southward (near Boston). They called this last area—where they appear to have found woods, corn and grapes—Vinland (Wineland) and it was under that name that it was introduced into the Norse literature of those days, though no one realized that a new continent had been discovered.

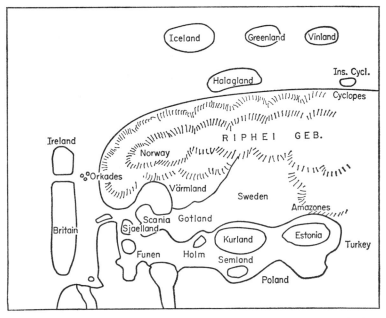

Fig. 3 The north-western part of the world as visualized by Adam van Bremen in about 1070 (after Tuinstra). The north is to the right above.

This history had a remarkable sequel in the fourteenth century, when a Norwegian expedition sailed to Greenland with orders to trace the colony settled there since the days of Eric the Red, of which nothing further had been heard since 1342. Failing to find the colony in Greenland, the expedition pushed on to America and landed there, probably on Rhode Island, where to this day there are the remains of a small, medieval Norwegian church near Newport. Part of the expedition possibly arrived in Hudson Bay, by sailing round Labrador from headquarters, and seems to have returned overland to Rhode Island. These men got back to Norway in 1364, after an absence of nine years.

It has already been said that the rest of Europe at that time knew little about these voyages, which are nevertheless entitled to be called voyages of discovery. Reports of them may perhaps have been scoffed at elsewhere, as mere travellers' tales; in any event they apparently aroused little interest. It is only recently that these stout-hearted expeditions of the Vikings have attracted attention.

We have dwelt at some length on this more remote history of the geographical picture of the world, because it is less well known than any other part of it. We shall deal more briefly with the next period of classical voyages of discovery, interesting though it is, selecting only a few of the most outstanding from many famous names and facts.

At first, the goals of the great and famous voyages of discovery undertaken by the Portuguese and Spaniards in the fifteenth and early sixteenth centuries were chiefly India and China. More had become known about these countries through the Arabs—who also appear to have brought back knowledge of the compass from China to the west, and who sailed across the Indian Ocean—and also from accounts of voyages such as those of the Venetian, Marco Polo, who visited and described China (the 'Cathay' of those days) and Japan. Meanwhile, European trade with the East had taken place only along the more direct route, for the most part over land. The need to reach the East entirely by sea, however, became more and more pressing, especially after the conquest of Constantinople by the Turks in 1453. Attempts were made to achieve this object by following two routes, one around Africa, the other straight to the west. The former was successful; the latter led to the discovery of America.

Under the direction of Prince Henry 'the Navigator', the Portuguese began to explore the west coast of Africa southward. At the time of his death in 1460, one-third of the entire coast down to the Cape of Good Hope had been explored, the Cape finally being rounded by Bartholomew Diaz in 1488. Vasco da Gama reached India that way in 1498. Meanwhile Christopher Columbus had sailed from Spain in 1492 to America, where he landed in the Bahama Islands (12th October 1492) thinking that he had reached Asia from the east. Columbus subsequently sailed three times to and from Central America.

In 1513, a European stood for the first time on the eastern shore of the Pacific; it was Balboa who, seeing a smooth sea stretching southward (owing to the trend of the coast), called it the 'Peaceful South Sea'. And in 1519 Fernando Magellan sailed westward from Spain with five sail, one of which returned three years later, having circumnavigated the globe, via the southern tip of South America, going through the Magellan Straits, right across the Pacific, by way of the Philippines (where the leader was killed in 1521), across the Indian Ocean and home round the Cape of Good Hope.

Within the space of thirty-five years (1486–1521), the map of the world had doubled in size, and that of the oceans trebled. And this was the work of

Portuguese and Spaniards, though some Genoese inspiration acted in the background. (Columbus, for instance, hailed from Genoa.)

It was a Spaniard, too, named Francisco de Hoces, who in 1526 reached the southern tip of America (later called Cape Horn) for the first time, and gazed upon the ocean to the south of it, which connects the Atlantic with the Pacific. This feat, however, passed almost unnoticed.

Right up to the second half of the eighteenth century, it was still generally believed that there was a 'Terra Australis (incognita)', an (unknown) southern land in temperate latitudes—a left-over from Ptolemy's map of the world—although it was realized that this land did not connect Africa with the Orient. Thus many maps—not only that of Ortelius (1570), but also much later ones—depict a continuous southern continent spread approximately along Latitude 50, separated from America by the Magellan Straits. Tierra del Fuego was part and parcel of this Southern Continent!

The Portuguese and the Spaniards were followed by the English and Dutch. Fifty years after De Hoces, the Englishman Francis Drake, having gone through the Magellan Straits but been driven back by north-west storms, sailed past Cape Horn and saw the ocean spread out to the south. Yet when, in 1616, the Dutchmen Le Maire and Schouten again rounded this cape—and now for the first time from east to west—it was as though it had only just been discovered, for from then on it was generally known as Cape Horn, which name they gave it.

Even these voyages did not banish the Southern Continent (imagined to be eminently habitable) either from the maps or from the minds of men. When the French navigator Bouvet discovered the island later named after him, he called it a cape on the Southern Continent. It was not until James Cook's second voyage round the world (1772–75) that it was generally understood that in the far south it is not land, but the sea, which dominates everywhere, to at least latitude 65° S. The true south polar land, that barren region of ice and snow, was not reached until the nineteenth century by such men as Bellinghausen (1820), Weddell (1823), Wilkes (1838–42) and James Clarke Ross (1842–43).

By the sixteenth century, Europeans had already penetrated far into the north. Again, these ventures were made partly with the aim of reaching India by other maritime routes, along a north-western passage around North America, or along a north-eastern passage skirting Scandinavia and Russia.

Apart from these, however, mention should first be made of the expeditions to North America made in the fifteenth century by John Cabot (a Genoese by birth, but in the service of the English), during which he discovered the shores of Nova Scotia and New England (1497); and by the Frenchman Jacques Cartier, who explored the basin of the St. Lawrence River (1544).

The object of Frobisher's 1576–78 expedition was the North-West passage. He reached the southern tip of Baffin Land. He was followed in these regions by John Davis, who sailed through the Davis Straits in 1586; Hudson, who discovered the Hudson Straits and Hudson Bay (1610), and Baffin who, in 1616, penetrated northward of the Davis Straits, far into the bay named after him (between central and north Greenland and Baffin Land), and reached the northern latitude of 77½ degrees.

The English also tried the North-East passage, but they gave up the attempt about 1560, after which the Dutch appeared upon the scene there. In the summer of 1594, Willem Barentsz got through to the west coast of Novaya Zemlja during a very favourable ice season, and went on into the Kara Sea. In 1596 Cornelis Rijp discovered Beren Island, while Barentsz and Heemskerk spent the winter of 1596–97 in Novaya Zemlja. Barentsz himself died on the way back to his fatherland, the Barents Sea preserving the memory of his name.

Nearly three centuries were to pass before anyone succeeded in making the whole of the North-East passage. In July 1878 Nordenskjöld sailed in the *Vega* from Sweden, passing, more than a year later, through the Bering Strait into the North Pacific, after spending the winter in the grip of the ice which had held him fast from the end of September to the middle of July, one hundred nautical miles to the west of the Bering Strait.

After many abortive attempts, including the great expedition under Sir John Franklin, between 1845 and 1848, which never returned, the North-West passage was for the first time achieved entirely by ship by the Norwegian, Roald Amundsen, who sailed in 1903 and emerged in 1906 through the Bering Strait into the Pacific Ocean.

Many more names associated with the exploration of the oceans could be mentioned but, so far as the Indian and Pacific Oceans are concerned, let us be content with just the Dutchman Abel Tasman who, coming from the Indian Ocean to the south of Australia, discovered Tasmania, the island called after him, and, farther to the east, New Zealand (1642); and Bering, the Dane in the service of Russia, who, in the north, sailed, in 1728–29, through the channel between the continents of Asia and America, now called the Bering Strait.

Lastly, we recall the true polar expeditions, those voyages of discovery which appeal so much to the popular imagination. There were the two Scoresby's, father and son (English whalers), the former sailing from Spitzbergen as far north as 81½°; Parry, who, likewise starting from Spitzbergen, reached 82° 45' (travelling over ice); Fridtjof Nansen who made his famous voyage in drifting polar ice with the *Fram* in 1893–96; and Peary, who between 1886 and 1909 made several attempts to reach the North Pole, and won through in the latter year. The South Pole, which, as we know, is situated, not in the sea but on the Antarctic Continent, was conquered in December 1911 by Amundsen, and in January 1912 by Scott.

We cannot leave the polar regions without mentioning the expeditions accomplished since 1937 by Russian and American scientists, by ice-breakers, by aeroplane and, last but not least, by ice-floe or ice-island.

The first great voyage on an ice-floe through the Arctic Ocean was made in 1937 and 1938 by a number of Russians under Papanin.

The first journey of American scientists on a floating 'ice island' (which does not consist of frozen sea, but is glacier-like ice some fifty metres thick and rather smooth) began in 1952 and lasted more than two years. Many other floating polar stations have been in action since then, including those established during the International Geophysical Year of 1957–58. At the present time there are a couple of more or less permanent floating weather stations in the Arctic Ocean, from which meteorological institutes receive daily weather reports.

A LOOK AT THE GLOBE

If we interrupt our historical excursions for a while and cast a glance at all that blue on the globe, a few general facts must strike us at once (cf. the maps of the world, Figs. 4 and 5). First of all, there is obviously far more water than

FIG. 4 The continental hemisphere (after Bos-Niermeyer's School Atlas; Wolters, Groningen); the regions which drain their waters into the three oceans are shown by different shadings.

land. Approximately 71 per cent. of the earth's surface is occupied by the oceans, the remaining 29 per cent. by the continents. The ratio is as 5 to 2.

In the second place we see that all the seas and oceans form an integrated unit and may therefore legitimately be called 'The World Ocean'. (The Caspian Sea and the Dead Sea could more properly be called lakes; their high salinity may be responsible for their description as 'seas'.) From any

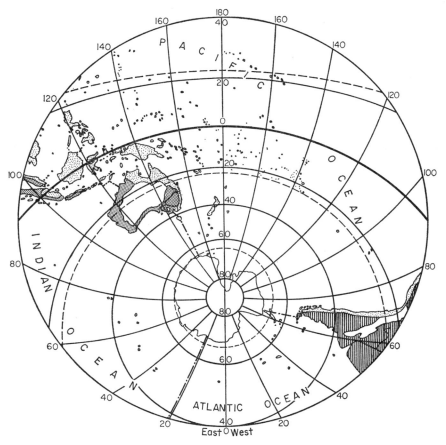

FIG. 5 The marine hemisphere (after Bos-Niermeyer's School Atlas; Wolters, Groningen); the regions which drain their waters into the three oceans are shown by different shadings.

point at sea one can reach any other required point at sea, across the sea or, at most, over sea-ice. In fact, the boundaries between the various oceans and seas are comparatively arbitrary.

The Atlantic Ocean is 'divided' from the Indian Ocean by the meridian through Cape Agulhas (20° E.) and its common 'frontier' with the Pacific Ocean is taken to be from Cape Horn to the South Shetland Islands. The dividing line between the Indian Ocean and the Pacific runs from the Malay Peninsula through Sumatra, Java, Timor and Cape Londonderry in

Australia, to Tasmania and thence directly southward (along the meridian of 147° E.) to Antarctica. Nowadays the Arctic Sea is regarded as belonging to the Atlantic, which is not unreasonable since, as is plain from Fig. 4, the Arctic is a marginal sea of the Atlantic. The Bering Strait, which is only 58 kilometres wide and 58 metres deep, divides the Arctic from the Pacific Ocean.

The continuous maritime area around the whole Antarctic Continent has been cut, by the divisions described above, into three portions, one for each of the three oceans mentioned. In this way the whole 'world ocean' is distributed among these three. (The Mediterranean and Baltic are marginal seas of the Atlantic Ocean; the Red Sea is a marginal sea of the Indian Ocean.)

The maritime area in the far south, an expanse of water spanning the entire southern hemisphere and itself having the dimensions of an ocean, is sometimes, and for a very good reason, called, in its entirety, the Southern Ocean or Antarctic Ocean. Apart from its coherence on the globe, this marine area also exhibits marked oceanographic and meteorological features in common. One outstanding feature, for instance, is the predominance of west winds in a large part of this ocean, which give rise to the powerful west wind drift, a broad, closed, west–east current of the upper layers of water. The line connecting the southernmost tips of the continents could serve as the northern boundary of the Antarctic Ocean.

It is the usual practice, when considering the distribution of sea and land, to visualize the globe in a certain position, namely with the axis of rotation pointing upward; we then divide it into a northern hemisphere and a southern hemisphere, finding at once that the oceans predominate far less in the northern than in the southern hemisphere. Whereas the ratio of water to land in the former is as 3 to 2, it is approximately as 4 to 1 in the latter.

Table I shows the surface of water and land for the thirty-six belts, each comprising five degrees latitude, into which the whole surface of the earth, from north to south, can be divided.

As will be seen, land predominates only between 45° and 70° N. (where the Eurasian continent lies) and between 70° and 90° S. (where the Antarctic continent is situated). Everywhere else, the oceans predominate; indeed, between 85° and 90° N. there is no known land at all, while from 40° to 65° S. only a small fraction of the entire surface is occupied by land.

Considering for a moment only the mid-latitude belt of both hemispheres, the ratio of land to water in the northern hemisphere is found to be approximately as 1 to 1, whereas in the southern it is 1 to 8. Hence the northern hemisphere offers far more living room to human beings than does the southern.

So far we have been dividing the earth in the traditional manner, namely with reference to the Equator. But geographically, in the literal sense of the word, (i.e. descriptive of the Earth), any other division is just as valid, and it can be quite instructive to take the Earth off its axis, as it were, and to have a look at it from a different angle. This has been done in Figs. 4 and 5, where the so-called 'marine hemisphere' has been placed opposite the so-called 'terrestrial hemisphere'. The difference between these two halves of our planet is very striking indeed.

Finally, if we look at each of the three oceans separately we shall see at once that the Pacific is by far the largest; the Atlantic is about half its size, and the Indian Ocean is a little smaller than the Atlantic.

Table 1

Distribution of water and land between the parallels. All the seas comprise 361,100,000 square kilometres or 70·8 per cent. of the earth's surface; all the land 148,900,000 square kilometres or 29·2 per cent. of the earth's surface.

	Northern Hemisphere					*Southern Hemisphere*			
Lat. (deg. N.)	Sea (million km²)	Land (million km²)	Sea %	Land %	Lat. (deg. S.)	Sea (million km²)	Land (million km²)	Sea %	Land %
90–85	0·98	–	100·0	–	0–5	16·79	5·33	75·9	24·1
85–80	2·55	0·38	85·2	12·8	5–10	16·90	5·06	76·9	23·1
80–75	3·74	1·11	77·1	22·9	10–15	17·21	4·42	79·6	20·4
75–70	4·14	2·33	65·5	34·5	15–20	16·15	5·00	76·4	23·6
70–65	2·46	6·12	28·7	71·3	20–25	15·45	5·05	75·4	24·6
65–60	3·12	7·21	31·2	69·8	25–30	15·44	4·26	78·4	21·6
60–55	5·40	6·61	45·0	55·0	30–35	15·78	2·97	84·2	15·8
55–50	5·53	8·07	40·7	59·3	35–40	16·48	1·17	93·4	6·6
50–45	6·61	8·46	43·8	56·2	40–45	15·83	0·59	96·4	3·6
45–40	8·41	8·02	51·2	48·8	45–50	14·69	0·38	97·5	2·5
40–35	10·03	7·63	56·8	43·2	50–55	13·39	0·21	98·5	1·5
35–30	10·81	7·94	57·7	42·3	55–60	12·01	0·01	99·9	0·1
30–35	11·75	7·95	59·6	40·4	60–65	10·30	0·03	99·7	0·3
25–20	13·35	7·15	65·2	34·8	65–70	6·82	1·76	79·5	20·5
20–15	14·98	6·16	70·8	29·2	70–75	2·60	4·14	38·6	61·4
15–10	16·55	5·08	76·5	23·5	75–80	0·52	4·33	10·7	89·3
10–5	16·62	5·33	75·7	24·3	80–85	–	2·93	–	100·0
5–0	17·39	4·74	78·6	21·4	85–90	–	0·98	–	100·0
90–0	154·70	100·30	60·7	39·3	0–90	206·40	48·60	80·9	19·1

The Atlantic Ocean is distinctly oblong in a north–south direction, and very irregular in shape compared with the other two. Its narrowing, almost to a neck of sea as one might say, between the eastern tip of Brazil and the bulge of Africa near Liberia, is quite striking. One could, in fact, almost look upon the North and South Atlantic as two separate oceans, though the division is external rather than internal. The distinctive feature of the North Atlantic Ocean is its very irregular contours. On both sides, especially the eastern side, large marginal seas and bays are found, such as the Mediterranean (with the Black Sea), the Bay of Biscay, the North Sea, the Baltic Sea, Baffin Bay, Hudson Bay, the Gulf of Mexico and the Caribbean Sea. By contrast, the contours of the South Atlantic are much smoother, as is also the eastern littoral of the Pacific Ocean from north to south. The western border of the Pacific Ocean, however, is indented considerably by the adjacent seas, such as the Sea of Okhotsk, the Sea of Japan, the East China Sea with the Yellow Sea, the South China Sea and the seas of the East Indian archipelago.

Finally, in the Indian Ocean the only bights of any significance occur along its northern margin from longitude 40° to 100° E., where we have the Red Sea, the Persian Gulf, the Arabian Sea and the Gulf of Bengal.

The coastlines enclosing the Atlantic Ocean, however, are longer than those of the Indian and Pacific Oceans together. Another striking, distinctive feature of the Atlantic Ocean is that by far the majority of the great continental rivers discharge into it (see Figs. 4 and 5).

Knowing as we do what an important part navigation has played in the history of civilization, we must realize that an irregular shoreline with many marginal seas and shielded bays providing good harbours, has always favoured the spread of culture. We have only to think of that large, almost enclosed sea, the Mediterranean, and of the coasts of India, China and Japan and western Europe.

Some details relating to the surfaces of various oceans and seas will be found in Table 3.

PROBING THE DEEP

The third dimension opens up an entirely new aspect of the exploration of the world's oceans. Exploration of the depths of the deep began far later than did that of its length and breadth; but for all that it already has its own history.

SOUNDINGS

From very early times the safety of those who ventured upon the sea depended on their knowing the depths of the waters close to the coasts. But as navigational safety was the sole object of this interest in the depths—or, more precisely in this case the shallows—the soundings taken were confined, for a long time, to the shallow waters found mainly along the coastline. The tool for these soundings was a plummet (usually of lead) attached to a plumb-line graduated in fathoms. The fathom is the classic measure for depth-soundings at sea and is approximately equal to the reach of an adult man between the finger-tips of his outspread arms; or, more precisely, 1·83 metres. When plumbing, the line, which was formerly always cord, was allowed to slip loosely between the hands; when the lead touched the bottom, the tension in the cord slackened, or ceased altogether.

It was obviously a difficult task to take soundings in deep water in this fashion. A certain geographer wrote, in the middle of the seventeenth century, that he had not come across a single seaman who had plumbed more than 200 fathoms. Apparently he had never heard of Posidonius's claim, in Grecian times, to the effect that he had established a depth of 1000 fathoms in the Mediterranean; (though it is not stated how this depth was measured).

It was not until the second half of the eighteenth century that greater depths were measured with certainty. In 1773, the English navigator

Phipps plumbed 683 fathoms in the Arctic Ocean. In 1840 Sir James Clark Ross took soundings in Antarctic waters to a depth of more than 2600 fathoms.

In those days strong hempen lines, of 6 millimetres thickness and more, were used, so it does not need much imagination to realize that several thousand metres of these not only weighed a good deal, but monopolized an enormous volume of space on deck.

Deep-sea soundings were a time-consuming business, even when winches were used. As the ship had to remain stationary, it meant taking in sail. Moreover, the mere paying out and hauling home of the line took literally

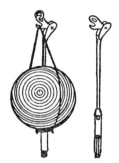

FIG. 6 Brooke's sounding-lead, with the weight on the left; without it on the right (after being hauled up).

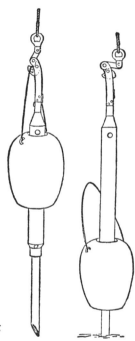

FIG. 7 Sigsbee's sounding-lead; left, during submersion; right, on touching bottom.

hours; and in the end it was often difficult to tell whether or not bottom had been struck.

About the middle of the nineteenth century, an American naval officer, Matthew Fountaine Maury by name, replaced the hemp line by a lighter one of sailcloth yarn to which he fixed a cannon-ball for 'lead'. With this he let the line run out quickly, and when the lead touched bottom it automatically detached itself from the line; it was therefore not hauled back with the line, which, for that very reason, was not required to be as strong and thick as those previously used. The release of the plummet was the invention of Maury's collaborator Brooke, and in some form or other is used to this day (see Figs. 6 and 7). It was at about this time that deep-sea soundings were becoming necessary for the laying of telegraph cables at sea.

The most important improvement was introduced by the British physicist, Thomson (Lord Kelvin) who, in 1874, replaced cord or canvas thread by thin steel wire (piano wire).

The present machines have steel piano wire $1-1\frac{1}{2}$ millimetres thick, wound on a winch drum. The wire passes over a counter which records the length of the paid-out line. The winch is driven by a motor for hauling from considerable depths. Modern sounding machines are, moreover, fitted with a device which stops the wire as soon as the lead touches bottom; this is a brake which, by being adjusted while the wire is being paid out, is able to hold up the weight of the wire alone and thus becomes effective the moment the lead touches bottom.

A deep-sea lead is specially constructed to release the weight (usually of iron and weighing 25–75 kilograms) from a rod or tube around which it is fitted. The tube can serve as a small corer, which penetrates a little way into the bed and brings a sample with it on its return journey. The weight remains below, to minimize strain upon the lead-line (which is not heavier than need be), and the risk of rupture when it is hauled up.

Notwithstanding all the improvements which have been made, wire-sounding by modern means is still a time-consuming business. It takes about one hour and a half to sound 5000 metres of water, that is, half an hour to pay out, and one hour to heave in. A sounding in 9000 metres takes three hours.

Until the introduction of echo-sounding, approximately 15,000 line-soundings had been made in depths of more than 1000 metres, 6100 of which were carried out in the Atlantic, 6300 in the Pacific and 2500 in the Indian Ocean.[1]

SOUNDING BY MEASURING PRESSURE

There are two other main methods of sounding the depths, one based on the principle of measuring the pressure, the other on that of echo-sounding.

As depth is approximately proportional to pressure, pressure gauging can reveal depth. One of the devices based on this principle is the 'Kelvin tube', which is a simple, sealed, water-pressure gauge. While this instrument is sinking, the water in the sealed limb (a glass tube) rises, owing to increasing pressure outside. The inner wall of the sealed limb is coated with a chemical substance which changes colour when it comes into contact with sea-water; this discoloration discloses the level reached by the water in the sealed limb, and also the pressure. The instrument is only used in comparatively shallow seas and, if not sailing too fast, the vessel need not stop for sounding to be taken with it.

Depth sounding by means of two thermometers should be mentioned in this context, because this method is likewise essentially a measurement of pressure. If an ordinary thermometer, calibrated at atmospheric pressure,

[1] This seems a lot, but in the Pacific it is only 1 to 27,000 square kilometres (an area almost the size of Belgium).

sinks down in the sea, the temperature it registers will be too high, because the pressure of the water compresses the mercury bulb, with the result that the mercury rises beyond the true level in the capillary. This is what happens in an unprotected thermometer. Now, if another thermometer, with its mercury bulb protected against excessive pressure by a very strong glass casing, is submerged to the same depth it will record the correct temperature. The difference between the readings of these two thermometers is a measure of the pressure and, therefore, of the depth at which the temperatures were registered. The readings are taken aboard, of course, but a special type of thermometer, called a 'reversing thermometer', is used for deep-sea soundings. This retains its registration after having been inverted *in situ*, so enabling those aboard to read off the temperature recorded in the depths. (Further details will be found in Chapter 2.)

Unprotected thermometers are often used to verify the depths at which oceanographic instruments (especially thermometers and water-samplers) operate during deep-sea observations. This is a very accurate method of depth-sounding, the margin of error seldom exceeding 0·5 per cent., whereas the depth derived from the length of the paid-out line may be very uncertain if the depth is considerable and the line oblique owing to drifting of the observing ship.

ECHO-SOUNDING

The echo-sounder, invented by the American research-worker Hayes in the early 'twenties of this century, marked a tremendous advance. The principle is clear; the vessel transmits a downward sound-signal which is sent back by the bottom, the echo being received in a kind of underwater microphone, which is called a hydrophone. A very accurate timer enables the time lapse between the transmission of the signal and the reception of the echo to be measured to within a fraction of a second, and from this interval, multiplied by the speed of sound in sea-water, the distance travelled by the sound, which is twice the depth, can be calculated; see Fig. 8.

Simple as this principle is, its practical application required great technical expertise. At first, echo-sounding was only successful in shallow to moderately deep waters, but present-day echo-sounders can be used to all depths, and produce results accurate to within one half per cent. This accuracy depends upon the precision with which the travelling time of the sound can be measured and also on how exactly the speed of the signal in the sea under the vessel is known. In modern instruments the time is recorded by a built-in mechanism which, as a rule, automatically converts the time interval into depth. For this, the instrument is adjusted to a given value of the speed of sound, usually between 1460 and 1500 metres per second.

The speed of sound in the sea depends on the temperature, pressure and salinity. It is, for instance, 1445 metres per second at 0° C, and 1 atmosphere pressure in sea-water with a salt content of 34·85‰, or parts per 1000, while at 20° C under otherwise the same conditions, it is 1518·5 metres per second.

The higher the temperature, the higher the speed of the sound; the same applies to pressure and salinity.

The effect of the pressure is to increase the speed of sound by approximately 18 metres per second per 1000 metres depth. Salinity also affects it, but this influence is comparatively constant in the ocean because there the salinity varies very little. Hence the speed of sound at various depths under a given spot at sea is determined mainly by the course of the temperature and of the pressure down below.

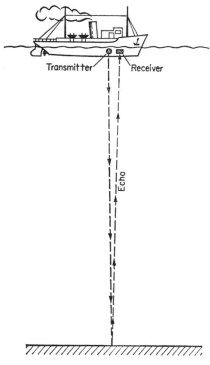

FIG. 8 Echo-sounding

The graph in Fig. 9 shows an example of the variation, with depth, of the speed of sound in the sea. We see that the lowest speed is at about 800 metres depth. It decreases at first with increasing depth, owing to the drop in temperature (except in the upper 50 metres); below 800 metres it increases with depth because the temperature decreases only gradually there, and the increasing pressure increases the speed.

One needs a graph something like this, therefore, to interpret an echo-sounding with the utmost accuracy; or at any rate one needs to know the speed at various depths in order to decide on the average speed in the vertical, so as to be able to derive the depth from the echo-time. Computed standard values of the average speed for various depths are used in practice for a given area. For example, if the echo-sounder is adjusted to a speed of

1490 metres per second, and with it a depth is found at which a standard average of 1485 metres per second obtains in the area concerned, one gets a corrected value for the depth by multiplying the value found by 1485/1490.

Instruments now in use record the sounded depths continuously, thus providing at the same time a complete profile of the bottom along the course followed (see Plate VI).

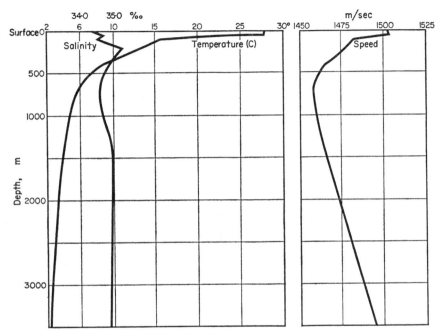

FIG. 9 Example of the course of the temperature, salinity and speed of sound with the depth, at a locality in the Atlantic Ocean (5° N., 15° W.).

The outstanding merit of the echo-sounder, of course, is that it saves so much time, and meanwhile the ship proceeds on its way; its disadvantage is that it does not provide a sample of the bottom, which a line-plummet may do. Nevertheless, we can learn something about the sea-bed from the nature of the echo; this may vary in distinctness, or may be diffuse; and that, to the trained observer, is revelatory as to the character of the reflecting surface (hard or soft bed).

In addition to the reflections from the surface of the bottom, reflections have, in some cases, been received from a deeper (internal) interface situated below the bed. This internal interface may be a surface of rock upon which a sedimentary layer of varying thickness is superimposed. The first reflection derives from the upper surface of the sedimentary stratum—the sea-bed— but, as the sound penetrates to some extent into this layer, a second reflection is received from the underside, where it rests on the rocky foundation. In

PLATE I

Stormy shore.

Above: Aboard the Netherlands weather-ship *Cumulus* on the Atlantic Ocean. A water-sampler with deep-sea thermometer about to be sent down.

Below: The water-sampler emerging from the deep.

several places it has thus been possible to determine the thickness of the sedimentary layer by the sound-signal's echo.

This is not all an echo-sounder can do. It has been known to detect schools of fish, while even layers with a dense population of animal plankton (especially copepods) can be betrayed by diffuse reflections of sound ('phantom bottom'; see Plate VII).

WHAT THE ECHO-SOUNDER HAS REVEALED

The number of deep-sea soundings made in the oceans has increased manyfold since hydrographers have had the echo-sounder. (Here is an example: before the *Snellius* expedition in the Molucca Seas there were

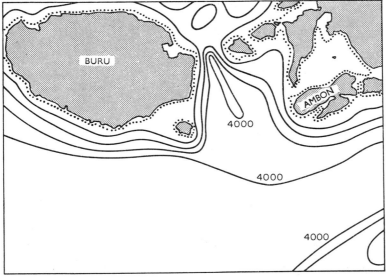

FIG. 10 Depth chart of the surroundings of Buru and Ambon according to the few soundings made prior to the *Snellius* expedition. (Cf. Fig. 11.)

records of 3000 wire soundings in water deeper than 200 metres. The work of this expedition has added 30,000 echo-soundings to this number.) Consequently, vastly more detailed depth data of a variety of marine areas have now been collected. So, whereas formerly all one could do was to map out the topography of the bottom in broad outline, on the basis of the comparatively scanty and widely scattered depth soundings recorded, there now exist topographical maps of the bottom in certain areas, which are as detailed as those of hilly or mountainous landscapes above sea level. The details missing from the old charts, which have since come to light thanks to the close network of echo-soundings, become apparent on comparison of the new charts with the old. (Cf. Figs. 10 and 11.)

It used to be generally held by oceanographers and geologists that there were only gentle slopes on the sea bottom; a landscape of the kind which above water would have been monotonously flat, with vast expanses of plains punctuated here and there by mere knolls and shallow glens, despite the fact that the *total* differences in height were considerable.[1] We now know that, in many places, the sea bottom is different. The truly fantastic valleys, with steep gorges which intersect the submarine slopes shelving from the continental margins down into the deep sea in many places, are extremely impressive. An astonishing number of these submarine canyons have been discovered along the coast of North America; one such is charted in Fig. 12.

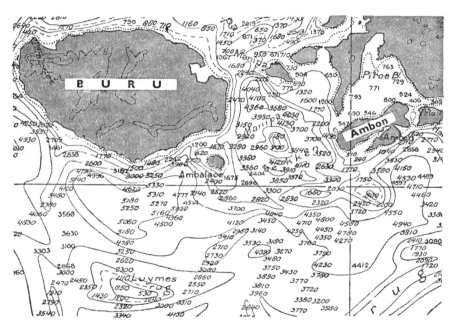

FIG. 11 Fragment of a depth chart regionally the same as Fig. 10, according to the many echo-soundings made by *Snellius*.

One other thing all too easily overlooked is that there is no point in collecting a great many records of depth-soundings unless an accurately located position is indicated with each measured depth, for only thus can a very exact, detailed map be drawn. Fortunately, the modern electronic devices for pin-pointing—notably Loran and Decca—with which shipping is equipped nowadays make it possible to satisfy this requirement. So, looking at a chart like that in Fig. 12, it is as well to realize that as enormous a number of accurate pin-pointings as of soundings has gone into the making of such a topographical picture.

[1] The only known exceptions were the slopes of some submarine volcanic cones, which can amount to as much as 40 degrees; see Fig. 18.

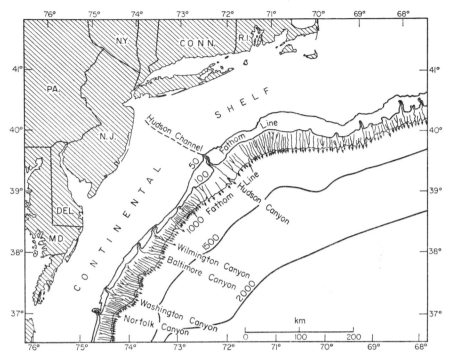

FIG. 12 *Above*. Part of the continental shelf and the continental slope along the East Coast of North America, with many submarine canyons. Depths in fathoms.

Below. The submarine Hudson canyon at the edge of the continental shelf (after Daly, *The Floor of the Ocean*, University of N. Carolina Press).

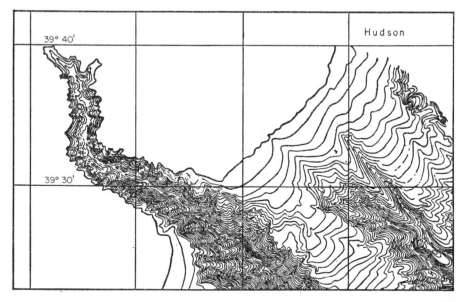

FROM THE SHORE INTO THE SEA

If we were able to walk from the shore into the sea upon its floor, we should notice that the continent was almost everywhere surrounded by a flat margin, known as the continental shelf, a terrace which, although it slopes down seaward, does so very gradually (average gradient 1 in 500). This continues down to a depth of roughly 150–200 metres (or 100 fathoms), the gradient becoming much steeper beyond that point, namely 1 in 25 to 1 in 15 on an average—apart from such irregularities as the submarine canyons.

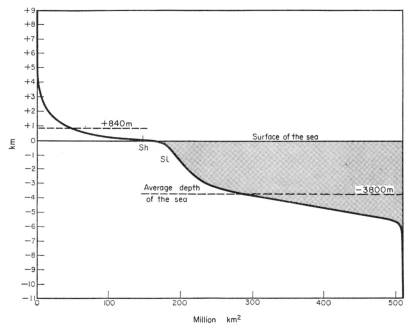

FIG. 13 Distribution of the various terrestrial elevations and marine depths. The surface of the earth's crust projecting above a given level of the ground can be read along the horizontal axis (840 metres is the average height of the land). The shallow margins of the oceans formed by the continental and island shelves are marked Sh while Sl indicates the continental slopes.

The downslope of the sea-bed outside the continental shelf is called the continental slope. The transition from one to the other of these zones is clearly to be seen in Fig. 12. Similar structures sometimes occur around islands, in which case we speak of an insular shelf and insular slope. That slope drops along a comparatively short distance to the great low-lying plains of the oceans, thousands of metres down, which stretch over by far the major part of the oceans of the world. They are sometimes called the abysmal deeps (from the Greek 'abyssos', which means bottomless, unfathomable).

Figure 13 shows a diagram of these three zones of the sea bottom. Here again, the slopes are exaggerated because of the difference between the depth scale and the horizontal scale. The whole of the continental shelf and continental slope rising from the floor of the ocean is called the *continental terrace*. The continental shelf varies in width from 0 to 1300 kilometres, the average width being 30 kilometres; the greatest width stretches from the north coast of Siberia.

As the deep areas (down to 6000 metres) comprise the major part of the total surface of the oceans, the average depth of the global seas and oceans is considerable, namely, 3800 metres. This is roughly four-and-a-half times the average height of land surface above sea level, which is 840 metres, though the highest mountain peak is not less high in that proportion than the deepest trough is deep; Mount Everest is 8880 metres high and the Marianas Trench in the Pacific Ocean is 11,000 metres deep. Hence, the floor of the oceans, the major part of which lies at a depth of several thousand metres, is not like a mirror image of the land surface, because the latter is largely made up of vast plains. And indeed, the volume of the seas is far greater than that of the land lying above sea level; the average depth of the oceans being four-and-a-half times the average height of the land, and the proportion of the surfaces being as 71:29, the volume of the oceans of the world is approximately eleven times that of land above sea level. Say that the water of the world's oceans had drained away; then the elevations on the earth's surface would fill up only an eleventh part of the volume of the vacated basins.

In the vast areas of the ocean floor, which are 3000–6000 metres deep, there occur depressions which are considerably deeper. One calls any such depression of more than 6000 metres a 'deep'. For a long time the greatest known deep was in the Philippine or Mindanao Trench, which was found by echo-sounding to be 10,500 metres. Here, in 1929–30, the Dutch *Snellius* expedition took a sample of the bottom by lead-line but, as the depth found was 10,070 metres, they were not exactly above the deepest spot. They did break a record, however, by bringing to the surface a water sample together with a temperature reading from a depth of 10,035 metres, which was deeper than a water-sampler and thermometer had ever been before.

Meanwhile, as has been hinted, the Mindanao Trench is no longer the deepest trough. In 1951 the British vessel *Challenger II* took echo-soundings in the Marianas Trench, halfway between the islands of Guam and Yap in the Pacific Ocean, and recorded a depth of 10,865 metres. Subsequently a wire sounding was also taken (not in exactly the same place), when a depth of 10,830 metres was plumbed, and a sample of the bottom was brought to the surface.

This record, too, however, has since been broken, namely by the Russian exploration ship *Vityaz* in 1957, during an expedition carried out within the framework of the International Geophysical Year, when a slightly greater depth was recorded by echo-sounding, likewise in the Marianas Trench. In 1959 this sounding was recalculated to 11,030 metres. It has to be borne in mind, however, that these figures are subject to a margin of inaccuracy of 50 metres.

The common practice is to name specific great depths in the oceans after the vessel which has found them; for example, we speak of the Snellius depth (10,070 m), the Cape Johnson depth (10,500 m), both in the Philippine Trench, the Challenger (II) depth (10,865 m) and the Vityaz depth (11,030 m), both in the Marianas Trench.

Table 2

Area proportions of the depth zones in the oceans of the world.

Depth Zone (metres)	Per cent.
0–200	7·6
200–1000	4·3
1000–2000	4·2
2000–3000	6·8
3000–4000	19·6
4000–5000	33·0
5000–6000	23·3
6000–7000	1·1
> 7000	0·1

Table 2 shows the percentage areas occupied by the various oceanic depth zones in relation to the surface. It will be seen that the 0–200 metre depth zone—the continental shelf—covers almost as large an area as the zone with depths of 200–2000 metres, which belongs to the regions of the far steeper continental slope; further, that depths of more than 6000 metres cover only a very small part of the ocean bottom, in contrast to the depths ranging from 3000 to 6000 metres (see Fig. 13).

MAPS OF THE BOTTOM LANDSCAPE

The word bathymetry, deriving from the Greek bathys, deep, means measurement of depth, so a bathymetric map is a depth chart, that is, a map which shows the topography of the sea bottom by lines of equal depth, sometimes embellished by different colours or shades to represent differences in depth. See the bathymetric map of all the oceans of the world facing page 316.

Certain sea-bed formations are now referred to in established terms, some of which are given below.

A *rise* is a long, broad elevation which rises gently and generally smoothly from the sea floor.

A *ridge* is a long, narrow elevation of the sea floor, with steep sides and more irregular topography than a rise. Sometimes the highest parts of a ridge project as islands above the sea. The Azores, on the Mid-Atlantic Ridge, is an example.

A *sill* is a ridge or rise separating a partially closed basin, trough or trench from another basin, or from the adjacent sea floor. The greatest depth over a sill is called the *sill depth*.

A *plateau* is the upper surface of a comparatively flat-topped, extensive elevation of the sea-floor, normally rising more than 100 fathoms on all sides.

A *bank* is an elevation of the sea floor located on a continental shelf or an island shelf and over which the depth of water is relatively shallow but sufficient for safe surface navigation.

A *basin* is a depression of the sea floor, more or less equidimensional in form, and not too small. When the length is much greater than the width, the feature is a trough.

A *trench* is a long, narrow depression of the deep-sea floor, having relatively steep sides.

A *trough* is a long depression of the sea floor, having relatively gentle sides, and is normally wider and shallower than a trench.

It would take us too far afield to enter into the details of the sea bed in the various areas of the world's oceans. Nor shall we dwell upon the interesting questions as to how the floor of the ocean came to assume these forms; for, as these questions belong to the domain of geology, they are outside the province of this book. Let us, however, consider some of the facts.

The following are among the best-known trenches: The Kuril Trench (10,500 m), the Japan Trench (with the Ramapo depth 10,400 m), the Philippine Trench (with the Cape Johnson depth 10,500 m), and the Mariana Trench (with the Vityaz depth 11,030 m), all in the western zone of the Pacific Ocean. Then, too, there are the Tonga Trench (10,880 m) to the south of the Samoa Islands and, in the eastern zone, beside the Andes Mountains, the Atacama Trench (8060 m). In the Indian Ocean we have the Sunda Trench or Java Trench (7455 m); while in the Atlantic Ocean there is the Porto Rico Trench (9220 m) and, at the margin of the Antarctic Sea, the South Sandwich Trench (8260 m).

As to the counterparts of the trenches, the ridges, we need only think of the Atlantic Ocean, cut through almost to its full length by the Mid-Atlantic Ridge. This ridge is 20,300 kilometres long and, following the general contours of the Atlantic Ocean, runs from the Antarctic in a vast S-bend to Iceland. Whereas basins more than 5000 metres deep occur on either side of this ridge, it is covered in most places by less than 3000 metres of water; in some, notably, from south to north, in Bouvet Island, Tristan da Cunha, Ascension, St. Peter and St. Paul Rocks, the Azores (on the Azores Plateau) and Iceland, it projects above the sea. There is only one spot, just to the north of the Equator, where there is a narrow, deep, transverse channel, the Romanche Trench, with more than 7000 metres' depth of water. In the southern hemisphere, at approximately latitude 30° S., there are two transverse ridges: the Rio Grande Rise on the west, connecting South America with the Mid-Atlantic Ridge and dividing the Brazilian Basin from the Argentine Basin; and to the east, the Walvis Ridge, running in a westerly direction from south-west Africa to the neighbourhood of

Tristan da Cunha, and dividing the Cape Basin from the Congo Basin. These two transverse ridges are very important features affecting deep-sea circulation in the Atlantic Ocean (to which we shall revert in Chapter 6).

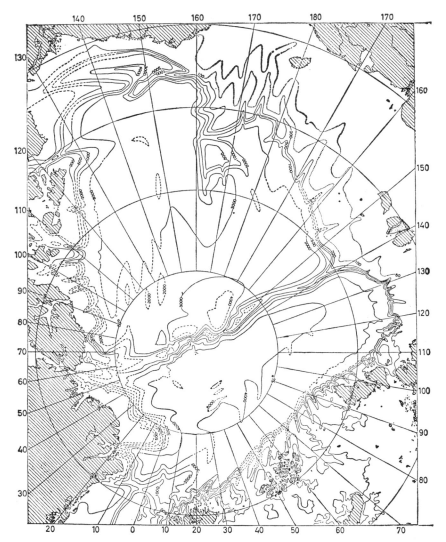

FIG. 14 Bathymetric chart (derived from a Russian source), of the Northern Arctic Ocean. Note the very wide Siberian continental shelf and the submarine ridge, the Lomonosov Ridge, right across the Arctic Ocean.

The same may be said of the Wyville Thomson Ridge, between the Faroes and Scotland, a section of the ridge which runs from Iceland to Scotland and divides the basin of the Norwegian Sea from the West European Basin. This ridge rises to 500 metres beneath the surface of the sea, and forms the barrier on the west to a narrow transverse channel about

1100 metres deep, namely, the Faroes–Shetland Channel. The Wyville Thomson Ridge divides the icy cold bottom water of the Norwegian Sea from the far less cold bottom water to the south of the ridge.

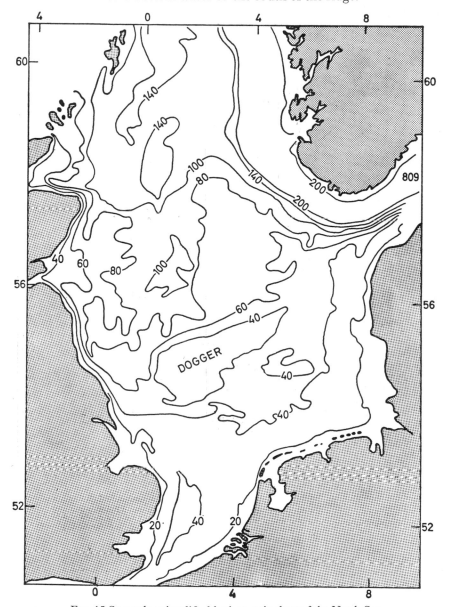

FIG. 15 Somewhat simplified bathymetric chart of the North Sea

We should not omit mention of the Rockall Bank in the North Atlantic, 500 kilometres west of the Scottish coast, from which rises that lonely rock Rockall, the habitat of auks and gulls.

2*

To complete the bathymetric map of the world (opposite p. 316) Fig. 14 presents a depth chart of the Arctic Ocean, which is not given full justice in the former. Two striking features appear on this chart: the very wide continental shelf off the coast of Siberia, and the submarine mountain ridge which runs from the New Siberian Islands, right across the North Pole to

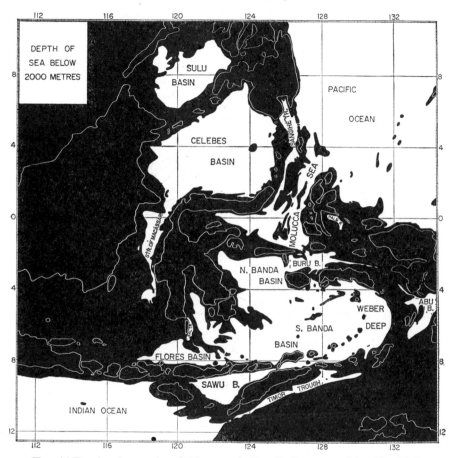

FIG. 16 Depths of more than 2000 metres in East Indian waters (after Van Riel).

Greenland. This chain of mountains on the sea bottom rises to 3000 metres and divides the Arctic Ocean into two basins. The range was discovered in 1948 by a Russian expedition drifting on a huge ice-floe; it was named 'Lomonosov Ridge' after a Russian scientist of the eighteenth century.

During the International Geophysical Year (1957–58) a similar American expedition discovered another, shorter range of submarine mountains, parallel to the Lomonosov Ridge, situated between the latter and Alaska.

Simple bathymetric charts are reproduced of two oceanic regions of some special interest, namely of the North Sea (Fig. 15) and East Indian waters (Figs. 16 and 17).

The only noteworthy feature of the North Sea which we wish to mention at present is the curved trench, more than 800 metres deep, which lies along the round extremity of southern Norway.

The *Snellius* expedition in particular, carefully and thoroughly probed the topography of the bottom of the Indonesian seas, at any rate so far as the eastern basins are concerned. In the western part of the archipelago the seas

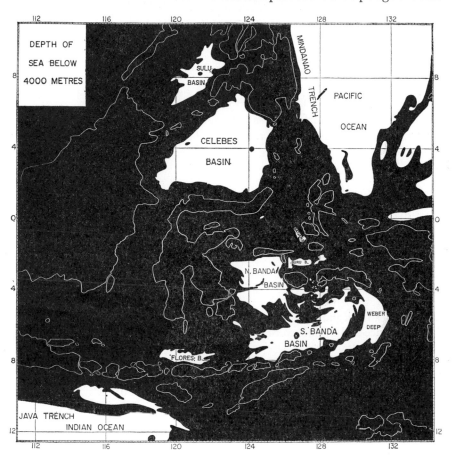

FIG. 17 Depths of more than 4000 metres in East Indian waters (after Van Riel).

are comparatively shallow; in fact, the large islands Sumatra, Java and Borneo lie on the Asiatic continental shelf. To the east of the line connecting the east coasts of Borneo and Java on the other hand, there is an extremely complicated array of roundish and oblong basins and trenches between curved ridges and chains of islands. The irregularity of the profile of the sea-bed is most clearly reflected in the irregular coastlines of many of the islands; we have only to look at Celebes, Halmahera and the like. Here and there a detached volcanic cone rises from the bottom of the sea, sometimes, but not always, raising its crown above the waves. The small island of

Gunung Api provides a good example of the former. It looks for all the world like a floating rock garden, but actually it is the peak of an impressively broad, submarine volcanic cone (Fig. 18).

FIG. 18 Gunung Api, an islet in the Banda Sea; actually the summit of an old, submarine volcanic cone, a cross-section of which is shown above (after Van Riel).

SURVEY OF OCEANS AND SEAS

Table 3 shows the surface areas, average depths and volumes of the three oceans (with and without their marginal seas), of some of the smaller seas and lastly, of the whole world ocean.

Table 3

Surface Area, Volume and Average Depth of Oceans and Seas

		Area (in millions km²)	Volume (in millions km³)	Average depth (m)
Atlantic Ocean	without	82·44	324·6	3930
Pacific Ocean	marginal	165·25	707·6	4280
Indian Ocean	seas.	73·44	291·0	3960
Arctic Ocean		14·09	17·0	1205
Mediterranean Sea and Black Sea		2·97	4·2	1430
Gulf of Mexico and Caribbean Sea		4·32	9·6	2220
Australasian Central Sea		8·14	9·9	1210
Hudson Bay		1·23	0·16	128
Baltic Sea		0·42	0·02	55
North Sea		0·57	0·05	94
English Channel		0·075	0·004	54
Irish Sea		0·10	0·006	60
Sea of Okhotsk		1·53	1·3	838
Bering Sea		2·27	3·3	1440
Atlantic Ocean	with	106·46	354·7	3330
Pacific Ocean	marginal	179·68	723·7	4030
Indian Ocean	seas.	74·92	291·9	3900
The World Ocean		361·06	1370·3	3795

FOUNDERS OF OCEANOGRAPHY

In the first part of this chapter, we traced the growth of the body of knowledge pertaining to the surface and lateral borderlines of the seas and oceans. We then turned our attention to the depths of the oceans, considered how the shapes of their floors were reconnoitred, and discussed the results of those explorations. The body of the world ocean—the 'waters of the sea' themselves—is situated between that surface and that bottom. The exploration of the realm of those waters already has a history of its own, young though it be; the science of physical oceanography is one of the latest branches of natural science.

We shall not now enter into details of the history of this science, only recalling the names of a few prominent figures of the past and present and of some important oceanographic expeditions and present oceanographic institutes. After that, the whole of this book will be devoted to a discussion of the results of this research obtained down the years; and historical names and facts will naturally crop up from time to time in connection with our subject.

James Cook was certainly one of the first, if not the very first, to lead a mainly scientific expedition. He had naturalists aboard on several of his voyages, and many temperature readings as well as soundings were taken. His best-known voyage was that of 1772–75, when he circumnavigated the Antarctic Ocean at approximately latitude 60° S.

In the years that followed, the growth of knowledge of the internal properties of the oceans depended largely on the development of suitable instruments with which to obtain reliable temperature readings in deep waters. There are two main difficulties. Firstly, there is the tremendous pressure to which a thermometer is subjected under these conditions, which causes the mercury to rise too high. Secondly, as the temperature is registered at a place beyond the reach of the observer, the reading has somehow or other to be 'fixed'.

The latter difficulty was at first overcome to some extent by the use of Six's maximum and minimum thermometer (1782). On the assumption that the temperature drops with increasing depth, the minimum thermometer registers the temperature prevailing at the depth attained. But it transpired later that this assumption was not always valid. In Arctic regions, Scoresby, as far back as 1811, found surface water which was colder than the water beneath it. He used insulated water-samplers to raise water for temperature determinations. This type of sampler provides another means of registering the prevailing temperature in deep waters, one that was also used, among others, by Maury (c. 1851), and is still used in the perfected form of the Petterson–Nansen water-sampler. The best solution of the problem of temperature registration, however, has been provided by the reversing thermometer. Originally this was a French idea (Aimé, 1843), but the London firm of Negretti and Zambra produced a later version (1878) which, in turn, was improved by the Berlin instrument maker, Richter.

Meanwhile, the other difficulty of excessive pressure on the bulb of a liquid thermometer had to be overcome. The answer was a thermometer protected against pressure. Sir James Clark Ross, during his Antarctic expedition of 1839–43, was among those who, with protected thermometers, recorded temperatures at various depths. He also measured the specific gravity at various depths. His soundings in more than 2000 fathoms, to which we have already referred, were the first which could truly be said to be deep-sea soundings in the full sense of the term. Lastly, although this is outside the province of this book, mention must be made of the important zoological material, an unsuspected wealth of animal life, which his expedition brought to the surface by dredging.

It is Matthew Fontaine Maury (1806–73) who has every right to be called the father of physical oceanography. This is not to say that he was the first to observe the physical properties of the sea; some of the facts related above are proof to the contrary. But he was the first to present the physics of the sea as a scientific discipline in its own right, side by side with marine biology.

Maury was an officer in the American Navy and had therefore spent much of his time at sea; he was later put in charge of the department of cartography and instruments, from which the U.S. Hydrographic Office developed.

He owes his high reputation not only to his own research work at sea (including his association with deep-sea sounding and the study of the properties of sea-water, to which reference has already been made), but also, and pre-eminently, to his magnificent work in collecting, analysing and interpreting virtually everything relating to the sea, observed not only by scientists but notably by the seafarers. He organized the centralized collection and interpretation of observations of weather, wind and currents made aboard merchantmen sailing the oceans of the world, working to a plan which, after a conference at Brussels in 1853, was accepted internationally and is followed to this day. He drafted climatological and oceanographic charts (notably wind and current charts) from which he drew up his extensive Sailing Directions. He wrote *The Physical Geography of the Sea*, which may well be called the first oceanographic textbook.

Maury was also one of the first to draw attention to the general external and internal circulation of the waters of the oceans; he compared it with the circulation of the blood in the human body.

FROM THE 'CHALLENGER' EXPEDITION TO THE PRESENT DAY

The most prominent event in the history of the exploration of the world's oceans in the previous century was the British *Challenger* expedition from December 1872 to May 1876. It was undertaken on the initiative, and under the leadership, of Wyville Thomson, a professor of geology and biology. The *Challenger* was a flush-deck corvette of the British Navy, and was equipped with the utmost care for its scientific task, with laboratories, dark room and so forth. In addition to the oceanographic records made of currents, temperatures, chemical composition and other properties of sea-water at all depths, meteorological, magnetic, geological, zoological and botanical observations were made, and material was taken on board. The ship carried a staff of research workers and traversed all the oceans. She sailed by way of Gibraltar and Teneriffe to the Cape of Good Hope, then to Antarctic waters as far as the ice barrier at nearly 67° S. Thence the expedition proceeded to Australia, from Melbourne to Hongkong, back via the Philippines, and along the coast of New Guinea northward to Yokohama. From Japan, the expedition sailed to Valparaiso (S. America), through the Magellan Strait via the Falkland Islands to Montevideo, then eastward to near Tristan da Cunha and from there northward to Portsmouth, whence it had sailed three and a half years previously.

Specialists from many countries worked over the collected material and the fertile results were published in a fifty-volume series entitled *Report of the Scientific Results of the Voyage of H.M.S. Challenger.* Two points emerging from this report, which should be mentioned, are the extremely low temperatures of the bottom water found to prevail in all deep basins of the ocean, and, in the biological field, proof that animals live right down to the greatest depths.

Little more than bare references will be made to just a few of the names of investigators and expeditions associated with post-*Challenger* developments. We repeat that the results of their work will be the subjects of the subsequent chapters of this book.

First of all, then, there is Sir John Murray (1841–1914), the successor of Sir Wyville Thomson. Murray was primarily a geologist and biologist, and as such was the crowning ornament of the British classic period of oceanography. It was he who, together with the Norwegian biologist and oceanographer Johan Hjort, organized that important cruise in the North Atlantic Ocean in the Norwegian ship *Michael Sars* (1910), joined by the physical oceanographer Helland-Hansen.

Murray's contemporaries were Alexander Agassiz, an American whose voyages of exploration, predominantly biological in intention, carried him, in all, across more than 150,000 kilometres of sea; and Prince Albert of Monaco who, in his private yachts, conducted some valuable work in the Mediterranean and North Atlantic Ocean, and who founded an oceanographic museum and laboratory in Monaco.

Next comes the great time of the Norwegian and German oceanographers. First among the Norwegians we have Helland-Hansen of the Geophysical Institute of Bergen, an institute which, with its own research ship, has been doing very important physical oceanographic work for many years, and which also deserves mention for what it has done in the theoretical field. Another outstanding name is that of Fridtjof Nansen, the polar explorer and oceanographer. The drift with the *Fram* in the polar ice from 1893 to 1896 is by no means his only contribution to oceanography. We should mention also Vilhelm Bjerknes the famous theoretician, and Walfrid Ekman to whom we owe the principles of the theory of wind-drift currents and a number of current meters. Finally, there is Harald Ulrik Sverdrup, meteorologist and oceanographer, polar explorer in Amundsen's *Maud* (1918–25), for a long time director of the well-known Scripps Institution of Oceanography at La Jolla (California), and lastly director of the Norwegian

Polar Institute at Oslo. The impressive German Atlantic expedition of the *Meteor* (1925–27) was undoubtedly the most epoch-making expedition of this century. It studied the whole of the middle and southern parts of the Atlantic Ocean very thoroughly, and we are indebted to its labours for much of our insight into the structure and 'organization' of this part of the oceans.

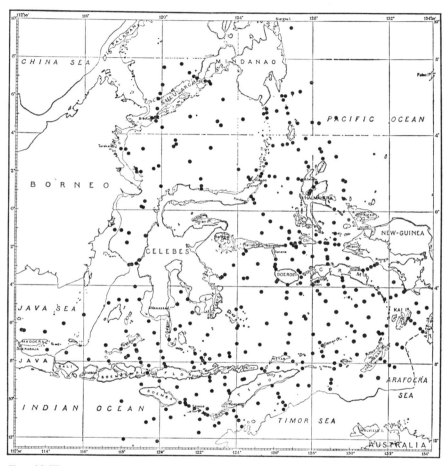

FIG. 19 The oceanographic stations of the *Snellius* expedition led by Van Riel (1929–30).

Shortly after the *Meteor* expedition, Denmark sent the *Dana* expedition round the world (1928–29) and the Netherlands rendered valuable services to oceanography when, in 1929–30, the great *Snellius* expedition, led by P. M. van Riel, explored the East Indian deep-sea basins. Thirty years earlier the Netherlands had had the *Siboga* expedition there, under the leadership of Max Weber; but this was principally for biological research, whereas the *Snellius* expedition was mainly concerned with physical oceanography. That this latter expedition was in truly great style is apparent from the map of Fig. 19, in which its 358 oceanographic stations are marked.

Before the war, Great Britain's main distant activities were centred on the *Discovery* expeditions in Antarctic waters.

Turning to the United States, we see that the two chief institutes dedicated to the study of the oceans are the Woods Hole Oceanographic Institution at Woods Hole (Massachusetts) on the Atlantic Coast; and the Scripps Institution of Oceanography at La Jolla (California) on the Pacific coast. Already, before the war, the former, led by Columbus O'D. Iselin, had done significant work relating to the Gulf Stream.

Japan also rendered good service in oceanographic research in the Pacific Ocean, before the war, while the Russians made important contributions to our body of knowledge in the Arctic Ocean.

Incomplete as this very brief summary of the period before the Second World War must be, that of post-war oceanography, which has made such enormous strides since about 1950, will necessarily be more so.

The United States have increased their fleet of exploration vessels (well supported by the navy) and have equipped oceanographic expeditions in the Atlantic Ocean—for a detailed study of the Gulf Stream among other tasks—as well as in the Pacific and Indian Oceans, expeditions which have provided many new data and generated new ideas.

Great Britain now has its National Institute of Oceanography, headed by G. E. R. Deacon, its new research ship being the third named *Discovery*. Further, there are (among others) the Fisheries Laboratory at Lowestoft, the Marine Biological Association at Plymouth and the Marine Laboratory at Aberdeen.

The Swedes performed a *tour de force* with their *Albatross* expedition round the world in 1947–48, and the Danes with their *Galathea* expedition (1950–52), likewise round the world. Germany has again come to the fore, with oceanographic institutes at Hamburg and Kiel, whence important research work at sea has been carried out under such leaders as G. Boehnecke and G. Dietrich. Also, the work of French and Canadian oceanographers should not be forgotten.

Last, but not least, Russia, too, has emerged with expeditions on the grand scale, not confining her activities to the Arctic Ocean, but also engaging in explorations of the great oceans, including the Antarctic Ocean. The Russian ship *Vityaz* has made extensive exploratory voyages, especially in the Pacific Ocean.

Some of these post-war expeditions were organized within the framework of the International Geophysical Year of 1957–58, which provided new stimuli for oceanographic research. Twice, for instance, an extensive oceanographic campaign was carried out in the northern Atlantic Ocean, in which vessels from various countries collaborated, all this under the auspices of the International Council for the Exploration of the Sea (a European organization).

A very impressive undertaking of the 'sixties was the International Indian Ocean Expedition (1962–65) which was planned by the Scientific

Committee on Oceanic Research (SCOR) and carried out under the auspices of the Intergovernmental Oceanographic Commission (IOC). During this expedition, research ships of many countries operated simultaneously in different parts of this hitherto least known of the oceans.

It would be remiss not to mention the fact that, in many countries, scientific research in the domain of fisheries plays a role by no means insignificant in the exploration of the sea. For this purpose the appropriate institutes have their own vessels.

In the Netherlands, too, the State Institute for Fishery Research, established at IJmuiden, has its own research ship. This, however, has been engaged mainly on biological research in connection with fishing in the North Sea. The Oceanographic and Maritime Meteorological Department of the Royal Netherlands Meteorological Institute specializes in the general field of physical oceanography. In the Netherlands, this involves predominantly North Sea problems, and the study of various problems connected with sea waves and surges, in addition, of course, to further study of the results of the *Snellius* expedition and the making of deep-sea observations aboard the weather ships in the Atlantic Ocean. One of the greatest problems raised by the North Sea with which this country has had to cope since the war is that of storm surges; and here considerable progress has been made. Currents, mixing processes and the water budget of the North Sea, especially in view of possible contamination (radioactivity), present an important problem for the immediate future. Efforts to solve this problem, and that of waves (which affects coastal defence and shipping) require the close co-operation of the various bodies involved, which include, apart from those already mentioned, the Netherlands Institute for Sea Research, at Den Helder, which is especially concerned with marine biology and marine chemistry, the Hydrographic Department of the Royal Netherlands Navy, the Geological Institute of Groningen University, and the Rijkswaterstaat.

Finally, a word about the international organizations having marine research within their terms of reference. The International Association of Physical Oceanography (affiliated to the Union Géophysique et Géodesique Internationale) is an organization for physical oceanography embracing the whole world. Further, the majority of European countries are associated with the International Council for the Exploration of the Sea, which has a permanent office at Copenhagen. This has both biological and physical oceanographical research on its programme, in connection with scientific fishery research among other things.

Among the bodies set up after the war are the Scientific Committee on Oceanic Research (SCOR), established by the International Council of Scientific Unions (ICSU) and the Intergovernmental Oceanographic Commission (IOC), which was established in 1960 under the auspices of UNESCO, and was the first world-wide organization covering the whole domain of oceanology.

SPECIAL MEANS OF INVESTIGATION

Seeing under Water

Before concluding this chapter, which has given a bird's-eye view of oceanic exploration, we must dwell briefly on two new means of studying the sea which, although hitherto employed to only a limited extent, are too interesting to be passed over, since they have enabled Man to look right *into* the deep realm of the sea, either directly or indirectly. These are, first, the bathysphere, bathyscaphe and various other diving vehicles, and secondly underwater photography.

We might also mention the submarine, but this is not used for the purpose of *seeing* under water. As a research vessel it has been used less for oceanic research than for the study of gravity (following Vening Meinesz). It is otherwise where the successful voyage of America's *Nautilus* is concerned. This submarine, coming from the Pacific Ocean in August, 1958, was the first ever to travel under the polar ice to reach the North Pole; whence she proceeded under the ice to the Atlantic Ocean. It will be obvious that such a vessel also opens up possibilities for marine research in those regions.

The bathysphere and bathyscaphe are the extreme and perfected versions of the various contrivances such as the diving-bell, the diver's helmet, the diving-suit and the aqualung, which were invented by man to enable him to spend some time under water. But, whereas these limit the venturesome to shallow water—where, nevertheless, there is a whole world of strange and wonderful things to see—the bathysphere and bathyscaphe have been designed to withstand great pressures in order to carry men and instruments down to great depths.

The bathysphere, constructed by the American engineer Barton, was a steel sphere capable of holding two people; attached to a ship's cable it was lowered into the sea. We know of the descents Barton made in 1934 (with the biologist Beebe) down to 925 metres, and in 1949. The deepest descent took place off the coast of California, and took him down to 1375 metres.

The *bathyscaphe*, an invention of Piccard's, is not suspended from a cable like the bathysphere, but floats freely under water, as an airship floats in the atmosphere. It is shaped like a small submarine with a metal sphere underneath in which the crew sits. The operation of a system of valves in the upper section admits sea-water to increase the weight of the craft and thus cause it to descend. The crew jettison ballast when the craft is required to ascend again. The first model, made in 1948, did not come up to expectations. In 1953 Piccard succeeded in reaching a depth of 3100 metres in the Mediterranean with an improved version, called the *Trieste*. Subsequent highly successful descents were those of the French bathyscaphe *FNRS* 3, in which Houot and Wilm of the French Navy reached a depth of 4050 metres in February 1954. This took place in the Atlantic Ocean, off Dakar. Lastly, in January 1960, the *Trieste* (in American service), with Jacques Piccard, son of the inventor, and the American Naval Officer, Walsh, aboard, went down into the Marianas Trench in the Pacific Ocean to 10,900 metres, practically the greatest depth occurring in the oceans of the world (see p. 22).

As the bathyscaphe is also able to propel itself horizontally under its own power, those on board can examine the sea bottom. Searchlights illumine the surroundings, which are observed from a porthole. The pressure on the walls and windows of the craft at 10,000 metres is no less than 100,000 kilograms per square decimetre!

Besides the bathyscaphe, various other sorts of diving vehicles have been constructed in recent years, but we shall not enter into details about these.

Successful attempts have been made in the past decades to take deep-sea photographs with an unaccompanied camera. The camera is, of course, watertight and resistant to sea-water. Up to the present *underwater photography* has been used mainly to obtain pictures of the sea bottom. For instance, as soon as a projecting arm fitted to the camera touches the bottom, it releases the shutter at exactly the right height to ensure a sharp focus of the bottom. A flashlight flashes simultaneously with the opening of the shutter.

Underwater photography provides geologists with valuable supplementary information about the sea bottom, in addition to the bottom samples obtained with soil-grabs and corers; this includes a variety of details (ripples for example) which show what the surface of the bottom looks like.

Such photographed features are a great help in the study of the processes involved in the formation of the bottom topography.

Furthermore, underwater photography is very useful to biologists, who are thus able to see photographs of living creatures in their natural environment, deep down in the sea. Plate V is a reproduction of one of these photographs showing a small part of the sea-bed with a few animals. This photograph was taken off the east coast of the United States, in the Atlantic Ocean.

Chapter Two

THE WATER OF THE SEAS

Roll on, thou deep and dark blue ocean!
(Byron)

EVERYBODY knows that sea-water is salt; but it is probably not common knowledge that it contains a large, varied collection of chemical substances in solution, namely, minerals, organic substances and dissolved gases. The study of these substances is a full-time job. And that is only the chemical side of the matter. What, however, do the substances, present in varying amounts, mean to all those organisms that live in the sea? This, too, is a subject of profound study, on which both chemists and biologists are engaged, for these problems lie on the borderline between chemistry and biology. Scientists are not only concerned with the substances occurring in appreciable quantities, like ordinary common salt, but equally with some which occur only as traces, like iodine. The whole constitution of sea-water is of the utmost importance to animate life in the oceans.

Now that constitution is governed in a major degree by the fact that all water masses in the oceans, from the surface down to the bottom, are in continual circulation. Although this circulation is very sluggish in many places, especially at great depths, it is nevertheless continuous. Obviously therefore, the composition of the sea-water at any given place and so, all life in it, depend to a very large extent on this circulation.

Reciprocally, the composition of sea-water also affects its movement. It would be fair to say that small differences in salinity are among the factors controlling water circulation in the mass.

We shall have more to say about these matters presently.

WHAT DOES SEA-WATER CONTAIN?

Let us see what sea-water contains in solution, apart from the (sometimes microscopically small) living organisms, and how chemists go about analysing sea-water.

To begin with, Table 4 on p. 40 shows the principal constituents of sea-water.

The reader will have noticed that common salt, or sodium chloride, does not appear in the table, despite our statement that it does occur in sea-water. This is because most of the dissolved substances in it are split up. Sodium chloride (common salt), for instance, splits up into an electrically-charged sodium particle (sodium ion) and a charged chlorine particle of opposite sign (chloride ion). The fact that these constituents are electrically charged—small though the charges may be—has important consequences. Not that a salt solution of the kind would thereby be electrically charged as a whole, for, as has been said, the two constituents into which the salt molecule has been broken down have opposite charges, as a result of which those charges in sum neutralize each other. What does happen, however, is that sea-water becomes a good conductor of an electric current, because the sodium and chlorine ions individually can carry their charges. If we boil down sea-water, however, we do not get sodium and chlorine separately; what we get is the salt sodium chloride.

Table 4

Principal Constituents of Sea-Water of 19 ‰ Chlorinity

Constituent	g/kg of Sea-water	Proportion to the Sum (%)
Chloride (Cl $^-$)	18·980	55·044
Sulphate (SO$_4$ $^-$ $^-$)	2·649	7·682
Bicarbonate (HCO$_3$ $^-$)	0·140	0·406
Bromide (Br $^-$)	0·065	0·189
Fluoride (F $^-$)	0·001	0·003
Boric Acid (H$_3$BO$_3$)	0·026	0·075
Sodium (Na $^+$)	10·556	30·613
Magnesium (Mg$^+$ $^+$)	1·272	3·689
Calcium (Ca$^+$ $^+$)	0·400	1·160
Potassium (K $^+$)	0·380	1·102
Strontium (Sr$^+$ $^+$)	0·013	0·038
	34·482	100·00
Water (with traces of other substances)	965·518	
Total	1000·00	

If this were the only component of sea-water, we could safely say that it contains common salt, though broken down; but as it also contains other substances, for example potassium and bromine, would we be justified in stating that potassium bromide is also present? We could do so; but then we could with equal right say that potassium chloride and sodium bromide are present, because the potassium and the bromine are not combined in the water, any more than are the sodium and chlorine. That is why no salts, no compounds, are shown in the table, but 'ionic' constituents. This is not to say that the residue after evaporation of a given amount of sea-water would consist of those constituents as shown in Table 4; it would consist of various *compounds* of those constituents; for example, magnesium chloride, magnesium sulphate, calcium sulphate, etc., and especially sodium chloride, because, as the figures show, the sodium and chloride predominate.

The last column gives the percentages in which the various constituents occur, not relative to the water but to their own sum; when added up they give 100 per cent. Apparently sodium and chlorine together constitute 85 per cent. of all solid substances dissolved in the sea. We say, advisedly, *solid* substances, because the gases are ignored in the last column for the reason that the gas content of sea-water is subject to considerable variation from place to place and from time to time. The other substances occur in fairly constant proportions, whether in the water of the North Sea, the Gulf of Mexico or the Antarctic Ocean. Note that we said the *proportions* are fairly constant; that is to say, the figures in the last column. It does not mean that the total quantity per litre of sea-water may not vary from place to place. As a whole, sea-water may be more or less 'dilute', so to speak, but the relative proportion of the dissolved substances is the same. Suppose we added a litre of fresh water to a litre of sea-water; then half as much would be dissolved per litre, but the relative proportion of the dissolved components would have remained the same. And that is approximately how things are everywhere in the sea.

The last column of the table, therefore, does not show how much dissolved solid matter there is in a litre of sea-water; for this we have to turn to the middle column. It will at once be seen, however, that the figures in this middle column are merely an example, because sea-water does not everywhere contain the same amount; but it is a good example, because it represents approximately the average, the figures standing for the number of grams of each component per *kilogram*, not per litre, of sea-water. Admittedly a litre of sea-water does weigh roughly a kilogram, but not exactly (it is a little more: usually between 1020 and 1030 grams). At the foot of that column will be found the figure for the total salt content as grams per kilogram of sea-water, or, parts per thousand by weight (indicated by the symbol ‰).

The list of components given here is far from complete. While it is true that these account for virtually the whole of the weight of the matter dissolved in the water, there are also elements, of which minute traces have been identified in sea-water, that may nevertheless be of importance to the economy of the sea and, apparently, are a necessity of life to certain organisms. Chemical analyses of sea-water have detected the merest traces of iodine, for example, which is an important constituent of some seaweeds; and copper, which occurs in the blood of crabs. Until recently, several chemical elements which had been found in marine organisms could not be demonstrated in sea-water itself by direct analysis; for example, cobalt in lobsters and mussels, nickel in molluscs, and lead in the ashes of various marine organisms. Even before these very elements had been chemically demonstrated in sea-water, scientists were forced to conclude from their presence in living creatures that they must be present there, and that the living cells were therefore better at extracting and concentrating these substances than were the chemists.

It is not really surprising to find that all these chemical elements occur in the sea as well as in the earth's crust. After all, rivers unceasingly carry down waste products of the land and mountains into the sea. Rain and snow fall on the mountains, the water runs down the slopes, the snow thaws in spring and the melted water descends in torrents; and all this water carries with it fragments of rock and soil as well as dissolved material, discharging this matter into brooks and rivers, which finally discharge their waters into the sea.

Seen in this light it is not surprising, therefore, that the sea should contain all those elements. The puzzling fact is rather that the proportions in which the components occur in sea-water and in rivers are so totally different. Whence comes that excess of sodium and chlorine in the dissolved substances of sea-water? And should not the supply from rivers constantly increase the quantity of certain substances in the sea?

Up to the present, no satisfactory answer has been forthcoming to the first question. So far as the second question is concerned, we have to bear in mind that the living organisms are also continually binding certain elements from sea-water and that some species incorporate them in their skeletons of silica or lime which, on the death of the organisms, sink as casts to the bottom, accumulate there and form sedimentary strata.

Radioactive matter also occurs naturally in the sea, albeit in exceedingly minute concentrations, for instance, uranium in concentrations of 1–3 milligrams per cubic metre and radium in concentrations of 0·03–0·13 milligrams per million cubic metres. In addition there are elements like radioactive potassium and radioactive carbon (radiocarbon or ^{14}C). We shall revert to this last-named at the end of the final chapter.

To wind up this summary of the various elements occurring in sea-water, let us work out the total stock of those substances in the oceans. We shall then see that the quantities in all the waters of the oceans taken together of even those elements of which traces could only be found in sea-water by extremely delicate analysis, are quite formidable.

The total volume of all oceans and seas together is estimated to be 1370 million cubic kilometres, or $1·37 \times 10^{18} m^3$, (1,370,000 billion[1] cubic metres). A cubic metre of sea-water is 1000 litres and contains an average of roughly 3·6 kilograms of dissolved salts. Hence the oceans and seas contain a total of $1·37 \times 10^{18} \times 3·6$ kg, or roughly 5000 billion tons of salts. Dried and spread over the whole earth, this would produce a layer 45 metres thick.

The iodine content of sea-water is approximately 0·05 milligrams per litre, which means that 1 cubic metre of sea-water contains 0·05 gram of iodine. This gives us a stock of 70 thousand million tons of iodine in all the waters of the oceans.

The gold content of sea-water is approximately 0·000006 milligrams per

[1] Billion = million × million.

litre, which comes to 0·006 milligrams in 1 cubic metre of sea-water. This gives us a stock of gold of eight million tons in all the waters of the oceans!

SALINITY DETERMINATION

For many purposes it is not necessary to know the concentrations of the individual elements in sea-water; it is enough to know the total salt content, or 'salinity'. The term salinity as used by an oceanographer does not mean *exactly* the same thing as the total salt content, but the difference is very small and need not concern us here. There are various ways of estimating the

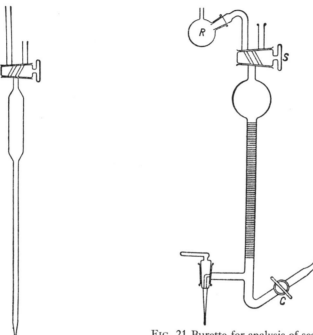

FIG. 20 Pipette for measuring out exactly a small quantity of sea-water for analysis.

FIG. 21 Burette for analysis of sea-water. The connection with the reservoir of the titrating fluid passes along *C*. The tap is on the left. *R* is a glass overflow cup; *S* is a two-way tap.

salinity of a sample of sea-water, but the most commonly used method is a chemical 'titration'. As we already know, the principal constituents of sea-water occur in very nearly constant proportions; thus to determine salinity it is sufficient to determine any one of the major constituents; the salinity can then be calculated by simple proportion.

The method generally used is to add to a measured quantity of the sea-water a solution of silver nitrate of precisely-known strength. The sea-water is measured with a special pipette (see Fig. 20) and the silver is added from an accurately graduated 'burette' (Fig. 21). A small quantity of potassium chromate or fluorescein is added to the water before titration; the silver reacts with the chloride and bromide in the water, forming a white precipitate of silver chloride and bromide. When all these ions are used up, the chromate or other 'indicator' produces a change in colour; chromate gives a brick-red colour, and fluorescein a rose pink. The amount of silver nitrate used can then be read off from the burette, and from this reading the concentration of chloride and bromide can be calculated. It is usual to assume, for the calculation, that all the salt reacting with the silver is chloride, and the figure obtained with this assumption is called the 'chlorinity'. Chlorinity, like salinity, is always expressed in parts per thousand by weight, that is, in grams of chloride in a kilogram of sea-water. Salinity is computed from chlorinity by multiplying by 1·805 and adding 0·03 to the answer. By means of the special glassware shown in Figs. 20 and 21, the salinity can be determined to a precision of about 0·01‰.

Another way of determining the salinity of sea-water is to measure the electric resistance. The resistance of a salt solution depends both on the concentration of salt and on the temperature. Thus a tube 10 cm long and 1 cm^2 in cross-section, filled with sea-water of salinity 34·5‰ at 15·0°C will have a resistance of about 236 ohms. If the salinity were half as great, the resistance would be about twice as much (actually a little less than twice). The temperature, however, also has a considerable effect; at 20°C the same sample would have a resistance of only 211 ohms. Thus to calculate the salinity from the resistance we must also know, or allow for, the temperature.

Various instruments, usually called 'salinometers', have been designed to measure the electrical conductivity of sea-water for the purpose of finding the salinity. In most of them the tube containing the water is mounted in a 'thermostat' designed to keep it at a constant temperature, usually 15°C. In some of them the thermostat also holds another, similar tube filled with 'standard' sea-water of accurately-known salinity and the meter compares the resistance of the standard with that of the unknown sample. The more accurate salinometers can measure the salinity to about 0·002‰, and they are much faster to use than the chlorinity titration. Salinometers can also be used very well on board research ships at sea, where the chemical method is difficult. Because of these advantages, they are tending to replace the chemical method for the most accurate work.

Instruments have also been designed which can be lowered into the sea from a ship, and which will measure the resistance of the surrounding water. In some, ingenious electric circuits compensate for the temperature variations of the water, so that the oceanographer on board the ship can read the salinity directly without needing to take samples of the water. These instruments are not as precise as the laboratory salinometers, but they make possible a very rapid survey of water conditions; in areas such as river estuaries, where large salinity variations are common, this rapidity makes it possible for example, to complete, during a few hours, a survey which would be quite impracticable by other means.

Other physical properties which are dependent on salinity are *specific gravity* and *refractive index* to light; both are also affected by temperature, but if either property can be accurately measured, and the temperature determined, it is possible to calculate the salinity. Instruments for measuring specific gravity are called *hydrometers*; Fig. 22 shows one type of hydrometer. Unless very elaborate and expensive apparatus is used, specific gravity and refractive index measurements are less precise as a means of determining salinity than are conductivity measurement or titration.

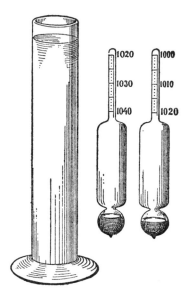

FIG. 22 *Hydrometer*. The graduation down to which the stem of the hydrometer sinks into the liquid indicates the specific gravity.

SALINITY VARIATIONS FROM PLACE TO PLACE

In the example given in Table 4 (p. 40), the salinity is calculated as 34·33‰. In the vast majority of places in the oceans, the salinity lies between 34 and 37‰; so it varies within narrow limits. In the North Sea it is predominantly between 34 and 35‰. See Fig. 138.

The salinity of the sea is lowest wherever there is much rainfall, or where many large rivers empty into the sea. In the places receiving a great deal of fresh water in this way, the salinity of the sea may be less than 34‰. In the Wadden Sea, for instance, the salt content is liable to vary from 34‰ to only a fraction of this figure close to the IJselmeer[1]; it is also less than 34‰ in the vicinity of Newfoundland, due not only to the fresh water discharged by the St. Lawrence River and the rivers of Labrador, but also to the pack-ice and icebergs floating down from the north. Here they give off their melt-water, which contains far less salt than does oceanic water; indeed, in the case of icebergs, the melt-water contains no salt. We shall have more to say about ice in the sea in Chapter 3.

The salinity of the Baltic is very low, less than 10‰ in most places; in the Gulfs of Bothnia and Finland it is as little as 5‰. This is because many

[1] It is 0·5–1·5‰ under normal circumstances in the IJselmeer.

rivers and rivulets discharge into them, while salt, oceanic water enters only slowly through the narrows connecting the Baltic Sea with the Atlantic Ocean. The surface salinity of the Arctic Ocean is likewise comparatively low, especially opposite the coast of Northern Siberia, where the great Siberian rivers discharge; but as this water remains on the surface (fresh water being lighter than salt water), the salinity at greater depths in the Arctic Ocean is nevertheless normal.

The salinity of the oceans is high wherever strong evaporation is continually extracting water from the sea, with the result that the water left behind holds a higher proportion of salt. This is especially so in subtropical regions, where the barometer reading is mostly high, and consequently there is much sunshine and little rainfall. In the Sargasso Sea for instance, in the middle of the Atlantic Ocean at about latitude 25° N., the salinity in summer is more than 37‰. The high salinity of the Gulf Stream, too, is due in part to the fact that some of its water comes from the Sargasso Sea. Salinity is higher still in the Mediterranean and Red Seas, being above 38‰ in the former and as much as 41‰ in the northern part of the latter. This is because these seas do not receive much fresh water either from rivers or from rain, while at the same time they are exposed to severe evaporation owing to their position; furthermore, being almost enclosed, they have scanty communication with the open ocean.

In the Mediterranean, that communication is maintained through the narrow Straits of Gibraltar. Here, water flows in from the Atlantic Ocean, notably along the surface, while at greater depth, a counter-current carries the much more saline water of the Mediterranean Sea over the sill of the strait into the Atlantic. (More follows on this subject in the final chapter.)

Chart 3, at the end of this book, shows the distribution of the surface salinity of the oceans in the northern summer. Broadly speaking, salinity is high in subtropical latitudes both in the northern and southern hemispheres. It is lower at moderate and higher latitudes where there is more precipitation, but also in the equatorial regions between the two subtropical belts. That is because there is more rainfall in equatorial regions than in the subtropical belts. (Meteorologists speak of the 'subtropical high-pressure belts'.)

SALINITY IN THE DEEP SEA

The differences in salinity which occur in the deep sea are smaller still than those at the surface. In all oceans salinity is between 34·5 and 35‰ at great depths. Just because the differences there are so small, it is necessary that the observations made should be carried out with the utmost possible precision, as within those narrow limits even *minute* differences in salinity produce small differences in specific gravity which affect the whole water circulation of the deep ocean. We shall be reverting to this in the last chapter.

DEEP-SEA WATER-SAMPLERS

Samples of sea-water are brought up from the depths of the oceans by special instruments called 'water-samplers' or 'water-bottles', of which there are various types, though they all operate on the same principle.

Such a water-bottle usually consists of a metal cylinder with openings at top and bottom so that, as it descends attached to a line, water runs freely through it. An Ekman water-bottle has round openings which are closed at the desired depth by top and bottom plates fitted with rubber gaskets. In the type known as the Nansen reversing water-bottle, in common use nowadays, the two openings are closed by plug-valves, each of which closes by a quarter

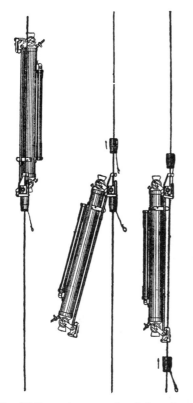

FIG. 23 Reversing water-bottle in action.   FIG. 24 Meter wheel.

turn. A Nansen water-bottle is illustrated in Figure 23. A series of water-bottles is always let down on the same line. Steel wire rope, about 4 mm thick, is generally used for work of this kind at great depths.

Each water-sampler carries one or two thermometer holders to take deep-sea, or reversing thermometers, about which more presently. As it descends, the water bottle is attached both above and below to the wire rope, below by a clamping-screw. The upper fixture, however, is detached by pressure upon a pawl, so that the sampler turns over, rotating about the lower point of support. Through this action the openings above and below are automatically closed by rotating valves.

The procedure is, then, to pay out the steelwire, attaching the water bottles to it at certain distances from each other, and thus drop them down into the deep (see Plate II). The sampler to go farthest down is attached first, and that which is to remain nearest the surface, last. The wire rope passes over a measuring wheel with a counter attached, from which the length of wire paid out can be read (see Fig. 24).

When the instruments have reached the desired depth, a drop-weight messenger is released along the wire. When this reaches the topmost sampler it falls on the pawl referred to above, with the result that the sampler turns over and thus hermetically seals itself. The drop-weight cannot pass this sampler, but it does detach another messenger previously suspended from the sampler (see Fig. 23); this now slides down the wire, acting upon the next sampler. The process is repeated until all samplers have turned over and are sealed. Under water, the speed of a messenger of this kind is roughly 200 metres a minute. When enough time has elapsed for the whole operation to be completed after the release of the messenger, the wire with its whole burden is hauled up, the water samplers are taken off one by one and placed on a rack which can hold a great number of them.

Any desired amount of the sample of sea-water for analysis can be drawn off into a bottle from the water-sampler by opening an air vent at the top of it and turning on a tap at its base. There are always one or more laboratories aboard an oceanographic research vessel for various sorts of work.

Thousands of metres of wire rope of about 4 mm thickness are needed to raise samples of sea-water from great depths—more than 10,000 metres at the deepest places. As this is in itself a considerable weight (about 70 kg per 1000 metres), a powerful electric winch is used which does the work at reasonable speed. Serial sampling is, for all that, a time-consuming business, at all events when great depths are involved.

For a full serial analysis it is the practice to obtain samples of water from the following depths: Surface, 10 metres, 20, 30, 50, 75, 100, 200, 300, 400, 500, 600, 800, 1000, 1200, 1500, 2000, 2500, 3000, 4000, 5000 and at every further thousand metres, and finally, at the bottom. As a rule, not more than ten water bottles are attached to the line at the same time; so, if the levels at which a water sample is required exceed this number, the operation has to be repeated. It is customary to append fewer instruments simultaneously to the wire at the greater depths than at the shallower ones. (See Fig. 25.) Hence the time required for a complete serial sampling depends on the depth of the ocean where one is operating. At 2000 metres, for instance, one will go down to 300 metres inclusive the first time and from 400 to 2000 metres inclusive the second time. Sometimes the upper series is then repeated once.

In such cases, the first series may take 45 minutes and the second roughly an hour. A station like that (with other things to do as well) will easily take

$2\frac{1}{2}$ to 3 hours. Almost eight hours, altogether, were spent by the *Snellius* expedition on the station above 10,000 metres in the Mindanao Trench.

There does exist an instrument called a 'sea-sampler' consisting of a combination of several small water samplers, each of which is fitted with a device that automatically closes it at a given depth. The underlying principle

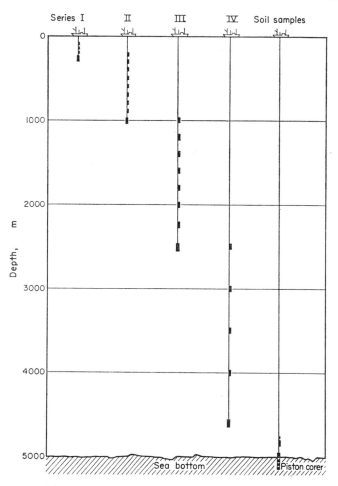

FIG. 25 Oceanographic station. The instruments (water-samplers) are let down in various series on the line.

is that the pressure attains a given value at the depth to which each individual sampler is adjusted. This instrument—which is not intended for great depths—can be immersed from a ship in motion. The line is paid out to a certain depth and then gathered in with a sample of water from each predetermined depth. But it is not a standard instrument yet; serial sampling as described above is still the classic method generally adopted, for the greater depths of any rate.

MEASURING TEMPERATURES AT VARIOUS DEPTHS

At present mainly two instruments are used to measure temperatures in the sea, namely, the reversing thermometer, which is fairly old and is still the standard instrument for precision readings at all depths in the ocean, and the bathythermograph, which provides less exact readings and is only used for the upper layers of water (at the moment down to 300 metres). The great merit of the latter, however, is that it works very rapidly in use; the vessel does not have to stop, as it does when reversing thermometers are used.

In recent years various other sorts of ingenious instruments have been constructed to record temperatures at various depths, but we shall confine our attention to the two types mentioned.

REVERSING THERMOMETERS

These are usually let down together with the water-sampling bottle, to which they are attached; but they can be let down separately, mounted in a turn-over frame which is fitted to the line.

The instrument is a mercury thermometer, the capillary of which narrows and gives off a small branch just above the mercury bulb. A short distance above that the tube loops and widens, but it becomes thin again in the straight piece which is graduated upside down, ending at the top in a second, smaller bulb. In this position (see Figs. 26 and 27), the mercury fills the lower bulb, the whole tube and a small part of the upper, smaller bulb. Naturally, the amount of mercury found above the constriction depends on the temperature; the higher the temperature, the more mercury will there be above the constriction. No reading can be taken in this position, but, if the thermometer is turned over, the mercury thread breaks off at the constriction owing to the weight of the mercury which is suspended under the constriction after the turn-over. This mercury descends into the small bulb, which is now at the bottom, and a reading can be taken from the graduated scale, which is now upright (Fig. 26). It follows from the foregoing that this reading is a measure of the temperature prevailing *at the moment when the thermometer was turned over*; hence the scale gives a direct reading of that temperature.

There remains one difficulty: when, after turning over, the thermometer is taken from the sea and is, therefore, exposed to a different temperature, the broken-off mercury filling the small bulb and part of the tube will expand a little, because the temperature above water is usually higher than in the depths of the sea. Allowance therefore must be made for this; so the reading, which depends upon the air temperature at which it is taken, is corrected by the taking of a reading of this temperature from a small auxiliary thermometer, which is fitted next to the main thermometer in the same glass casing.

The casing of thick glass, which encloses the whole unit, serves to protect the thermometer against the high pressure prevailing in the depths of the

Above: Catch of copepods seen under the microscope.

Below: The floor of the sea at a depth of 1800 metres, with a sea spider and a few serpent-stars. The white object on the line is a fish-hook. The dark cloud is caused by the arm of the camera touching bottom. (Photograph D. M. Owen.)

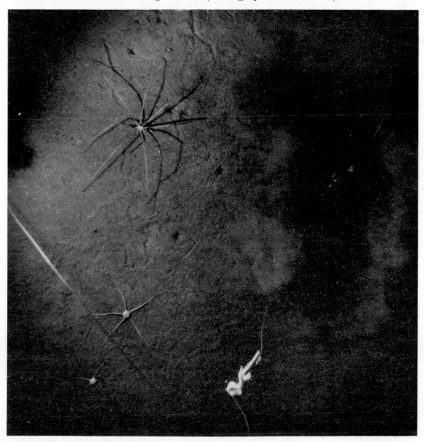

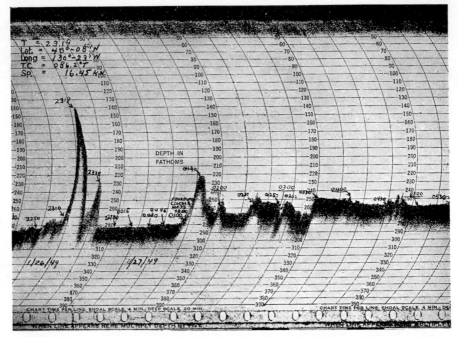

Example of an echo-sounding record. The depths are in fathoms. (Photograph U.S. Hydrographic Office.)

Echo-sounding record with 'phantom bottom', which rises at sundown (arrow). Here the echoes are caused by a layer very rich in certain planktonic creatures. This echogram was recorded in the neighbourhood of Miami, Florida. (Photograph Hersey and Moore.)

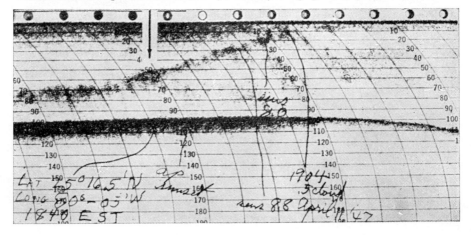

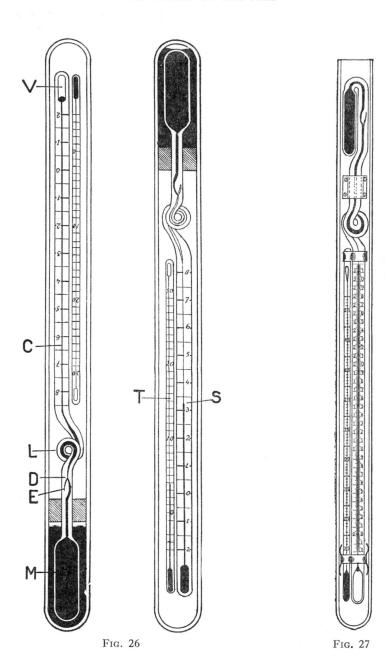

FIG. 26

FIG. 27

FIG. 26 Protected reversing thermometer. On the left, upright (while descending); on the right, turned over (while being raised and read). M = mercury bulb; V = accessory bulb; C = capillary; E = branch; D = break-off point; L = loop; S = temperature reading; T = auxiliary thermometer.

FIG. 27 Unprotected reversing thermometer.

3

sea. We know that the pressure increases by about 1 atmosphere per 10 metres' descent so that the prevailing pressure at 100 metres' depth is 10 atmospheres, at 1000 metres 100 atmospheres and at 10,000 metres 1000 atmospheres. If the glass bulb were not protected, this pressure would compress it to such an extent that the thermometer reading would be far too high; hence the thick glass casing. The lower part of this outer case is filled with mercury, which surrounds the mercury bulb. This is to ensure better transfer of heat between the surrounding sea-water and this mercury bulb.

The reversing thermometer was introduced by Negretti and Zambra of London in 1878, and has become the standard instrument for temperature recording in the deep sea. The best current instruments give a temperature reading accurate to within 0·01°C.

The type described above (Fig. 26) is called a *protected* reversing thermometer, to distinguish it from *unprotected* reversing thermometers, which are also used (Fig. 27).

As we have seen, the effect of submarine pressure is to squeeze extra mercury out of the large bulb, if the mercury container is not protected. Consequently, if we have an unprotected reversing thermometer beside a protected one, the former's reading will be too high, and the difference will provide us with a measure of the prevailing pressure down below. We can deduce the pressure from this difference and with it, therefore, the depth, because the pressure is related to the depth. Hence an unprotected reversing thermometer combined with a protected one serves as a pressure or depth gauge.

Unprotected reversing thermometers are so constructed that the apparent temperature is raised by about 0·01°C per metre of water. For example, if the protected one registers 6·43°C and the unprotected one 17·68°C, the difference, amounting to 11·25°C, indicates a pressure of roughly 1125 metres of water.

It is necessary to know precisely (by calibration) the apparent temperature rise equivalent to 1 metre of water in order to be able accurately to determine the depth; but, given this knowledge, one can measure the depth to a precision of about one-half per cent.

THE BATHYTHERMOGRAPH

Although other instruments have been devised for recording the prevailing temperatures in the oceans, we do not intend to tax the reader's patience with as detailed a description of them as we have just given of reversing thermometers. There is one, however, which has come much to the fore since the Second World War and which, we think, merits a little closer attention; it is the bathythermograph, an invention of A. F. Spilhaus.

A thermograph is, literally, a 'heat-writer', hence a temperature-recording instrument. As was explained earlier, the prefix 'bathy' means 'deep'. It is, therefore, an instrument that registers the temperature at various depths. Its outstanding merit is the speed with which it does what is required of it. The vessel does not have to stop, continuing on its way while the fairly heavy instrument, attached to a metal wire, descends into the sea. If the wire is paid out and hauled up again by a motor-driven winch, the whole operation can be completed in about five minutes.

The instrument does not go down to very great depths. Some go 50 metres, some to 135 metres and others down to 270 metres. So it by no means supersedes reversing thermometers for deep-sea work. Nor is its precision comparable to that of the latter. But it does quickly give a detailed picture of the temperature in the upper layers of the sea. Figure 28 illustrates the kind

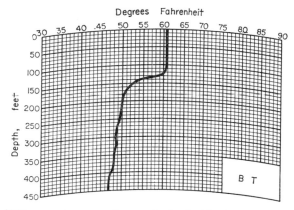

FIG. 28 Temperature recording as obtained with a bathythermograph.

of recording one gets. The black line is a graph from which the temperature can at once be read against the depth; the vertical scale divisions show the temperatures, while the slightly curved lines from left to right are the depth lines. Each point of the black line belongs to a given depth, which can be read on the left (in feet); the position of the point in question between the vertical lines gives the temperature prevailing at that depth in degrees Fahrenheit, and can be read at the top.

In this case we see that, at the spot where the recording was taken, the same temperature as at the surface prevailed down to 36 metres, after which it dropped with increasing depth, first rapidly and then more slowly.

A bathythermograph does not emerge from the water with a graph like this. All it has is a small, dark-coated glass with the line which is black in our graph showing white, having been scratched out of the coating; and there is no graduation on the glass at all. The picture we see in Fig. 28 is obtained by the use of the dark glass with its white line as a negative; it is magnified, while another glass, the 'calibrating glass', which carries the graduated scales as a grid, is held against the plate and photographed with it; thus the ultimate picture shows the temperature line and scales as in Figure 28.

Many thousands of recordings have been taken with this instrument, especially by naval vessels; for these recordings can be used to estimate what the propagation of sound (the direction of which is influenced by the distribution of temperature in the layers of water) will be like, which is a necessary datum for detecting submarines by means of horizontal sound-tracking (Asdic, Sonar).

The bathythermograph itself is illustrated in Plate VIII.

TEMPERATURES IN THE SEA

Figure 28 gives us some idea of temperature distribution in the upper layers of the sea, at any rate in those parts of the ocean *not* too far north or south, i.e. at moderate and low latitudes outside the areas belonging, and adjacent, to the Polar Seas.

We said that Fig. 28 gave us *some* idea of temperature distribution, because, although this is *often* as represented there, it is not invariably so. Notably, there is not always an 'isothermal' upper layer (a layer of the same temperature at different depths). On sunny afternoons, for instance, if there is not too much wind, the temperature is highest on the surface of the sea, so that it is lower everywhere beneath it. And even if there is an isothermal layer, owing to mixing of the waters, the thickness of that layer is liable to vary considerably. That depth was 36 metres in Fig. 28, but sometimes it may be as much as 150 metres, especially in the cold season. The layer immediately below it, in which the greatest drop in temperature takes place is called a *thermocline*. We shall touch on this again in our final chapter.

The temperature of the surface water varies very much in the different parts of the oceans of the world. Whereas in the North Sea it may vary between (roughly) 5°C and 18°C (cf. Figs. 139 and 140), it may sometimes rise to as much as 30°C in such tropical parts as the China Sea and Gulf of Mexico, and higher still in some almost enclosed border seas. Almost notorious in this respect is the Persian Gulf, where a water temperature of 33°C is not exceptional. The average temperature distribution on the surface of all oceans in the month of August is shown on Chart 2 at the end of this book.

Now, however, let us get down into the depths. The drop in temperature, the beginning of which is to be seen in Fig. 28, continues, and at great depths—2000 metres and more—the water is ice-cold in all seas, including those in the Tropics, the temperatures varying from a couple of degrees above zero to almost two degrees (Celsius) below zero in the Polar Seas. In the latter seas the water is around freezing point at all depths as well as at the surface.

It is a known fact that the freezing point of salt water is not at 0°C but lower, and the saltier the water, the lower it is. Ocean water only begins to freeze at −1·9°C.

Two typical series of observations, illustrating the described course of the temperature in the deep sea, are given in Table 5. One series comes from a station in the tropics, the other from a station in Antarctic waters; both were reported by the German *Meteor* expedition in the South Atlantic.

Table 5

A Tropical (*left*) and Antarctic (*right*) Observation Station in the South Atlantic Ocean
(*Meteor* Expedition)

Depth (m)	Temp. (°C)	Salt (‰)	Depth (m)	Temp. (°C)	Salt (‰)
0	25·52	36·12	0	1·63	34·15
50	25·58	36·11	50	1·35	34·17
100	22·92	36·43	100	−1·50	34·38
150	17·28	35·93	150	−0·30	34·59
200	12·79	35·25	200	0·40	34·67
300	8·77	34·80	300	0·41	34·68
400	7·46	34·65	400	0·37	34·70
600	5·75	34·52	600	0·29	34·70
800	4·42	34·48	800	0·20	34·695
1000	3·95	34·60	1000	0·11	34·685
1500	3·97	34·91	1500	−0·07	34·68
2000	3·29	34·96	2000	−0·255	34·67
2500	2·90	34·93	2500	−0·36	34·67
3000	2·775	34·92	3000	−0·42	34·66
4000	1·73	34·83	4000	−0·55	34·64
5000	0·72	34·72			
5500	0·43	34·685			

TEMPERATURE, SALINITY AND SPECIFIC GRAVITY

We find then that, generally speaking, the temperature drops with increasing depth; generally, we say, because here too there are exceptions. Very occasionally, warmer water is found under a colder layer above, as when a cold air stream rapidly cools off the surface while the water below retains its warmth. The same may happen on quiet winter nights, when the surface water cools through radiation more quickly than the water underneath it.

A situation of this kind is only temporary, on the surface. But it also occurs in some places in the depths of the ocean, particularly in very deep basins, when the temperature, which is only a degree or two above zero (or lower) rises slightly at further increasing depth. An example will be found in Table 6. These temperature readings were taken by the *Snellius* expedition in 1930, notably in one of the very deepest trenches, the Mindanao Trench to the east of the Philippines. It will be noted that, as from 3500 metres, the temperature rises slightly at increasing depth.

A temperature distribution of this kind is not just temporary, it is practically permanent; we know that the temperatures are scarcely apt to change at all at these great depths.

A question now arises which we shall have to consider. It is easy enough to see why colder water lies under warmer water, for the colder water is heavier. But how can warmer water—however little warmer—come to be under colder water? Can that lighter water remain permanently under the heavier? How can this be?

We may remember what we learned at school about the specific gravity of water, which is highest at 4°C because water cooling to below 4°C again begins to expand; so that, when the temperature drops below 4°C, the specific gravity does not increase, but decreases again. Thus water of 1°C is

Table 6

Snellius Station 262 (Mindanao Trench)

Depth (m)	Temp. (°C)	Salinity	Sigma
0	28·8	34·44	21·7
50	28·24	34·30	
100	25·74	34·69	23·3
150	20·24	34·885	
200	15·20	34·605	26·5
300	10·50	34·44	27·8
400	8·60	34·47	28·6
600	6·48	34·52	29·9
800	5·35	34·53	31·0
1000	4·47	34·55	32·0
1500	3·10	34·585	34·5
2000	2·24	34·605	36·9
2500	1·82	34·64	39·2
3000	1·65	34·66	41·5
3500	1·585	34·67	43·7
4000	1·595	34·67	45·9
4500	1·645	34·67	48·0
5000	1·715	34·67	50·1
6000	1·855	34·67	54·3
7000	2·005	34·68	58·4
8000	2·16	34·69	62·4
9000	2·31	34·68	66·4
10,000	2·43	34·67	70·1

lighter than water of 2°C and that of 2°C is lighter than that of 3°C. All very well, but this applies to *pure* water, not to sea-water in which so much salt is dissolved. The highest specific gravity of sea-water is not at 4°C, but at its freezing point, at all events if its salt content exceeds 24‰. Hence the lower the temperature, the heavier does sea-water become. So the riddle is not solved yet.

So far, we have been considering only the influence of temperature upon specific gravity. Of course the salt content also affects it, so that slightly warmer water can sometimes be heavier than somewhat cooler water, if the former contains more salt. But a glance at the third column of Table 6 shows that the solution does not lie here either.

There is, however, yet another determining factor involved in the specific gravity of sea-water; that is the *pressure*. With increasing pressure, the volume of a certain mass of sea-water with given temperature and salinity decreases somewhat. True, the compressibility of water is only slight, but enormous pressures are involved at the depths of the ocean, namely, approximately 500 atmospheres at 5000 metres and roughly 1000 atmospheres at 10,000 metres. Owing to those high pressures, water at the same temperature and salinity, has a slightly higher specific gravity (because it is more compressed) at a depth of 10,000 metres than at 5000 metres. And so it may come to pass that, notwithstanding the somewhat higher temperature, water at greater depth may have a little higher specific gravity than has water at less depth which is colder. That is also the situation in the case under discussion. The fourth column of Table 6 shows the specific gravity. The figures in this column, headed with the Greek sigma, give the difference of the specific gravity from 1 and that multiplied by 1000; for example, 25·6 means that the specific gravity is 1·0256.

This nevertheless does not explain how a temperature distribution such as was found by the *Snellius* expedition in the Mindanao Trench can continue to exist. It is a question of the stability of layers of water, which should be formulated as follows: assuming a disturbance of such proportions that a given quantity of water is displaced from its own level to a higher or lower one, will the prevailing forces of pressure restore the previous state of affairs (when the equilibrium was *stable*), or will they push the displaced water further still from its own level (when the equilibrium was *unstable*)? If there are no differences in salinity, the answer depends upon the temperature of the displaced water. Say that it has been displaced upwards, the condition will be unstable if, *after the displacement*, the water is warmer than its surroundings, but stable if it is colder than the new environment, because if warmer it is lighter, if colder it is heavier, under equal pressure.

Now, however, we come to the crucial point. The temperature does not remain unchanged if a compressible substance undergoes reduction of pressure and hence expands. This is called adiabatic cooling through expansion; we see the reverse, i.e. adiabatic heating through compression, at the base of a bicycle pump. Now water displaced upward is under reduced pressure, and therefore expands a little, whereby it cools down slightly. Thus, to find out whether the water layers are stable or unstable, we have to know how much cooling takes place during a certain upward displacement. We shall say more about this in our final chapter; at the moment it will suffice to note that it appears from the calculations that, even where temperatures rise at increasing depth in the Mindanao Trench, the stratification of the waters still remains stable, except, probably, the very bottom layer resting on the floor of the ocean, which receives a little extra warmth from the earth.

Lastly, we have to ask why it is that the temperature at those great depths increases towards the bottom, instead of continuing to decrease in the normal manner. This question is tied up with the whole problem of deep-sea circulation, which is to be discussed in the final chapter. The question relates to an exception to the rule of temperature distribution; so full justice cannot be done to the answer until the cause of the rule itself is understood. All we wish to say at present is that the icy cold prevailing everywhere at great depths has its origin in the polar regions, whence icy water descends and flows through all deep ocean basins. Now this cold bottom water can only enter a basin like the Mindanao Trench over the far shallower margins— over a sill—whence it drops some thousands of metres along the slope of the basin to the ultimate depths. As it does so, the pressure increases and the water is slightly compressed, which causes a rise in temperature (adiabatic heating). Hence the somewhat higher temperatures down below.

GASES IN SEA-WATER AND THE PART THEY PLAY

As the sea is in continual contact with the atmosphere, we should naturally expect to find some, at least, of the gases in the latter to occur in solution in the sea. Water certainly can contain dissolved gases, and sea-water contains both nitrogen and oxygen, the two main constituents of air. It contains carbon dioxide, too, of which only a small amount is present in the air, but which is nevertheless necessary for the maintenance of life on earth; for carbon dioxide and water are the two raw materials from which, with the help of sunlight, plants manufacture the indispensable carbohydrates (sugars and starch). They do it with their chlorophyll. Animals cannot do this, so the animal kingdom as a whole *ultimately* depends on plants for nourishment; carbon dioxide is therefore an indispensable 'raw material' to all animate nature, including the human race, because this eventually profits by what plants do with it.

Despite the small quantity of carbonic acid (carbon dioxide, CO_2) present in the atmosphere (see Table 7), it stands in no danger of being depleted, because living organisms, in turn, make it, notably during the 'combustion' or 'oxidation' of compounds containing carbon atoms (C), this combustion being necessary for a variety of functions, such as heating and energy. Oxygen is used up for that oxidation, but it is generated by the assimilation of carbon dioxide in chlorophyll, referred to above.

This, expressed in formulae, becomes:

Plants: $CO_2 + H_2O$ + solar energy $\rightarrow$ carbohydrates + O_2.
Humans, plants and animals: Organic substances + O $\rightarrow CO_2 + H_2O$
+ usable energy or heat.

All this also happens in water. Unless there were carbon dioxide and oxygen in water, plants and animals could not live in it. So it is a good thing that the gases of the atmosphere dissolve in sea-water.

Table 7 shows the proportions in which nitrogen (N_2), oxygen (O_2) and carbon dioxide (CO_2) occur in the atmosphere, and how much of each is absorbed by sea-water of 12°C exposed for a sufficient time to air of one atmosphere. These gases will therefore occur also, roughly in these quantities, at the *surface* of the sea, provided its temperature is 12°C. The lower the temperature and the greater the concentration of a particular gas in the atmosphere, the more of it does water absorb.

Table 7

Proportions of Nitrogen, Oxygen and Carbon Dioxide in Air, and Maximum Quantities in Sea-Water of 19‰ Chlorinity (34·33‰ Salinity) at 12°C in Contact with Air of 1 Atmosphere.

	Nitrogen N_2	*Oxygen* O_2	*Carbonic Acid* CO_2 (and H_2CO_3)
Proportions in normal air	78%	21%	0·03%
Equilibrium values in sea-water of 12°C	11·1 ml/l	6·2 ml/l	0·3 ml/l

Nitrogen: Nitrogen predominates both in sea-water and the atmosphere, but less so in water than in air; whereas it fills 78 per cent. of the volume in air, it represents approximately 64 per cent. of the total of gases in solution (comprising mainly nitrogen and oxygen) in water. Apparently nitrogen dissolves less readily in water than does oxygen.

So far as we know, nitrogen in water is of little significance to living creatures, apart from a few bacteria, which manufacture ammonium salts and nitrates from it. These bacteria exist in several places on or near the bottom. They do not, however, appear to play an important part in the whole economy of the ocean.

Oxygen: sea-water has two sources of oxygen, namely (1) the atmosphere and (2) the plants which, with sunlight, manufacture carbohydrates from water and carbon dioxide. Both these sources are, therefore, at and near the surface of the sea; at greater depth the atmosphere is far away; and at the same time it is too dark to be a habitat for green plants. Oxygen, however, is consumed everywhere, even in the depths, because creatures do live there which use oxygen; moreover, oxygen is combined by the decomposition of organic waste products, dead remains of vegetation sinking to the bottom, and dead animals.

The picture, in a few words, is as follows: oxygen consumption takes place everywhere; most oxygen is produced at the surface, the amount declining gradually with increasing depth, because less and less light penetrates and the number of plants decreases by degrees. Near the surface there is overproduction; at the greater depths 'overconsumption'; in between there is a level where production and consumption are just balanced, called the 'compensation depth'. Here is an example: according to explorations in the Gulf of Maine (on the east coast of the United States), the compensation level lay, in summer, at a depth of 24–30 metres. Some oxygen does usually travel downward as the result of turbulent mixing of

3*

surface water with layers below it; but in many places such blending does not go deeper than one or two hundred metres.

This would imply that, as a rule, there would be no more oxygen in the water at greater depths than these, were it not for a certain regular water refreshment brought about by the continual slow *water circulation* within the oceans.

In certain areas the surface water sinks gradually and then spreads horizontally. This occurs mainly in the northern parts of the Atlantic ocean and in the Antarctic (but not only there). And, in other places, water, from the depths rises to the surface. Here, the colder the water is, the more oxygen is it able to absorb. Sea-water of 0°C can contain one and a half times as much oxygen as can sea-water of 20°C. Solubility also depends to some extent upon air pressure, to which it is directly proportional; but the variations of the air pressure are not more than 5 per cent. on either side of the mean. Lastly, the solubility of oxygen in salt water is a little below that in fresh water; sea-water in equilibrium with the air will contain roughly 20 per cent. less oxygen than will fresh water of the same temperature.

A picture of oxygen distribution will be found in Fig. 134, where lines of equal oxygen content have been drawn. There we see that at the surface (above) the oxygen content is considerably larger at higher latitudes (far to the north and far to the south) than in the warmer tropical waters; this is in accordance with the temperature difference. We also see that there is an appreciable amount of oxygen almost everywhere, right down to the floor of the ocean, despite the great distance from the sources of oxygen; so much so, in fact, that there is more oxygen at 3000 metres' depth under the Equator than at the surface. This is because water (*above right* in the figure) coming from the north drops down in the northern part of the Atlantic Ocean, bringing a continual, slow supply to these depths. We shall deal in greater detail with this water circulation in the final chapter.

Oxygen may be completely absent from some almost enclosed seas, where there is no such 'ventilation' of the deep waters. The bottom of the Black Sea is one example, and some Norwegian fjords with high sills provide another.

As several big rivers empty into the Black Sea, its upper layer, a hundred fathoms deep, has a comparatively low salt content (16‰); it is considerably lighter than the deep water, which is richer in salt (hence heavier). A stratification of this kind is said to be 'stable', which means, among other things, that little mixing takes place between the upper and lower layers. The upper water does contain oxygen, but because there is no vertical circulation, the lower water does not. Malodorous hydrogen sulphide (H_2S) instead is present in the water there; consequently no animals can live below that depth of a hundred fathoms, only certain (anaerobic) bacteria which do not need oxygen, and which subsist on waste products descending from the upper layer. It is these which produce the H_2S. An example of a similar situation is to be found in Kau Bay in Halmahera (see Fig. 29).

Carbon Dioxide: whereas the amount of carbon dioxide in the atmosphere comes to only 0·03 per cent. by weight of the total, it constitutes 1·6 per cent. of all the gases dissolved in sea-water, hence fifty times as much in proportion. This is due to its excellent solubility in water which, per litre, absorbs a slightly larger amount of carbon dioxide from the atmosphere than a litre of air contains. But, where sea-water is concerned, there is another factor. As base-forming metals like magnesium and calcium occur in the sea in a *slightly* larger quantity than the corresponding acid residues are able to neutralize; or, put differently, as sea-water is slightly alkaline, carbon dioxide

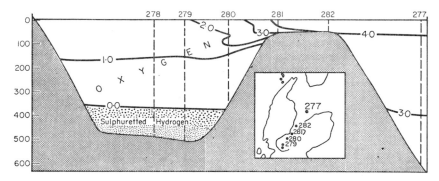

FIG. 29 Cross-section through Kau Bay in Halmahera, with oxygen distribution in ml/l, according to observations made by the *Snellius* expedition (after Kuenen, *Realms of Water,* Cleaver-Hume Press Ltd., London). The numbers along the top stand for oceanographic stations.

can be combined in it as carbonates and bicarbonates. If, however, for some reason, such as considerable consumption of carbon dioxide by vegetation during the lightest part of the day, the amount of free carbon dioxide in the sea decreases, these carbonates (CO_3 groups) and bicarbonates (HCO_3 groups) will readily give off CO_2. They therefore provide a large reserve for the carbon dioxide content, usually many times the quantity of free CO_2 circulating in sea-water. So the plants, weeds and vegetable plankton there are unlikely to suffer from a shortage of carbon dioxide. At night, when carbon dioxide is not consumed, but is produced by breathing, some of it is again chemically combined, hence stored up.

ORGANIC SUBSTANCES

Sea-water contains a diversity of substances of vegetable and animal origin, in addition to salts and gases in solution.

As a rule, dead plants and animals will sink to the bottom. This, however, is a very slow process, and if they are not eaten by other living creatures on the way, they will have partly or wholly decomposed before they reach the bottom. Thus, a variety of substances in solution are present in sea-water, which though only a small fraction counted as a percentage, yet form an enormous stock taken over a whole ocean. This stock, admittedly, comes to rest for the most part at depths where it ceases to be profitable as food for plants; but we know that the general, though slow, circulation of oceanic waters maintains a permanent redistribution. Just as it carries oxygen to great depths, so does it bring organic foodstuffs to the upper layers—*inter alia* in regions of 'upwelling' (see Chapter 6), which is particularly pronounced along the west coasts of North and South Africa and North and South America (California and Peru).

LIFE IN SEA-WATER

A bucket of sea-water contains a good deal more than merely dissolved salts, gases, organic substances and, perhaps, a small amount of undissolved material. There is Life in it, living creatures.

Now this book does not deal with the biology of the oceans, for the author is not a biologist; but our description of the waters of the oceans would be incomplete without some mention of the living matter in them. In this respect, we are concerned mainly with the *plankton*, a word meaning all drifting and floating organisms in the sea, largely unable to move independently, and so just as passively borne by the currents as are the inanimate

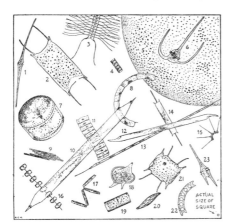 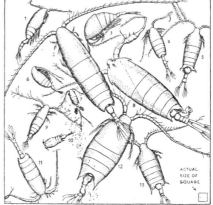

Figs. 30–31 Various species of vegetable (*left*) and animal (*right*) plankton. All vegetable species except 1, 6, 18 and 23 are diatoms. In both illustrations the small square in the right-hand bottom corner shows the actual size of the whole (after Hardy).

substances in the sea. This applies more particularly to phytoplankton, that is, the vegetable plankton. There are some species of zooplankton—animal plankton—which are capable of a semblance of swimming, but, for all practical purposes, these, too, are entirely at the mercy of the motions of water. This also holds for spawn and helpless larvae, which are likewise classified as plankton, even if the adults are swimmers. The individuals making up plankton are often of microscopic dimensions.

As plants generally need light, the phytoplankton is mainly confined to the upper 100 metres. The *diatoms* are the best-known group of microscopic phytoplankton, and with the dinoflagellates, are the most important as food for the animal kingdom. They constitute the 'meadows of the sea', upon which, in the ultimate, all animal life subsists. This does not mean, of course, that all marine animals are vegetarians; on the contrary! But animal life could not exist in the sea without these submarine meadows, for animals cannot live *only* on each other; there must also be herbivores among them. In the animal world of the seas these are predominantly the very small relatives of the shrimps, known as copepods. Various kinds of diatoms and copepods are illustrated in Figs. 30 and 31. (See also Plate IV.)

These living organisms occur in astounding numbers. The number of diatoms at a given moment in the Kiel Bight has been estimated at 6000 per cubic centimetre, an estimate based on the catch in a plankton net (a very fine-mesh silk net) taken from what was gauged to be $1\frac{1}{2}$ cubic metres of water running through the net. It has been estimated that the yield of a certain region in the Irish Sea averages 10 tons of aqueous vegetable material per acre, which does not compare unfavourably with the yield of cultivated land. However, there are also vast oceanic areas which are very barren.

Generally speaking, the chemical constitution of marine vegetation is not very different from that of meadow hay. Diatoms have approximately the same percentage of proteins and fats, a little less of the hydrocarbons but considerably more 'ash', thanks to their siliceous shells.

As to the meadow *animals*, notably the copepods, it is estimated that the North Sea sustains between a quarter and one million of these little creatures per square metre.

Herrings live on copepods; copepods live on diatoms; diatoms live on whatever is in solution, and on the great ultimate source of energy . . . sunlight.

LIGHT IN THE SEA

Descending beyond 100 metres or so into the sea we come upon a realm of perpetual night. So, if we speak of light in the sea, we can, on the whole, be referring only to the upper layer, some 100 metres 'thick', which, compared with the depth of the oceans, is really quite thin.

Does this mean that there is no light at all at great depths? The Norwegian oceanographer Helland Hansen investigated this in 1910, during a voyage of exploration in the *Michael Sars*, by immersing an instrument, containing photographic plates, in the sea. It was in the vicinity of the Azores, at about noon, in June, and therefore when the sun was high in the heavens. One plate, which he exposed for 20 minutes at a depth of 500 metres, showed considerable darkening after it had been developed. He sent down another plate to 1000 metres and exposed it for 80 minutes. This, too, displayed some darkening after being developed, but only to a slight extent. Finally, there was no trace at all of any reaction to light on a plate exposed for 120 minutes at a depth of 1700 metres.

We therefore have no right to say that there is no light at all at 500 or 1000 metres; but, for all that, it is as dark as night down there; for a photographic plate would show some reaction to light, even on one of our darkest nights.

Complete darkness certainly prevails at a depth of a couple of hundred metres. There are, however, a few deep-sea fishes which are capable of putting on a light under certain conditions. These may, therefore, be wandering stars in this otherwise moonless and starless night. An amazing world.

If we hold up a bottle of sea-water against the light, it appears to be quite transparent, as clear as crystal. The light goes right through it. So how can it be so dark down below? The answer is simple: even if light passes through a layer of water, this does not mean that the whole one hundred per cent. of the light traverses it. Let us assume that one metre of sea-water lets through 90 per cent. of the incident light. The next metre of sea-water then lets through 90 per cent. of that 90 per cent., so that the layer of two metres lets through $0.90 \times 0.90 = (0.90)^2 = 0.81$, or 81 per cent. of the light. In the same way a layer of three metres lets through $0.90 \times 0.90 \times 0.90 = (0.90)^3 = 0.729$ or 73 per cent. We can continue like this, and we shall then find that a layer ten metres thick still lets through a fraction of $(0.90)^{10} = 0.35$ or 35 per cent. of the incident light. That is quite a lot. A layer one hundred metres thick, however, lets through only $(0.90)^{100} = 0.000027$ or 0.0027 per cent.; hence the light intensity at a depth of one hundred metres would only be about $1/400$ per cent. of that above. All this is on the assumption that every metre of sea-water lets through 90 per cent. of the incident light. We shall see presently whether this percentage agrees with that actually found in the seas and oceans.

If no more than 90 per cent. passes through, where is the missing 10 per cent.? It is partly *in* the water. In other words, the water *absorbs* part of the transmitted light; the water molecules themselves do it; the substances in solution in the sea-water do it; any undissolved particles drifting in the water, or plankton, do it. The light absorbed by the matter in sea-water can do various things, chief among which is to supply some warmth to the water.

Apart from absorption, however, there is a certain amount of *scattering* of light. To a certain extent, light entering from above is everywhere scattered in the water in various directions, sideways and even backwards, which means loss to the straight penetrating rays. This scattering is caused both by the water molecules themselves, and by any undissolved particles of matter, gas bubbles and the like, that may be there.

Hence absorption and scattering together weaken the direct penetration of light rays into water. The total diminution which is the sum of these two effects, is also sometimes called 'absorption', the word being used in a broader sense than that implied by us in the foregoing. A better term is *extinction*; so we get: extinction = loss from absorption + loss from scattering. The loss found by observations in the sea is always the sum of these two terms. In the above example, the extinction in a metre of water was 10 per cent.

Pure water is highly transparent, at any rate to the major part of visible light. Here we arrive at a complication on which we have not yet touched, namely that extinction may be different for different colours of light. As the reader knows, the wavelengths of visible light range from approximately 0·4 to 0·8 micron; 1 micron (μ) = 0·001 millimetre. The shortest visible wavelengths are in violet, the longest in red. Pure water is most transparent to blue light (wavelength about 0·48μ) and least so to red. It is practically opaque to infra-red rays, i.e. rays of even longer wavelength than red. Thus, for example, as large a percentage of 'light' of 1μ wavelength is absorbed in a layer of water one metre thick as of yellow light in a layer of a thousand metres.

Here are a few figures showing the percentage loss of light of different wavelengths in a metre of pure water.

Table 8

Loss of light, per cent., in one metre of pure water
(1μ = 0·001 mm)

	Violet	Blue	Green		Yellow	Orange	Red
Wavelength (μ)	0·40	0·46	0·50	0·54	0·58	0·64	0·70
Loss of light (%)	4	1·6	2·6	4	7	21	40

A table like this should be used with some circumspection. It is no good multiplying these figures, which are valid for one metre, by ten, to get the loss in ten metres. The last two percentages would, in that way, come to an absurdity, since a loss of 210 per cent. or 400 per cent. is quite impossible. The correct calculation is as follows: say that the loss is 2·6 per cent., then the transmission must be 97·4 per cent., or 0·974. The transmission through two metres is then 0·974 × 0·974 = 0·9487; hence the loss in two metres is 0·0513, or 5·13 per cent. This actually is double the loss in one metre, approximately, but if we take twenty metres the transmission becomes $(0·974)^{20}$ = 0·5905, and the loss therefore 0·4095 or 40·95 per cent., which is by no means the same as twenty times 2·6 per cent.

The foregoing examples refer to pure water and the figures in the table were the results of laboratory tests. Other laboratory experiments have now shown that *salts* dissolved in water increase the absorption to only a very minor extent. That being so, one might think that the loss of light in sea-water differed little from extinction in pure water. We have to remember, however, that sea-water is more than a solution of salts in water; and we shall therefore have to transfer our observations to the sea itself to find out what the extinction in it really is. How are we to go about it?

The oldest device for estimating the transparency of sea-water is the Secchi disc, a disc of 30 cm diameter, painted white, which is let down into the sea. The clearer the water is, the greater will be the depths at which the disc can be seen through the water. Therefore, the depth at which it vanishes from sight is a measure of the transparency of the water and the extinction is obviously in inverse proportion to this depth. It is generally assumed that in water of fairly good transparency the loss of light per metre (in the sense explained above) is equal to 1·7 divided by the depth at which the disc ceases to be visible.

We have already mentioned another method, namely that used by Helland Hansen as far back as 1910, when he exposed photographic plates under water.

The most accurate data are obtained with a photo-electric cell, which is allowed to descend in the sea and records the light intensity by emitting a small electric current which can be measured at once aboard the ship. There are two alternative ways of applying this method; (1) by merely measuring, at various depths, the intensity of the daylight transmitted from above; or (2) by using one's own underwater source of light and, with the photo-electric cell at a given distance—say one metre—from it, measuring the quantity of light transmitted through that metre of water (this quantity then being compared with the quantity of light received when there is no sea-water between the source of light and the photo-electric cell). The instrument with which the latter measurements are made is known as a transparency meter; it is also called a turbidimeter. One can also place filters of different colours in front of the photo-electric cell to measure the effects proper to the various parts of the spectrum.

All the observations so far made have shown that (1) the extinction in sea-water is usually far greater than in pure water; (2) the difference varies for the several colours of the spectrum in the sense that, with the exception of the very clearest oceanic water, the colour best transmitted is no longer blue, but green, and sometimes also yellow; (3) considerable differences exist between the kinds of sea-water of various places.

Table 9

Loss of light, per cent., in one metre of sea-water (according to Jerlov)

	Violet		*Blue*	*Green*		*Yellow*	*Orange*	*Red*
Wavelength (μ)	0·30	0·40	0·46	0·50	0·54	0·58	0·64	0·70
Oceanic water most transparent	16	4	2	3	5	9	29	42
Oceanic water least transparent	57	16	11	10	13	19	36	55
Coastal water average		63	37	29	28	30	45	74
Coastal water least transparent		90	76	62	50	41	52	81

Table 9 sums up several of the results obtained, but it must be borne in mind that these figures do *not* apply to the topmost few metres of water, for there is always far greater extinction immediately under the sea surface due to the presence of such things as foam or air bubbles. Consequently, these figures are not necessarily an easy guide to the light intensity at various depths.

The three phenomena mentioned above are clearly reflected in the table. A very striking difference is that in transparency between the water of the open ocean and coastal waters. Two examples of each type of sea-water are given. It need hardly be said that there remains considerable variation in both, and that, furthermore, there is a gradual transition between them.

It should not be imagined that, apart from the topmost layer of water, the transparency of sea-water at a given place is the same at all depths. Many measurements, made with the transparency meters already mentioned, have, on the contrary, made it plain that superimposed layers of water are liable to differ considerably in transparency. For instance, it often happens that a maximum turbidity is detected in a layer at a certain depth, notably the layer showing the steepest drop in temperature (*thermocline*, see Fig. 28), where, apparently, there is an accumulation of drifting material. Sometimes, too, water masses of very different degrees of turbidity occur side by side. Thus transparency can serve as an (inverse) measure of the quantity of drifting material (particles of silt, plankton or plankton waste) present in sea-water, and as a typical feature of certain kinds of water.

The average figure for extinction in oceanic water at depths of more than three metres can be taken at roughly the ten per cent. per metre given above as an example. The waters of the oceans in the higher latitudes are usually less transparent, however, on account of the abundance of plankton in them.

As stated, the topmost metres of the sea are everywhere by far the least transparent; for example, at 5 metres' depth in the open ocean we already have to allow for a loss of 82·5 per cent., so that as little as 17·5 per cent. of the incident light reaches there. Some figures found for greater depths in average oceanic water are given in Table 10.

Table 10

Illumination at various depths

metres	0	10	20	50	130	200
%	100	9·5	3·7	0·31	0·0005	0·000,002

Down at 130 metres the light intensity has decreased to only 1/200,000 of that immediately under the surface. If we consider that, owing to reflection, the light intensity immediately under the surface of the sea is less than the strength of illumination *on* the sea; and that the light of the full moon is also approximately 1/200,000 of that of the sun, then we must realize that here, 130 metres down, the prevailing light is comparable to moonlight. But at a depth of 200 metres, the light is again 250 times weaker, which is comparable to a moonless night. All this holds for average oceanic water; conditions in coastal waters are far worse.

An area of exceptionally transparent water is the Sargasso Sea, in the western part of the Atlantic Ocean, near the Bermuda Islands.

The distribution of vegetable life in sea-water naturally depends largely on the transparency of the water. The more transparent it is, the farther will sunlight penetrate and the greater will be the depth at which plants consuming carbon dioxide can subsist, provided they have enough food to live on. Accordingly, in a region like the Sargasso Sea the 'compensation depth', to which reference has been made (the depth at which oxygen consumption and production by plants are in equilibrium), is at a far lower level—namely 80 metres under the surface—than in all kinds of coastal waters, where 25 metres may well be the level found.

It will also be evident that plant plankton is dependent upon the position of the sun as well as on the transparency of the water. If sunlight falls vertically upon the water it will go straight through, and will not be refracted; but if it falls obliquely upon the water, it is refracted in such a manner that its submerged path is steeper than its incidence. If the sun is very low and the sea calm, so that light falls at a very small angle on the surface, it is so markedly refracted that it still runs into the water at an angle of 48·5 degrees with the surface.

The position of the sun is important mainly on account of the varying degree of reflection involved. A smooth sea-surface reflects only 3 per cent. of the incident light with the sun's altitude at 50 to 90 degrees, but not less than 40 per cent. with an altitude of 5 degrees. Less light is reflected from a low sun if the surface of the sea is rough.

THE COLOUR OF SEA-WATER

The purest sea-water looks blue. This is because, within the spectrum of the incident light, *blue* is the colour scattered most by water molecules, so that more of the blue than of the other components of the light is radiated back from the water under the surface. This blue appearance is due therefore to the same cause as that which produces the blueness of the sky. We refer to this effect briefly as 'selective scattering'. There is, however, the additional fact that blue is absorbed least of the various colours in pure oceanic water, and is therefore most readily transmitted (and returned).

Deep blue is the colour of the water of the open oceans, especially in tropical, subtropical and mid-latitude regions; less so is it in the seas at high latitudes. Those who have hitherto seen only the North Sea and English Channel are astounded when, for the first time, they see the deep blue waters of the Atlantic Ocean, or make the acquaintance of the Mediterranean.

The blue of the oceans is a token of the purity of their waters; it signifies that they contain little organic life and few organic waste products. This blue has been called the 'desert colour of the oceans'! The Sargasso Sea, for instance, is a 'desert' of this kind.

But there are other regions, close to the coasts and on banks, where the sea is much more green than blue; so is it with the surface water originating in high latitudes. The difference between the blue water of the Gulf Stream and the more greenish, colder water that flows on its western and north-western side (off the American coast) is striking.

Green sea-water owes its coloration to a variety of organic material, either living, or as waste products. According to analyses made by the German chemist Kalle, a certain substance of vegetable origin (a product rather like humic acid) which he calls the 'yellow substance', dissolved in sea-water, is predominantly responsible for this hue; yellow mingling with the natural blue produces green.

Apart from this, the phytoplankton itself, if present in abundance may discolour the sea-water, at the same time making it far less transparent. Thus, in spring, when increasing solar radiation and consequent warmth enhance the production of phytoplankton—the 'blooming' of the diatoms—the waters of some vast coastal regions become brownish-green. Later in the year the colour returns to blue.

On occasions the sea may even become russet-coloured in certain places. This is usually due to the presence at the surface of the sea of very dense populations—millions of cells per litre—of a kind of algae called dino-flagellates. The Red Sea[1] owes its name to this phenomenon, as does the so-called Vermillion Sea (the Gulf of California).

THE MIGRATION OF ANIMAL PLANKTON IN RESPONSE TO LIGHT

Biologists have discovered another remarkable phenomenon, with which, incidentally, fishermen were already acquainted. During daylight, especially in summer when the sun is high, there are few animalcules to be found in the uppermost layers of sea-water. Most of them are then congregated twenty metres or more down. In the open oceans the biggest catches of animal plankton taken in daytime come from even deeper layers. It is, however, a very different matter when the sun goes down and the dusk merges into nightfall. Then all plankton animals capable of vertical displacement gradually ascend. They obviously shun strong daylight in the upper layers, and seek out the places where the light is dim. The nearer this prevalent dimness rises to the surface as the sun sets, the higher do they come. At night, when it is dark everywhere, they cease to show any preference for a given depth; but at early light in the morning, they gather together again and sink down, lower and lower as the sun rises higher and higher.

These facts have been discovered not only from catches made in nets, but also by echo-sounding, when layers containing many of certain kinds of animal plankton have been detected (see above and Plate VII).

[1] Here the bearer of the colour is an alga called Trichodesmium erythraeum.

Chapter Three

ICE IN THE SEAS

The ice was here, the ice was there, the ice was all around.
(Samuel Taylor Coleridge,
The Rime of an Ancient Mariner.)

ICE and snow reign supreme in the far north and the far south of our Earth, its two most inhospitable realms which are white in summer and endlessly shrouded in the darkness of night in winter.

Looking at the earth as a whole, we can distinguish various regions in most of which western Man, at any rate, is not in his natural element. Actually, Man is only more or less at home in the varied landscapes of the moderate climatic zones. The other great realms—those of the virgin forests in equatorial and tropical regions, of the deserts and tundras in subtropical and northern regions, of the incommensurable expanses of water covering seven-tenths of the earth's surface, and of the polar regions—are essentially alien to him. This notwithstanding, or perhaps just for this reason, these realms attract him; many men have been enthralled by the lure of the unknown, and the vastness of these tracts. That is why people have ventured into primeval forests, into the deserts and tundras, and many have set out upon the kingdom of the seven seas, while others have been drawn to the polar regions, the most inaccessible and forbidding of all. Nowhere is the Unknown so impressive as in the polar regions, than which there are none more remote and untrodden. Therein precisely lies the lure of those regions.

The call of the Eternal Ice.

The heartbreaking battles with the elements necessary to invade the polar regions and to penetrate ever farther, defy description. We are not going to practise hero-worship; but it is a fact that no voyage of discovery has exacted so much courage and dogged perseverance from human beings as has the exploration of the polar regions.

The Norsemen may have been the first to steer their ships towards the Pole and, little by little, to penetrate the shroud of mist, ice and wintry darkness of these solitary tracts.

We may suspect, as does Nordenskjöld,[1] three possible motives for these tentative steps into the unknown, namely the desire to be the first to see and

[1] *The Geography of the Polar Regions*, The American Geographical Society, New York, 1928.

report on something hitherto never seen; the drive to face and overcome danger; and the prospect of drawing some profit from the venture. These are motives which may well have taken root and grown, and which were simply obeyed without much ulterior thought being given to exalted general human ideas—such as were subsequently ascribed to those pioneers for their glorification—or to ideals worthy of a 'hero'. The first two motives are in Man's blood, so to speak. As to the third, we think it more likely that the organizer, if there was one, of such expeditions, rather than those who undertook them, may have been inspired by that motive, at any rate if by 'profit' we mean economic profit.

In the past hundred and fifty years there has been a further incentive for such explorations, the hope of gains in scientific knowledge; this sort of 'profit' usually does engage the enthusiasm of the protagonists themselves. Or, to reverse the statement, the exponents of the scientific disciplines involved often accompany such expeditions. An example which at once springs to mind is that of Sverdrup, who himself spent years in the Arctic.

Reference has so far been made only to the polar seas. But in winter, ice returns regularly to other seas as well; for example, the Baltic, notably the Gulfs of Bothnia, Finland and Riga; the Sea of Azov, the Bering Sea, the Sea of Okhotsk and, of course, the north-western parts of the Atlantic Ocean, around Greenland, Labrador and Newfoundland. Let us not forget that these latter oceanic areas are in direct communication with the Arctic Ocean; in fact, many oceanographers regard the Arctic Ocean as a large marginal sea of the Atlantic Ocean, with which it fundamentally certainly does form a single unit (see Fig. 4). With the Pacific Ocean, on the other hand, it is connected only by the narrow Bering Strait. Accordingly, the ice encountered in the north-western parts of the Atlantic Ocean in winter and spring derives largely from the Arctic.

Matters are simpler in the south where scarcely any ice is found in the sea outside the belt encircling the South Polar continent, apart from a few coastal waters around islands, where ice may occur in winter; and, apart, of course, from the icebergs which sometimes drift considerably farther northward than the pack-ice.

Before proceeding to discuss the more general physical aspects of ice in the sea and its distribution, there is an important distinction which we have to make.

SEA-ICE, ICEBERGS AND ICE ISLANDS

Although *icebergs* certainly are ice in the sea, they are *not* sea-ice. By 'sea-ice' we mean ice formed within the sea. This is not true of icebergs, which are formed by glaciers or by shelf-ice (a special kind of glacier about which more will be said later). Hence icebergs consist of typical fresh-water ice, i.e. old snow-ice; actually, therefore, they are products of the land, not of the sea. To distinguish them from sea-ice, we might alternatively speak of 'land-ice in the sea', but this term would include river-ice that had entered the sea. Whereas the latter calls for little further definition, however, there is much more to be said about icebergs.

Since 1950 we have known of another form of drifting ice in the Arctic Ocean, more akin to icebergs than to sea-ice, namely *ice islands*, a number of which float about in the Arctic and whose birthplace is the extreme north of the Canadian Archipelago.

We shall first consider sea-ice proper, that is to say ice formed in the sea from sea-water. It can be subdivided, notably in the north, where a distinction is made between *Arctic pack* or *true polar ice, pack-ice* and *fast ice*. We shall, however, first deal with the generation, properties and forms of sea-ice in general.

SEA-ICE

THE FREEZING POINT OF SEA-WATER

Most people will have noticed that the sea takes longer to freeze than do ponds and lakes. This is partly due to the fact that the sea cools down far less quickly than land, and, therefore, than lakes and ponds which are surrounded by land. Moreover, the freezing point of sea-water is lower than that of fresh water because sea-water is a solution of salt; salts in solution lower the freezing point in approximate proportion to the concentration of the solution. The temperatures of the freezing point for various values of the salinity are shown in Table 11.

Table 11

Freezing Points of Sea-Water

Salinity ‰	0	10	20	30	35
Freezing point °C	0	−0·53	−1·08	−1·63	−1·91

It appears that average sea-water of approximately 35‰ salinity does not begin to freeze until the temperature has dropped to 1·9°C.

ANOTHER REASON WHY SEA-WATER DOES NOT READILY FREEZE OVER

It is not only the lower freezing point of salt water than of fresh (lakes, for instance) which necessitates more cooling before ice is formed on its surface. There is another factor. The greatest specific gravity of sea-water, unlike fresh water, is *not* at 4°C. If it is sufficiently saline, sea-water of −1°C is heavier than that of 0°C, the latter is heavier than sea-water of +1°C, and so forth; the colder it is, the heavier.

This does not hold for pure water. Such water at 4°C is heavier than that of 5°C, but water of 3°C is *lighter* than that of 4°C. Below 4°C the specific gravity diminishes again with further decreasing temperature. For this reason water of 0°C can lie on water of +1° or +2°C. Put differently: it is possible, with fresh water, for only the topmost water to cool down to freezing point, without sinking down if the water below it should be a few degrees warmer.

It is otherwise with sea-water, provided its salt content be at least 24·7‰. As it cools down, its specific gravity increases progressively until freezing point has been attained. Therefore, if the sea is cooled from above and, as a result, the surface water becomes colder than the water underneath, it will sink downward and water from below will take its place. Hence the surface water cannot possibly drop to freezing temperature as long as the water beneath is not almost equally cold.

All this is on the assumption that there is not much difference in salinity above and below. If the upper water contained considerably less salt than the water below, it *could* be colder and yet be able to float, thanks to its lower salt content. Should this not be so, however, the whole mass of water must evidently cool down almost to freezing point before ice can be formed on the sea. Accordingly, in winter and summer the basins of the polar seas are largely filled with water of temperatures near to freezing point. Only the upper layer warms up slightly in summer, especially in the vicinity of the coasts which are free from ice at that time. That upper layer has then again to cool down to its full depth before ice will form once more on its surface.

It will be evident from the foregoing that the shallower the open sea, the sooner can ice be formed on it, because there is less water to cool down. That is why, when the summer is over, ice first begins to form on the shallow coastal waters of the polar seas.

GROUND-ICE

In autumn a fisherman in the Baltic may suddenly find his boat surrounded by grey ice-floes to which, sometimes, seaweed and stones are clinging. This is called ground-ice because it was obviously formed on the bottom. Ground-ice is also met with in river beds, in lakes and in certain shallow parts of the polar seas where a strong current is running.

The reason why ice is formed sooner at the bottom than above in such cases is that water may become supercooled under certain circumstances; that is to say, it cools down to below freezing point without solidifying, notably if there are no freezing nuclei present to serve as points of attachment for the water molecules and thus to initiate the process of solidification. A diversity of solid particles, more especially sand and siliceous stones (and, naturally, particles of ice itself, e.g. snow crystals), serve as such freezing nuclei. If there are no particles of this kind in the water, and if it is churned by rapid flow or by the wind while cooling proceeds, it may become supercooled right down to the bottom. But, as the bottom often does offer the necessary points of attachment (sand, stones), able to act as freezing nuclei, ice will be formed on the bottom in that case.

Another name for ground-ice is anchor-ice.

THE FORMATION OF SEA-ICE

The appearance in the water of small clouds of microscopically tiny particles of colloidal ice, so-called, which at first only make the water slightly turbid, is the first sign of freezing. These first minute particles of ice are more or less discoid and form the cores of growing crystals. When they have developed further, these ice crystals become hexagonal needles one to two centimetres long. They change the appearance of the surface of the water, which dulls over, as it were, and no longer reflects the sky.

These ice crystals consist of pure ice, *without any salt*. Only the water molecules coalesce to form these crystals; the salt remains behind in the fluid water. Hence the water around a recently formed ice crystal will be somewhat more saline than the original water, since a small amount of pure water has been withdrawn and the nearby water which has not yet frozen is burdened with the discarded salt; it has therefore become a little heavier and sinks down. It is replaced by uprising water with the initial salt content.

This can continue for quite a time. New fresh-water ice crystals are continually being formed from the sea-water of, say, 35‰, or the crystals already formed grow further; the surrounding water becomes slightly heavier than it originally was, drops down and makes way for other water of 35‰. Soon there is a whole lattice of crystals resting on the surface of the water; then some crystals begin to grow vertically downward. Later on, cross-connections are built up between these vertical crystals, so that ultimately there is a widespread structure of small, enclosed spaces, cells still containing water, but shut off from the outside world by little walls of ice.

At the instant when a cell of this kind is enclosed, the contents are still of the same composition as the water outside. So, if one lifts a lump of this sea-ice out of the water, one will not really be holding just a fragment of ice alone, but ice—and pure ice at that—in which many tiny cells with sea-water are enclosed everywhere. Thus, although a fragment of this 'ice' does contain salt, this salt does not, firstly, reside in the ice substance, itself of recently formed ice, but in the 'brine' filling the cavities between the ice crystals; secondly, the average salt content of such a fragment is lower than that of the water from which it was formed. For, let the whole fragment of ice weigh one kilogram, and let it contain 800 grams pure ice and 200 grams sea-water, then there is 35‰ of 200 grams, or 7 grams of salt to 1 kilogram of sea-ice; consequently, the average salt content is only 7‰. Sea-ice of 7‰ has come into being from 35‰ sea-water. What has happened to the residual quantity of salt? As we have seen, this has made a quantity of sea-water heavier and has dropped down with it.

Suppose sea-ice like this, containing cells with sea-water, continues to freeze; then, not only will the ice begin to accumulate underneath, but, with continued withdrawal of heat, ice will also begin to settle out of the enclosed sea-water. Up to the moment of this enclosure, the temperature of that sea-water had remained $-1\cdot9°C$ (the freezing point at 35‰ salinity) and the withdrawal of heat had not served to lower the temperature, but only to form ice of freezing temperature. Now, however, things are different. Once a certain quantity of sea-water is enclosed, the salt content of the residual brine increases irrevocably with further deposition of ice from the contents of a cell, as it is once again 'fresh' ice that settles out. As Table 11 shows, however, the freezing point drops with increasing concentration of the contents of the cell, which, incidentally, is also dwindling in size. This means that, with continued withdrawal of heat, the temperature in the ice will have to drop still further. Although, as this temperature drops, a little more ice is constantly being deposited from the brine in the cells within the sea-ice, at the same time the freezing point of the contents of the cell likewise falls, and the temperature therefore has to be constantly dropping further for progressive freezing to take place inside. Ultimately, the contents of the cell become so concentrated that certain salts reach their limit of saturation and begin to crystallize out on the cell wall. From that moment we get salt crystals among the ice crystals.

Laboratory experiments have shown that sodium sulphate crystals begin to form at $-8 \cdot 2°C$ and that the sodium chloride starts to crystallize out at $-23°C$. Yet, at such low, and even lower, temperatures, minute quantities of fluid, exceedingly concentrated salt solution were always found to be present in the ice.

For all that, the total salt content of this ice does not alter as a result of the dropping temperature and the consequent processes taking place within the ice. Nor does it when, subsequently, the temperature rises again and there is a partial internal thaw of the contents of the cells, at any rate not until the thaw has progressed to the point where the cells open and 'brine' is able to run out, as often happens with 'old' ice.

If sea-ice is not too old, the degree of its salinity depends mainly on the circumstances under which it was originally formed. If the ice is formed suddenly and grows quickly, as it does at low air temperature, or if there is intense cooling through a high, cold wind, then ice crystals are formed at great speed and many cells holding sea-water are enclosed; the salt content thereby becomes high. But if the crystals grow slowly, comparatively little sea-water is enclosed and the salt content remains low.

Table 12

Salt Content of Sea-Ice

Air temperature at which the ice was formed °C	−16	−26	−30	−40
Salt content of the ice ‰	5·6	8·0	8·8	10·2

This table is based on observations made by Sverdrup during the Norwegian expedition in the *Maud* (1918–25). It shows that ice of higher salinity is formed at lower temperatures than at temperatures which are not so low. The observant reader will have noticed that the highest salt content noted here (10·2‰) is still considerably lower than that of the sea-water from which the ice is formed. The average salt content of the waters of the Arctic Ocean at the surface is 31‰; that of polar ice is, on an average, only 7‰.

THAWING SEA-ICE

As we have said, if the temperature begins to rise after a time, and the interior of the ice thaws sufficiently for the cells to come into contact with each other, the salt solution in those cells can, owing to its weight, sink down, leaving behind the upper parts of the mass of ice with many empty cells and, therefore, with far less salt. If this thawing process goes far, those parts of the ice masses projecting above water may become entirely porous and lose all their saline water. By this time the old ice has become fresh water, and is drinkable. In summer, owing to this melting process, 'pools' of potable fresh water may ultimately be formed on the fields of ice; and many a polar explorer has been thankful to come across them. Sverdrup, for instance, who, as oceanographer, went in the American submarine *Nautilus* to the Arctic Ocean (in 1931), tells of how the expedition was entirely dependent for a time on these melt-water pools, as the drinking water aboard had somehow become unfit for consumption.

SPECIFIC GRAVITY OF SEA-ICE

We have now seen that sea-ice is not a pure solid, but contains a certain amount of 'brine' at every temperature and a given salt content. For example, sea-ice of 10‰ salinity at $-3°C$ is essentially a conglomerate of 20 parts of salt water and 80 parts of pure ice.

Like freshwater-ice, sea-ice is always lighter than water. Its specific gravity depends notably on the amount of enclosed air, and varies between 0·86 (in the case of old upper ice) and somewhat more than 0·92. The former is considerably below the specific gravity of pure ice, which is 0·916 near freezing point; the latter is above it, owing to the salt content.

THE THICKNESS OF POLAR ICE

Polar ice is not, of course, equally thick everywhere and at all times. There is polar ice and polar ice. We shall see presently that we differentiate between the permanent 'polar cap' in the Arctic Ocean, travelling pack-ice and landbound fast-ice; while in the Antarctic Ocean there is, instead of a polar cap of sea-ice, a continent with what is known as 'shelf-ice' on its margins.

The thickness of the true polar ice, the Arctic pack, is usually 2 to 3·5 metres. In one place Nansen found an average thickness of 3·65 metres. In one freezing season (autumn, winter and spring), ice in the Arctic can become 2 metres thick. None of these figures allows for piling-up of broken ice causing what are called 'hummocks', which may assume far greater vertical dimensions than those mentioned. These hummocks, however, are not the result of the normal growth of ice, being formed, rather, by compression caused by icefields driven by wind or current against each other. As another consequence of the latter, the 'polar cap' is not just an unbroken landscape of ice, but always has crevasses, gullies and lanes and, in summer, even larger stretches of open water.

We shall have more to say about the dimensions of these accumulations and pressure ridges of ice presently.

MORPHOLOGY

Morphology is the science of forms, the word being derived from the Greek word morphè, meaning form.

Ice in the oceans can assume a variety of forms, depending on the conditions under which it comes into being, also on wind and current causing it to crack or to pile up, and, lastly, on conditions governing thawing. In course of time various words were adopted to describe the different forms. Some scientists did what they could to put this terminology into some sort of order, and eventually the classification suggested under the auspices of the World Meteorological Organization (WMO) was generally accepted. This means, for one thing, that this terminology is adopted, as far as possible, in reports made by ships about observed ice,[1] and in warnings issued about the presence of ice near shipping lanes. This ice warning service was organized by the international Conferences for the Safety of Life at Sea, the first of which was held in 1913 after the notorious disaster to the *Titanic*, which resulted from collision with an iceberg in 1912. Further reference will be made to it in a later part of this chapter.

As to the various kinds and forms of ice in the sea, we already know that the primary differentiation to be made is between true 'sea-ice', i.e. ice formed from sea-water, and 'land-ice', in which category icebergs come first and foremost, deriving as they do from glaciers, hence the land, and consisting of virtually fresh ice containing scarcely any salt at all.

A whole list of terms is in use for sea-ice, some of which we shall consider in more detail. This vocabulary comprises some terms derived from Russian, and others from the language of the Greenland Eskimos or Esquimaux. The following descriptions are illustrated in Plates X–XIV inclusive.

TYPES OF RECENTLY FORMED ICE

Ice crystals: These are thin, pointed, oblong platelets, no longer than a couple of centimetres. They consist of pure ice without salt.

Slush: This word is used for collections of ice crystals which, having coalesced little or not at all, form a thin layer. Slush gives a greyish or livid tinge to the sea's surface and eliminates its wind-ripples. It makes little or no noise when a ship sails through it.

[1] These communications form part of the weather reports sent out by ships by arrangement with the WMO.

Ice-rind: In calm water, slush is apt to freeze over at low temperature to harder ice, which is called an ice rind. This type of ice is prevalent in places where the surface layer is not very saline, as in bays and fjords, and also between floes of old ice, where fresh melt-water freezes when it spreads over the colder sea-water between the floes. An ice rind is less than 5 centimetres thick, thinner than 'young ice' (see below), and comprises all the transitions from thin freshwater ice to slush.

Pancake Ice: When there is a fair amount of movement in the water and the air temperature is low, the slush freezes to detached cakes of ice which grow in size and assume the shape of round discs with raised edges. These edges are formed by collisions between the discs and also by the attachment of freezing slush. This is called pancake ice. The raised edges are not always formed if the water is fairly calm. An ice rind broken up by a swell may become pancake ice through collision and friction of the fragments. In normal cases the 'pancakes' are 0·5–1 metre across but sometimes as much as 1·5–3 metres.

Young Ice: This term stands for stretches of more or less smooth ice, more than 5 centimetres, but less than 20 centimetres thick, usually, but not invariably, formed by the coalescence of pancake ice and often identified by a pattern of rings. Young ice is greenish-blue and moist at the top; it is tenacious and to some extent flexible and is not readily fragmented by a swell.

Winter Ice and Polar Ice (old Ice): By 'winter ice' we mean ice at least 20 cm thick which was formed in the course of one freezing season; so it is less than a year old, but is nevertheless no longer 'young'. As it still contains a fair amount of salt, it is not very hard.

Sea-ice more than a year old contains less salt and is therefore hard. It is called polar ice or old ice.

Both types can be further classified into various forms and sizes. As far as the form is concerned, we have the following definitions for special cases:

Flat, or Level Ice: Ice of even thickness (more than 20 cm) with a smooth surface. It is usually formed by the accretion of young ice. In unexposed places this ice soon becomes so thick that it remains unbroken for long periods, often the whole winter. In the open sea, newly-formed flat ice tends to break up soon. A swell breaks it up into small floes of regular shape, but wind and currents transform it into floes of irregular shape and size. The next thing is that the floes collide, thereby losing the character of flat ice, because fragments of ice attach themselves to the margins. As a rule, therefore, flat ice is not more than a year old.

Hummocks: The repeated collision of thick ice-floes or ice-fields, often involving enormous pressures, causes local accumulation of ice-floes which, in turn, may coalesce into irregular, massive hillocks consisting of broken lumps of ice, which are called hummocks. These are liable at times to reach a height of ten metres above sea level. Frequently, too, they are arrayed in long ridges or ranges, and they are then called pressure ridges. Enormous embankments of this kind, up to a height of 20 metres, may be formed when fields of ice are pressed against a shore.

Where ice more than a year old prevails, the hummocks and pressure ridges which came into being during a previous summer or winter lose their angular shapes in the process of temporarily melting and freezing again, and acquire a more rounded outline.

Growler: This is a floating fragment of ice derived from a hummock, pressure ridge, glacier or iceberg, with a cross-section of at least half a metre, but not more than ten metres.

The following is the current terminology for the *dimensions* of winter ice or ice more than a year old:

A *field* is an expanse of coherent ice, the limits of which cannot be seen with the unaided eyes from the crow's nest of a ship. Hence it must extend at least several kilometres.

A *large floe* is at least 200 metres wide.

A *small floe* is less than 200 but at least 10 metres wide.

An *ice-cake* is less than 10 metres wide.

Here are a few more terms relating to sea-ice:

Fast-ice is a strip (sometimes a very broad one) of coherent ice bordered on one side by the coastline.

Ice-foot is the belt of fast-ice which has frozen fast to the shore and does not move with the tide.

Sikussak is a term derived from the language of the Greenland Eskimos, and means a kind of land-fast ice of many years' standing which does not drift away, and is found, for instance, in fjords of the north coast of Greenland. In large measure its formation is aided by snowfall and snow-drift and it therefore has a certain kinship to glacier ice.

Anchor Ice (or ground-ice) was referred to a few pages back.

ICEBERGS AND ICE ISLANDS

LAND-ICE IN THE SEA

'Land-ice' occurs in the sea, as does sea-ice, if we understand land-ice to be all ice not formed by the sea itself, hence that which in its native state does not contain sea salt. This type includes the most spectacular kind of ice in the sea and the most dangerous, under some circumstances, to shipping, namely icebergs.

Apart from these (and the 'ice islands', about which more is to follow), there is another kind of land-ice which makes its way to the sea; that is river ice. The great rivers of Siberia and of the northern part of America, more especially, discharge quantities of their ice into the Arctic Ocean in spring and early summer. This does not happen in the Antarctic.

ICEBERGS: GLACIER ICE

Icebergs are formed by the 'calving', as it is called, of glaciers on the coast. Greenland in the north and Antarctica in the south are the chief producers of icebergs, next in importance being some glaciers on some of the islands situated in or around the polar seas.

To understand icebergs we have to know something about glaciers. Confining ourselves to the glaciers occurring in the polar regions and extending down to the coast, we distinguish four types, viz.,

(1) *Inland ice* is an ice-sheet covering a large area, only allowing pinnacles of rock to project here and there.

(2) *Valley glacier* is a glacier following the course of a valley.

(3) *Piedmont glacier*, or expanded-foot glacier, is a terrace of ice which spreads out at the foot of one or more valley glaciers at the base of the mountain(s).

(4) *Ice barrier*, or *shelf-ice*, is a layer of ice which stretches out from the shore (from inland ice) into the sea.

Inland Ice: The foremost examples of this type are the ice that covers the whole of the interior of Greenland, an area of two million square kilometres; and the ice covering the major part of the Antarctic Continent, an area of no less than ten million square kilometres. Something similar on a far smaller scale is found in Spitsbergen.

Ice of this kind is most likely to be created in an area for the greater part encircled by a range of mountains forming a parapet, as it were, within which the ice can pile up and cover the whole enclosed landscape.

Travelling inland from the sea one first comes upon the boundary range, and behind that an expanse of ice. In Greenland this ice is 3400 metres thick in some places, a thickness which can be measured by echo-sounding. The word 'nunatak' is borrowed from the Greenland Eskimos to denote an isolated mountain peak which projects through the ice sheet.

Sometimes there is a break in the range along part of the circumference of the land-ice and this immediately borders the sea, as, for instance, in Wilhelm II Land, where in some places there is a wall of ice on the coast 40 to 50 metres high.

There are also numerous small islands bordering the coast of Antarctica, which are completely covered with a coat of ice; the rocky ground underneath can only be seen at low water.

Valley Glaciers: These are often the offshoots of an ice-field of the foregoing type, which is then the reservoir that feeds the valley glaciers.

We are best acquainted with the Alpine valley glaciers, but glaciers of this type also occur quite commonly in polar regions, especially along the littoral of Greenland. Notably on its western coast, the glaciers assume enormous dimensions. Between latitudes 69° and 71°40′ N., and so covering a distance of 300 kilometres, there are 14 large and several smaller glaciers. At about 78° N., on Smith isthmus, the Humboldt glacier has a front 110 kilometres wide; it ends at the edge of the sea as a wall of ice 90 metres high.

Other iceberg-producing valley glaciers occur in Spitsbergen, Franz-Jozef Land, Novaya Zemlya, Northland and in North America in some islands of the Canadian archipelago, notably Ellesmere Island and Baffin Island, also in Alaska, where several valley glaciers reach the Bering Sea and there calve icebergs.

Valley glaciers, usually fed by the inland ice, also occur on the borders of the Antarctic continent. When, as they often do, they slope fairly steeply down to the sea, they are comparatively short. In Victoria Land this length varies from 10 to 100 kilometres, and the width from 5 to 15 kilometres. The Beardmore glacier, which Scott and Shackleton climbed on their way to the land-ice of the Antarctic Continent, is the largest known valley glacier, being 200 kilometres long and 25 to 55 kilometres wide.

Piedmont, or Expanded-Foot, Glaciers: These spread out on flat terrain at the foot of mountains. They may do so where the lower end of a valley glacier extends laterally over such a plain and a vast field of ice is thus formed which sometimes connects two or more valley glaciers. Some call only this latter type a Piedmont glacier.

Piedmont glaciers cover, *inter alia*, parts of the Antarctic coast, such as Adélie Coast and Alexander Land and, more especially, coastal regions of Terra del Fuego and Alaska. They are often terraced.

Shelf-Ice or Ice Barrier: This has been called shelf-ice because it is ice which spreads on the sea above the continental shelf, and so beyond the coastline proper, which is in fact masked by it. Near the actual coastline an ice barrier of this kind rests on the bottom—hence the continental shelf—but farther out to sea it floats on the water.

The best-known example is afforded by the Great Barrier, to which the name of Ross was given. This covers more than half of that huge bay of the South Polar Continent, the Ross Sea, situated on either side of longitude 180 and occupying an area of 900 by 950 kilometres, larger than France! Where this ice rests on the water, it more or less follows the movements of the tide. Under the pressure of the inland ice and of the glaciers running down to the coast from the interior, the ice of the Great Barrier is slowly but surely moving northward at the estimated rate of approximately 400 metres a year. But out to sea, where its height above the water varies from 2 to 50 metres, it is constantly 'crumbling', with the formation of vast table-icebergs.

The Ross Sea is not the only place in Antarctica where shelf-ice is found. It also occurs, though not on this vast scale, in the western and southern part of the Weddell Sea and at nearby Wilhelm II Land.

In the North Polar region, notably off the fjords of the north coast of Greenland, an ice formation—called, after the Eskimos, sikussak—is found. This is allied to shelf-ice and is a transitional form between the latter and fast ice. Because, unlike fast ice in most places, it does not disappear in summer, accumulation (also of snow) down the years has made it very thick and it has taken on a structure similar to that of glacier ice.

The thick ice-sheet fringing the north coast of Ellesmere Island (to the west of the northern tip of Greenland) is an even clearer example. This can truly be said to be a kind of shelf-ice. It is the cradle of the 'ice islands'.

Ice Islands: This is the name given to those individual, heavy, flat sheets of ice (see Plates XVI and XVII) which drift around in the Arctic Ocean, and are far thicker than ordinary polar ice. Their thickness may easily amount to 50 metres, 5 metres of which project above water. The surface area of the largest known ice island is approximately 1000 square kilometres, but there are other, far smaller ones. There are estimated to be about a hundred of them, but most of them are small. Because of their origin, they consist of a kind of glacier-like snow-ice. They differ from icebergs mainly in having a far longer life owing to the 'favourable' climate in which they subsist. The first ice island reported has barely changed at all since 1946.

That they have in all probability been formed by the breaking of shelf-ice that borders the north coast of Ellesmere Island is deduced from the striking resemblance of the two surfaces, both of which are conspicuously undulating. It cannot be said that the ridges of the parallel waves are very high; they are at most about six metres, and on some ice-islands (probably more weathered) they are far lower. The distance between the crests is between 150 and 300 metres. The occurrence of small lakes and rivulets on them only goes to show that the term 'ice islands' was aptly chosen.

The discovery of ice islands provides subject-matter for a story unto itself, which we shall relate when we come to discuss the Arctic Ocean.

FORMATION OF ICEBERGS

Valley glaciers have every right to be called ice-rivers, for a glacier is not a motionless mass of ice. Even if the foot of a valley glacier remains at approximately the same place, this will not mean that there is no movement in the ice; on the contrary, glacier ice 'flows'. It is able to do this because its internal structure is somewhat different from that of freshly formed ice, which consists of fairly large, coherent crystals. Glacier ice is snow-ice of many years' standing, and is of slightly plastic consistency. Moreover, ice under heavy pressure is liable to begin to melt somewhat, and thereby to become 'lubricated' at the bottom so to speak.

Under the influence of gravity operating downward along the slopes, and possibly also under the influence of the pressure of land-ice (which lies behind the Greenland valley glaciers for instance and, because of its great size, exerts enormous pressure) the mass of ice of a valley glacier slowly glides downward. Alpine glaciers do this at the rate of about one metre in four days without the fact being noticeable at their snouts, because there the ice melts away as fast as it comes down. The rate of travel of the valley glaciers issuing in the fjords on the east and west coasts of Greenland, however, is often more than 10 metres, and sometimes as much as 20 metres, a day. And this is the cause of icebergs being formed. As the tongue of ice at the foot of the glacier slowly slips into the water, at some time a huge fragment suddenly breaks off. This, as we have already said, is called 'calving'.

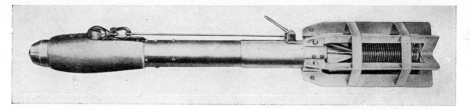

Bathythermograph

Ekman current meter

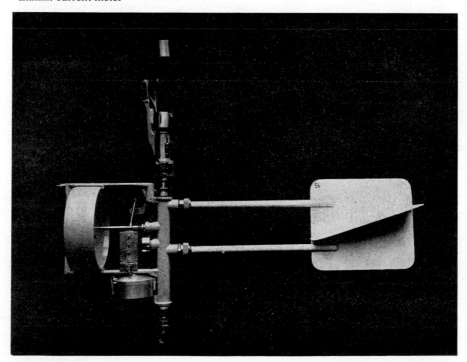

Above: Three kinds of polar ice; aerial view: Young ice, broken and shifting (above and right), winter-ice (centre and below) and ice more than one year old with pressure ridges.

Below: Pancake ice in the Antarctic Ocean. (Photograph W. Vervoort aboard *Willem Barendsz.*)

The process might be described somewhat as follows: the sea-water (or perhaps fjord-water) erodes the ice mass underneath, especially in summer, and the part above breaks off through its own weight. This is all the more likely to happen if, after ebb-tide, the water level is low and no longer buoys up the ice mass sufficiently. This is how the iceberg is born.

Matters are somewhat different in the Antarctic region, where the great ice-cap dips towards the sea, mainly not in the form of glaciers but as barrier ice or shelf-ice. The difference between the situation here and in Greenland can be seen by comparing the two diagrammatic cross-sections in Fig. 32. All the same, the ice barriers of the south likewise calve.

At the edge of the Ross Barrier the ice moves at the general rate of approximately one metre a day, but locally sometimes four times as fast.

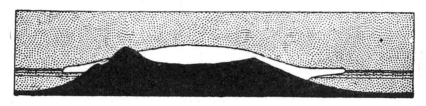

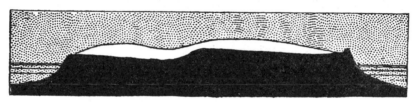

FIG. 32 *Below:* Diagrammatic cross-section through Greenland. *Above:* Diagrammatic cross-section (on a smaller scale) through Antarctica (after Smith). It should be observed that not all of the Antarctic coast is occupied by shelf-ice.

SHAPES AND CHARACTERISTICS OF ICEBERGS

Whereas the valley glaciers deliver icebergs of comparatively limited horizontal dimensions, the chunks that break away from an ice barrier may be some tens of kilometres in length, sometimes in fact as much as one hundred kilometres. These are called *table bergs* or *barrier bergs* (see Plate XV).

Unlike the table bergs of the south, which are usually fairly regular in shape, at all events in their youth, most of the northern icebergs (the great majority of which are supplied by the Greenland valley glaciers and therefore enter the Atlantic Ocean) are of irregular shape, sometimes indeed quite fantastically so. This is partly due to distortion of the tongues of the valley glaciers by the accidented floor of the valley. Furthermore, an iceberg is liable to capsize in course of time, because its altered balance, which is due to erosion and melting of its submerged base, causes it to turn turtle. Wind and rain, sun and ocean waves of course, are likewise governing factors.

4

Icebergs assume an astounding variety of shapes, from fairly uniform geometrical figures to castles with turrets, domed structures or minarets, and mountains with peaks and gorges, while in some there may be deep clefts, fissures or cavities. Falls of melt-water have been seen to cascade down giant bergs, while bunches and fringes of icicles suspended from projecting edges have been observed in others. Photographs of some icebergs will be found in Plates XVIII–XXII.

The intrinsic colour of glacier ice, which is best seen in transmitted light, is bluish-green. On the outside, icebergs usually appear to be white like snow, owing to the strong reflection of light. They are sometimes coloured in patches by diatoms; silt bands or strips of bluish, transparent ice are also frequently seen on them.

On clear days an iceberg is visible from a considerable distance, even if it is still beyond the horizon, with only its peak showing. But in fog—and there happens to be a great deal of it at sea in the vicinity of the Newfoundland Bank, where more icebergs occur near the shipping lanes than anywhere else in the world—an iceberg may well loom up within one hundred metres. So the navigational blessing of radar will be patent to all!

It is a known fact that icebergs often have projections under water which are just as dangerous as submerged reefs; consequently, a ship keeping at a respectful distance from the visible part of an iceberg may nevertheless collide with it.

As the specific gravity of iceberg-ice is on an average four-fifths to six-sevenths (varying with the amount of air enclosed in the ice), the underwater volume of an iceberg may generally be expected to be something like four to six times that of the projecting part. It is not only a question of vertical dimensions, but essentially of volumetric proportions. Thus the draught of an iceberg may be far less than four times its height, as the underwater part is often broader than the upper part, at any rate in the case of castle-shaped or pyramidal icebergs.

When the movement of wind-driven pack-ice is different from that of the deeper layers of water—which may be governed by a sea current running deep down—an iceberg may follow an entirely different course from the pack-ice,[1] because the major part of its volume is immersed in this deeper water. Advantage has sometimes been taken of this fact by mooring a ship to an iceberg, to the end that it be towed through the pack-ice!

THE HEIGHT OF ICEBERGS

Most icebergs do not tower more than 50 metres above water; quite an impressive height, for all that! And do not forget that five times as much may be under water. Accurate measurements in the north have seldom shown more than 75 metres freeboard, but very occasionally an iceberg 100 metres tall (about the height of a cathedral tower and spire) has been seen.

[1] Conversely, the pack-ice may tow icebergs along with it.

A height of 200 metres has been reported from the south, but this height is doubted. Scott says that the majority of icebergs measured during his expedition did not exceed 35 metres in height.

BREAK-UP AND MELTING

As an iceberg travels farther and farther from its birthplace, and becomes older, its volume gradually declines. This may happen in three ways, namely, by calving, by melting and by erosion.

Born by the calving of a glacier, an iceberg which casts off a part of itself is likewise said to *calve*. When this happens, what remains of the iceberg is usually thrown off balance and it capsizes. Often, indeed, it calves more than once.

Melting This generally takes place in cold water along the water-line. If an iceberg has capsized once or several times, a melt edge, or melt edges, will clearly define the previous water-line(s); a fine example is to be seen in Plate XX. In comparatively warm water, melting takes place predominantly in the lower part and there is frequent calving. That the air and the rays of the sun can melt the upper part, small waterfalls often bear witness.

A noise of varying intensity sometimes accompanies the melting of an iceberg above water. Observers have compared the loud noise heard when sunshine is accelerating the process of melting to the clatter of rain on a flat roof. In other cases it is more like a distant murmur. It is caused by the release of many tiny air bubbles which have been enclosed under pressure ever since the formation of glacier ice from snow.

Erosion This is due to the scouring action of waves and rain. Waves are capable of washing out whole grottoes (comparable to the caves hollowed out by the breakers on rocky coasts) and portals in the wall of ice. Or else a valley is formed right across the iceberg between two peaks; then, if erosion of the whole mass continues, the iceberg sinks down deeper, the floor of its transverse valley will be submerged and the two peaks, projecting separately but connected underneath, will form a twin iceberg.

Something more will be said at the end of this chapter about the speed and destruction of icebergs in the Atlantic Ocean.

THE POLAR REGIONS

Let us now examine in greater detail those homelands of ice, the polar regions in both hemispheres. The ice situation in these regions is shown in Figs. 33, 34 and 36, which summarize the data collected during many voyages down the years.

The salient difference between the two polar regions is apparent at a glance: a big sea around the North Pole, albeit a sea of ice; a vast continent around the South Pole, though covered with ice and snow.

All around the Arctic Ocean continents alternate with seas and oceans: we find successively the continent of Europe and Asia (Siberia), the northern part of the Pacific Ocean, the continent of North America (Alaska and Canada) with its adjacent islands, including Greenland, and then the northern Atlantic Ocean. In the south we find by contrast, all around the Antarctic continent, a closed ring of water connecting the Atlantic, Indian and Pacific Oceans.

This geographical difference between the northern and southern hemispheres is responsible for their differing climates. As the greatest frigidity is found, not above the water, but above continents, it is North Siberia which is the coldest in the north (at any rate in winter), not the Arctic Ocean. Hence the Pole is not the coldest place in the north, but it *is* in the south because there it is situated on the Antarctic continent.

On the other hand, although the climate around the polar region in the southern hemisphere—say along the 60th parallel—is bleak and inclement, it is nevertheless comparatively uniform; whereas in the northern hemisphere, along the 60th parallel running through Russia, Siberia, the Bering Sea (the north of the Pacific Ocean), Alaska, Canada, Hudson Bay and the northern tip of Labrador, the southern tip of Greenland, the North Atlantic Ocean and, lastly, southern Norway, the climate varies enormously. One has only to compare the south of Norway with the north of Labrador. Nor is it merely a question of differences between land and sea climates; there is a marked difference in the sea itself, notably in the Atlantic Ocean between the western parts, into which a cold sea current (the Labrador Current) flows from the north, and the eastern parts, where comparatively warm water coming from the south (the Gulf Stream) keeps the ocean free from ice up to high latitudes.

The ice situation in the Antarctic Ocean is simpler than in the Arctic.

THE ANTARCTIC OCEAN

ICEBERGS

Travelling southward from the more 'moderate' latitudes of the southern hemisphere (see Fig. 33), we first come to a region where icebergs are liable to be seen in all seasons. This region begins in the Atlantic Ocean immediatey to the south of latitude 40°; in the Pacific Ocean at about 50° S., and in between these two latitudes in the Indian Ocean; from there it stretches to the edge of Antarctica, the birthplace of the icebergs.

The northern boundary of the area in which icebergs occur can, of course, be drawn only tentatively. An iceberg has undoubtedly been encountered from time to time to the north of the line drawn in the chart, which marks the *average* northern boundary. On 30th April 1894 a drifting piece of ice was reported as having been seen at 26°30′ S., 25°40′ W., a place between South Africa and South America, only 180 nautical miles from the Tropic of Capricorn! This is the most northerly point at which we know the remains of a southern iceberg ever to have been seen. Icebergs scarcely ever travel as far as this. They are exceptional to the north of latitude 35° S. in the

Atlantic Ocean, to the north of 45° S. in the Indian Ocean and to the north of 50° S. in the Pacific Ocean.

Why, we may ask, are icebergs able to penetrate farther north in the Atlantic Ocean, especially on the western side, than in the other oceans? The answer is that this is due to the cold sea current on the western side of

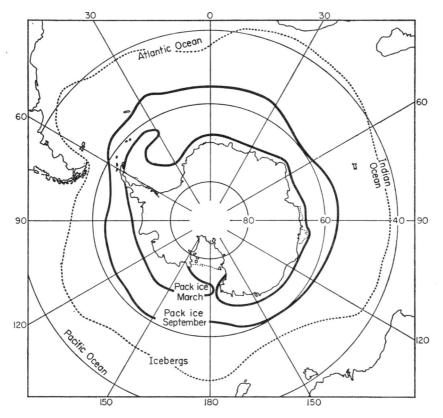

FIG. 33 Average northern boundary for icebergs in the Antarctic Ocean and average pack-ice boundaries at the end of the winter and end of summer.

the Atlantic Ocean which, coming from the south-east bends north-eastward along the Falkland Islands (near the southern tip of South America); it is called the Falkland Current, and it is more or less the counter-part of the Labrador Current of the northern hemisphere. The ice carried along by the Falkland Current comes predominantly from the Weddell Sea. Icebergs are encountered every year, especially in October, November and December, that is, in the spring and early summer of the southern hemisphere, far to the north of the Falkland Islands. Accordingly, the average boundary line of the iceberg area bulges notably northward on the chart in the western South Atlantic Ocean.

As to the frequency with which icebergs occur in the Southern Seas, this does not vary much with the season, vastly in contrast to the North Atlantic, in which icebergs are most frequent in spring and early summer. Generally speaking, October and November appear to be the months when they are most numerous in the south. This is due to the release of the icebergs from the pack-ice in September and October (the southern spring). They reach farthest north from November to February; floating icebergs are fewest in number during the southern winter, viz. from May. As to the total number, several thousands of them are certainly adrift every year in the Antarctic Ocean.

By far the majority of the south polar icebergs are of the tabular type owing to their origin in the barrier ice. A photograph of one of these appears in Plate XV. Though usually less fantastically shaped than their northern counterparts, these Antarctic icebergs are no less imposing by virtue of their monumental size. In their youth, most of them are at least 400 metres long, but many are as much as 1500 metres. Icebergs, which could really more aptly be called ice-islands, of 5 to 20 nautical miles in length have been seen. On one occasion indeed, the length reported was 50 miles. In 1840 a ship observed one of these from afar for several days; her captain, Dumont d'Urville, thought it was land and called it Clarie Land. . . .

Southern icebergs seldom reach a height exceeding 50 metres. Although table icebergs are of comparatively simple shape in their youth, as time goes on the constant action of the waves (sometimes high ones) works upon their contours which become crenellated and eroded with grottoes.

In addition to this type there are also some icebergs in the south which derive from valley glaciers and are therefore similar to the Greenland icebergs.

THE PACK-ICE OF THE SOUTHERN SEAS

If we pursue on the chart (Fig. 33) our journey southward, during which we first encountered the boundary line of the iceberg area, we shall eventually come across pack-ice at higher latitudes.

The first indication of the approach of an ice-field is 'ice-blink', a white gleam in the sky just above the horizon, notably if there are any clouds about. It is caused by scattering of the light reflected upwards by the ice-field and is often observed before the ice itself comes into view. Naturally, this is not confined to the southern hemisphere any more than is another sign of the approach of ice-fields, namely, a diminution of sea movement and swell when the ice lies to windward, or in the direction whence the swell comes.

There is another special sign of the nearness of pack-ice in the Antarctic Ocean, which usually has a fairly clear northern boundary there. It is the presence of birds, which use the ice as their front-line base. The snow petrel (*Pagodroma nivea*), for instance, never goes farther than 100 miles from pack-ice. Furthermore, a fairly abrupt drop in the temperature of the sea-water is consistently found ten to twenty miles to the north of the ice boundary; it is a drop of 1° or 1·5°C, e.g. from 0°C or −0·5°C in winter to −1·5° or lower still.

By pack-ice in the Antarctic we mean all floating ice-fields consisting of comparatively flat slabs of ice. At the edges of these slabs there are crumbled-off fragments or rims of ice caused by friction between the large floes which are almost invariably kept moving by wind and currents.

As there is far less impediment to the movements of the ice-fields here, with water all around, than in the Arctic Ocean, there is less fragmentation and piling-up of the pack-ice of the south than in the north, and it therefore consists of far more extensive ice-floes. Here the accumulations caused by lateral pressure (hummocks) are seldom more than 3–4 metres high. Pressures comparable to those in the Arctic only occur in the Weddell Sea.

All expeditions to these parts have reported on the pack-ice in the seas around Antarctica since James Cook's circumnavigation of the South Polar Continent in 1772–75. But it was not until 1925 that organized exploration of the distribution of the ice in these regions was undertaken, notably by the British expeditions in the *Discovery*, *Discovery II* and the *William Scoresby* and also by the whaling expeditions, particularly those of the Norwegians. Finally, much new information about pack-ice has been obtained in latter years, through several Antarctic expeditions, such as those of Byrd (American), the Norwegian–English–Swedish expedition of 1950–52, the Antarctic expeditions on the occasion of the International Geophysical Year of 1957–58, and by aerial reconnaissance.

Figure 33 shows the extreme seasonal positions of the pack-ice boundary, namely, the average position of the northern boundary after the winter (in September and October), when the glacial area has advanced farthest, and the average limit at the end of the summer (in March), when this limit has retreated farthest. Certain parts of the coasts of Antarctica, e.g. to the south of Africa and of Australia, are entirely free of ice in some summers, the major part of the west coast of Graham Land becoming so every summer. This usually happens in late summer or early autumn, though in 1938 *Discovery II*, sailing along the Adélie Coast, found that there was no pack-ice left as early as the middle of January.

It is in the Antarctic spring, September and October (corresponding to our March and April) that the ice boundary is situated farthest north. The increasing warmth of the sun has by then begun to thaw some of the ice admittedly, but this also entails a certain amount of loss of cohesion between the ice-fields which, under the influence of wind and currents, are able to spread over a somewhat larger area, particularly in the Atlantic sector. Then, in November, the ice boundary begins at last to retreat, first fairly slowly, but by December it begins to break up and disappear on a large scale. Towards the end of that month, when the sun stands highest in the heavens, vast areas, especially in the Atlantic sector, become ice-free.

In all seasons there is a belt of pack-ice in front of the mouth of the Ross

Sea, situated on the Pacific side of Antarctica; but it has long been known that water is found to the south of this pack-ice in high and late summer. During its southward voyage in January 1936, the *Discovery II* expedition found that this belt was some 650 kilometres wide. Behind it they came upon ice-free water, from latitude 73½ S. to the great Ross Barrier. When the vessel returned northward a fortnight later, the width of the ice-belt was still 250 kilometres.

Something similar happens in the Weddell Sea, situated opposite the western part of the Atlantic Ocean, with the difference that the entrance to the Weddell Sea is entirely open on its eastern side in summer, as can be seen on the chart (Fig. 33). After the ice has broken up and the ice boundary has retreated, there remains a broad tongue of ice to the south of the Atlantic Ocean, still stretching far eastward, as far as longitude 30° E., in December, but which retreats during the summer to Graham Land in the west. In January 1915, for example, the *Endurance* penetrated through a tongue of ice roughly 1000 kilometres wide in the neighbourhood of the Weddell Sea, and found open water behind it at 72° S.

Graham Land is to the west of the Weddell Sea. The west-going current along the continent bends to the north here (owing to the presence of the peninsula) and forms the Weddell Current which, farther up, then bends back to the north-east and begins to run parallel to the West Wind Drift. It is this looping of the cold Weddell Current which is responsible for the long, broad tongue of pack-ice which, as we have seen, is still lying off the Weddell Sea at the beginning of summer, when there is already open water farther south.

We have already pointed out that the boundary lines sketched in on the chart merely represent average boundaries; the actual boundary line seldom runs as uniformly and evenly. Vessels sailing alongside the margins of the pack-ice at some distance have always found them twisting and winding, with deep inward and outward bends.

As will be clear from Fig. 33, there are far greater displacements of the ice boundary in the Atlantic section of the Antarctic Ocean in the course of the seasons than, say, in the sector of the Pacific Ocean. For one thing, the ice boundary in the latter sector does not push anything like as far northward in spring, and for another, its ice is not subject to the same degree of demolition in the summer and autumn.

Ocean currents are largely responsible for these and similar variations. It is a known fact that the ice-fields in the polar seas are constantly drifting, a movement caused by the wind and general ocean currents.

THE GREAT ICE BARRIER

Pushing southward through or over the pack-ice off the Ross Sea (which is roughly due south of New Zealand), there is often found, as we have seen, open water stretching to a great distance. This was an unexpected and pleasant surprise to the first polar explorers who were trying to reach the continent. But, after they had crossed this open stretch of sea, they found their way barred by a vertical wall of ice rising out of the sea, varying in height from a few metres to 70–80 metres above the water and spanning the whole width of the Ross Sea, a distance of more than 700 kilometres. The ice-cliff in question is aptly called the Great Barrier, or the Ross Barrier, after James Ross who first discovered it.

It was not until later that attempts were made to pass this wall on foot. Once on top of it, the voyager sees spread before him a huge expanse of almost flat ice, along which he can proceed for mile upon mile without having to climb more than a few metres. The surface of this ice is reminiscent of inland ice, except that it surpasses it—if such, indeed, be possible—in desolate monotony. It was across a plain of ice like this, at least comparable in size to a country like Sweden, and possibly vaster, that Shackleton, Scott and Amundsen began their treks to the South Pole.

This glacial plain consists for the major part of snow-ice of many years' standing, and is therefore more like land-ice than sea-ice. It can, in fact, be regarded as a continuation of the glacier-ice with which the Antarctic Continent is almost entirely covered. This continental ice was actually formed like one huge glacier by the accumulation and compression of snow down the centuries, to a compact sheet of ice, which, however, instead of coming to an end on the margin of the continent, slips over it in many places into the surrounding shallow water. There it rests partly on the bottom—the 'continental shelf'—farther out, however, on the water.

This ice is really a transition from land-ice to land-fast sea-ice of many years' standing. It is called 'shelf-ice' because it spreads over the continental shelf which, as we know, is the comparatively flat part of the sea-bed stretching along the edge of a continent, usually to where the depth is about 200 metres (or 100 fathoms). This shelf-ice occupies most of the Ross Sea. Byrd's expeditions and the Norwegian–English–Swedish expedition mentioned above had their permanent observation bases (Little America and Maudheim) not far from the edge of this ice.

Another extensive shelf-ice plain covers the interior part of the Weddell Sea to the south of the Atlantic Ocean.

We already know from the history of icebergs that shelf-ice is not immobile; through compression of the inland-ice it is being pushed very slowly (for example at one metre a day) outward, and from this shelf-ice stem most of the southern icebergs that we have considered earlier in this book.

WINTER ICE AREAS OUTSIDE THE SOUTH POLAR REGION PROPER

Hitherto, we have been discussing the seas around Antarctica[1] only. The reader may wonder whether the sea freezes anywhere else in the southern

[1] The words Antarctica and antarctic are derived from 'arctic', which relates to the North Polar regions, and 'anti', meaning 'opposite'.

4*

hemisphere. It does, but in only a few places outside the actual South Polar region. Winter ice occurs chiefly along the South Georgia coasts (54° S.) and those of the Sandwich Islands. On the other hand, the straits of Tierra del Fuego (53–55° S.) and the bays of the Kerguelen Islands do not freeze over.

THE ARCTIC OCEAN

Figure 34 gives a bird's-eye view of the seas and glacial regions around the North Pole. We shall ignore the icebergs for the time being.

We see here three areas of sea-ice, namely within the great central core, the permanent 'polar cap' of sea-ice, called the 'Arctic pack', which comprises the major part of the ice area, and around this two other belts, the pack-ice, or drift-ice and the (land-) fast ice.

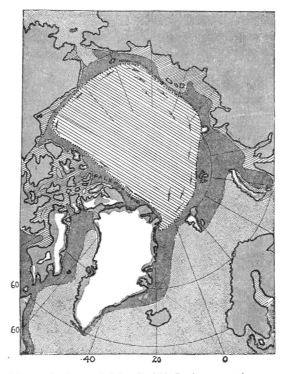

FIG. 34 The glacial areas in the north (after Smith). In the centre the great polar cap; fast ice along the coasts; in between these and farther south the looser pack-ice, indicated in a darker shade.

In this case we mean by pack-ice the belt of drifting sea-ice, situated between the vast polar cap and the fast ice, which for the most part was not formed locally but has drifted from elsewhere, and is less permanent and less coherent than the Arctic pack.

THE POLAR ICE OR ARCTIC PACK

Separated by the shifting pack-ice from the fast ice or the coast, there lies the ovoid, permanent polar cap of ice, a glacial area as vast as European Russia or the U.S.A.—approximately six million square kilometres. The long axis of the oval runs from Spitsbergen to west Alaska; the boundary of this area lies furthest south along the northern coast of Alaska (latitude 72° N.) and furthest north near Spitsbergen and Franz Jozef Land (81½° N.). The North Pole itself is not situated in the centre of this area; that centre is called the 'Ice Pole' or the 'Pole of Inaccessibility' and its exact position is 84° N. and 175° W.

On comparing the boundary of this area with the course of the depth lines of the Arctic Ocean (see Fig. 14), it must strike us that this boundary more or less follows the thousand-metre line.

It would be a mistake to picture the Arctic[1] pack to oneself as one coherent, flat floor of ice. First of all there are always fissures in it, gaping crevasses or fairly broad open lanes, especially in summer, but also in winter. Secondly, in most places the ice-fields are uneven, owing to piled-up ice pushed by lateral pressure. Both conditions are due to the fact that the ice masses are never at rest, but are continually shifting, away from each other and upon each other, as a result of wind and current. It is estimated that in summer ten per cent. of the surface of the polar cap consists of water forming open patches between separate ice-fields, and open strips and lanes. This is only an estimated average for the summer months; the quantity of open water naturally depends on the meteorological conditions prevailing during those months, and therefore varies from year to year.

A known phenomenon caused by the presence of open water is what polar explorers call *water sky*; bands or widths of open water throw dark patches on banks of cloud, as they reflect less light than does ice. It is the converse of ice blink.

The Arctic pack can be described as consisting for the major part of ice several years old, predominantly in the form of vast fields, (i.e. coherent expanses of which the limits cannot be seen from a ship's masthead), greatly misshapen by interlocking under pressure, as a result of which piles of ice have been heaped up, and hummocks formed, imparting a highly accidented appearance and incomparable strength to the whole for huge distances.

The thickness of the polar ice, apart from piled-up ice and hummocks, varies on an average from 2–3½ metres. Through years of freezing, melting and freezing again, these hummocks have become absolutely massive, rising vertically in places up to 25 metres. Disregarding these, we can say that the thickness at the end of winter is 2½–4 metres, and at the end of summer, 1½–3 metres.

[1] Arctic means pertaining to the North Pole region and is derived from the Greek word arktos, meaning bear (referring to the constellations Ursa Major and Ursa Minor, which stand in the north).

Large surfaces of simple ice formed solely by constant freezing through and through are seldom found in polar ice. It appears that, where this does happen, about 2 metres of ice are formed in one season. In the event of continuous growth, the ice becomes approximately 4 metres thick; this is the limit attained by freezing alone in about 4 years, for owing to this great thickness, there is eventually so little loss of heat by the water through the ice that the ice ceases to grow underneath. Usually however the ice has been broken up at least once within a year.

The ice-fields of the Arctic pack usually have a border of hummocks and pressure ridges, as a result of collisions with other, similar, drifting ice-fields. It is now easy to see why, under such conditions, the polar regions are far from being landscapes where perpetual stillness reigns.

We know that varying drift at the mercy of current and wind sets up tensions in the ice; but there is yet another cause, namely local differences in expansion or contraction which occur when the ice-fields cool down or become warmer, and lead in one case to a pile-up, and in the other to cracking.

Even ice-fields are found only where, thanks to exceptionally favourable conditions, prolonged cohesion has enabled the ice steadily to increase in thickness.

MOVEMENT OF POLAR ICE

East winds predominate in the polar region, and they are responsible for the average east–west movement of the ice. This movement, as seen on a chart (Fig. 34) produces a clockwise circulation. Owing to the rotation of the earth, this wind-drift of the ice and water is accompanied by a tendency to shift towards the right, hence towards the interior of the polar region. Consequently, at the time of its greatest mobility, the ice tends to press up towards the middle, and to relax the pressure along the margins of the polar sea.

With regard to the circular movement mentioned, it should be added that the movement of the waters between Novaya Zemlya, Spitsbergen and North Greenland is led into somewhat different channels. In the Barents Sea, the last offshoot of the Gulf Stream drives Atlantic water in a northerly direction and, between Spitsbergen and Greenland, Atlantic water passes northward along the west coast of Spitsbergen, while polar water flows southward along the east coast of Greenland.

There is, however, a further complication in the interior of the polar sea. As we saw in Chapter 1, the Arctic Ocean is divided into two oceanic basins by the submarine mountain ridge called the Lomonosov Ridge. This affects the circulation of the water. Where the movement extends to some depth, two distinct circulations tend to be formed in the two basins, the water along either side of the Lomosonov Ridge flowing towards Greenland. That is why many drifting voyages are apt to end near Greenland. First there was that of Nansen in the *Fram* (in 1893–96), which was followed by several similar expeditions, some of which are shown in Fig. 35, either in ships like the Russian ice-breaker *Sedov* (October 1937–January 1940), or on ice-floes or ice-islands.

Because the wind, though blowing predominantly from the east, does so by no means consistently, the direction in which the ice-fields move is likewise very variable, as is evident from the zig-zagging lines representing the routes of these expeditions. Both Nansen and Sverdrup (who, in the

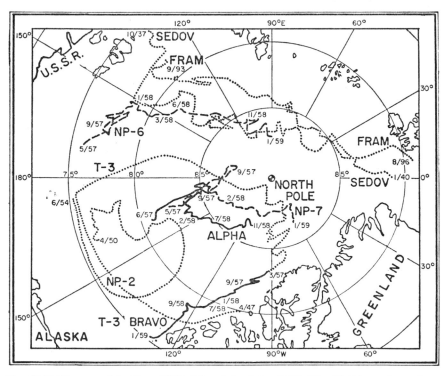

FIG. 35 Drift routes of the *Fram* (1893–96) and the *Sedov* (1937–40), of drifting polar stations and of ice-islands. (Alpha = A, Bravo = B, NP = North Pole stations.)

Maud, was locked in the ice to the north of Siberia in 1922–24) noted that if the wind blew steadily for a time from one direction, the movement of the ice adjusted itself so that the ice travelled at an angle of about 30–40 degrees to the right of the direction of the wind. As we know, this is due to the deviation caused by the Earth's rotation, which is characteristic of wind-drift currents (see Chapter 6).

'*NORTH POLE*' STATIONS

In May 1937 an aeroplane landed four men on a large drifting ice-floe at only 20 kilometres from the North Pole. The leader of this little band of Russian explorers was Ivan Papanin. They camped for nine months on this ice-floe, making all kinds of oceanographic and meteorological observations, and transmitting the latter regularly by radio.

They had expected the ice-floe to take at least a year, if not much longer, to reach the edge of the polar ice, but it did so much more quickly. The ice at once set course from the Pole for Greenland. The variable winds naturally did not permit the voyage to follow a straight line, but it subsequently proceeded southward at gathering speed and at the end of nine months, during which it had travelled 2500 kilometres, station 'North Pole' in the pack-ice of the East Greenland Current had already arrived at 70° N. There the men were picked up.

After the war, the Russians took up the threads again and equipped stations 'North Pole' 2, 3, 4, etc. in succession; indeed, since April 1954 one or two teams have been working continuously on drifting stations.

During the International Geophysical Year of 1957–58 the Americans also established an observation post on a drifting ice-floe ('Station A'). But before that they had set up a station on something different from a slab of sea-ice, namely on an ice-island which was called T 3.

THE DISCOVERY OF THE ICE-ISLANDS

Although the existence of ice-islands in the Arctic Ocean (see p. 82) had been known earlier to the U.S. Air Force, the fact was not made public until 1950. The story of their discovery goes back to 1946 when, on 14th August, a reconnaissance aircraft of the USAF flew over the polar ice at a distance of 500 kilometres from the north coast of Alaska, and there showed up on its radar an enormous drifting mass of ice which was clearly different from the surrounding polar ice. For the time being it was called Target X, or TX, and subsequently $T1$, and its discovery was treated as a military secret.

For the next three years, in the course of the regular meteorological flights over the Arctic Ocean, crews frequently observed $T1$, either visually during rare clear periods, or by radar in the dark or when an overcast sky or fog made visibility poor. Drifting farther and farther away from the route of the meteorological flights, $T1$ was finally lost to view. The last time it was seen, on 6th October, 1949, it was more than 2500 kilometres away from its position when first detected. $T1$ measured approximately 27 × 32 kilometres. At that time no other ice-islands had been discovered.

In May 1950, the crews of the regular meteorological flights to the north of Alaska were ordered to search diligently for ice-islands. Their efforts were at last rewarded on 21st July when a second ice-island, $T2$—a little larger than the first one, namely, 30 × 32 kilometres—was sighted. It subsequently appeared that $T2$ had shown up on a radar photograph on 19th July, but had not then been reported. Encouraged by this success, the crews intensified their search, and on 29th July a third ice-island, $T3$, was detected. It was 8 × 16 kilometres, a good deal smaller than the other two.

The surfaces of all three islands were in very distinct relief, taking the form of a system of approximately parallel waves. This relief was at its most pronounced in $T3$, which was probably younger than the other two.

As it turned out later, $T3$ had already appeared on photographs taken in April 1947 and July 1948. $T1$, the first ice-island to be sighted, was ultimately rediscovered in August 1951, twenty-two months after it had last been seen. Since then, neither $T1$, $T2$ nor $T3$ has been lost to view.

After these discoveries, the photographic files of the USAF were, of course, assiduously scanned for indications of the existence of more of these islands. The scrutiny was not in vain, for two fairly large ones were detected, though they have since been lost. One of them is particularly interesting, because there is one photograph in the series on which the island appeared, which shows the place whence it must have come. This is a place on the north coast of Ellesmere Island where a large 'bite' out of the shelf-ice shows up. The ice-island is assumed to have broken off there in 1946, at the starting-point of its travels.

In March 1952 an American expedition, led by Air Officer J. O. Fletcher, landed on $T3$ for the purpose of making meteorological, oceanographic and geophysical observations. This station was maintained until May 1954. Another working-party of scientists was posted there for several months in 1955, and in 1957, on the occasion of the International Geophysical Year, the United States again established an observation post there, this time for a longer period. This observation station was called Station B, because another such station, called Station A, had been set up on a large ice-floe in another part of the Arctic Ocean.

Station B had the benefit of fairly extensive scientific equipment, including a good-sized oceanographic laboratory. Readings were regularly taken of depth, current, temperatures, salinity and other oceanographic quantities, from which it became evident that the effect of Atlantic water (the Gulf Stream) is still noticeable at certain depths in the middle of the Arctic Ocean; for, whereas the temperatures are below $0°C$ in the upper layers and near the bottom, the waters are above this temperature (with a maximum of $0·5°C$) at depths between 270 and 1000 metres. The average rate of drift of $T3$ was four kilometres a day, with a maximum of fourteen kilometres a day.

We have already dealt with the essential nature of ice-islands.

FAST ICE

On the shore side of the Arctic Ocean there is a border of fast ice for nine months of the year. This can best be described as a non-drifting expanse of ice attached to the land, in its entirety less than a year old, and caused by the freezing of the sea starting out from the land. This ice is not completely immobile, because, beyond a certain distance from the shoreline, it goes up and down with the tide. The belt, which is attached to the shore, and which does not follow the movements of the tide, is called the ice-foot. Owing to these movements a large fissure, running parallel to the shore, is often formed between the ice-foot and the rest of the ice; but fresh ice forms in it later.

The limit of the ice is set, approximately, by the 12-fathom line, that is the depth-line of roughly 22 metres. So, wherever there is a vast expanse of shallow water alongside the shore, with the 12-fathom line far from the coastline, the belt of fast ice is wide; but where the sea bottom dips comparatively steeply from the shoreline, the belt is narrow. The former prevails, for example, along the wide Siberian continental shelf. There the fast ice stretches out to 480 kilometres beyond the shore in places, notably off the mouths of the rivers Yana and Lena. These extensive, uninterrupted sheets of ice are a unique phenomenon, even for the Arctic Ocean, where otherwise the ice landscape is intersected by open fissures or lanes of irregularly formed stretches of open water.

It is not only owing to its shallowness that the water off the Siberian coast near the mouths of the great rivers lends itself to the growth and spread of fast ice; it is also because the river-water there keeps the salt content down.

An important factor favourable to the formation of land-fast ice off open coasts is the presence of stranded hummocks. As the larger specimens draw about 12 fathoms, they thus mark the 12-fathom line and there form a line of fortifications as it were; for the fixed ice is exposed to pressure from the pack-ice, which threatens to break it up, while there comes a similar threat from the swell induced elsewhere in open areas.

A curious phenomenon is the *polynya*—a Russian word meaning a fairly extensive area free from ice and enclosed by ice-fields—to be seen locally at the outer edge of the fast ice. A permanent one is the great Siberian polynya stretching along the edge of the fast ice from the north of the New Siberian Islands to Kolynuchin Bay. It has been suggested that the existence of this polynya is due to the prevalence of certain strong winds, which keep this region 'clean'.

The many straits, bays and passages between the islands of the Canadian archipelago are likewise propitious to the formation of fast ice in autumn, the islands and peninsulas protecting it from the effects of wind-waves and swell.

In a few of the fjords of Greenland's northern coast some of the fast ice may fail to melt in summer, whence, in the course of many years, an amazingly thick kind of ice has formed, fed moreover by snowfall and therefore assuming a structure approximating that of glacier ice, hence allied to the shelf-ice of Antarctica. It is called *sikussak*, a word borrowed from the Eskimos.

The solid ice in the fjords and bays of west Greenland is an important factor in the life of icebergs formed there, for it holds them fast in winter and spring, right up to May, and does not let them go until it is itself broken up.

PACK-ICE (DRIFT ICE)

Pack-ice—which is generally understood to be displaced sea-ice deriving either from the margins of the Arctic pack or from land-fast ice, part of which always comes adrift in spring—will be found between the belt of fast ice and the Arctic pack. It is less compact and therefore more mobile than the latter, usually thinner and having less extensive floes. As there is no fast ice in summer, there is only pack-ice between the Arctic pack and the shore. In August, the strip of water off the coast of Eurasia has on an average 50 per cent. of open water and 50 per cent. of pack-ice, which may be taken as an average for the whole stretch of this strip from Novaya Zemlya to the Bering Sea, except for certain unfavourable places where ice-fields are apt to hang about and pile up, for example in De Long Strait, between Wrangel Island and the continent of East Siberia at 179° E., in the strait between North Land and Cape Chelyuskin, the region of the Taimyr Skerries (rock islands) and in the southern part of the Kara Sea. Places like these always proved to be obstacles in the path of former expeditions trying to complete the North-East passage from western Europe along Siberia to the Pacific Ocean, or the other way round.

Nowadays the Russians maintain a shipping trade of sorts along the whole Siberian north coast in summer, mainly in August and September. They have set up meteorological and oceanographic observation posts all along the route, and reconnaissance flights are made over the ice for the benefit of this traffic. Convoys, assisted by ice-breakers, then sail either from western Russia or from eastern Siberia to the great Siberian rivers, like the Jenissei, the Lena, the Indigirka and the Kolima.

The distribution of the pack-ice is governed by the more or less permanent great sea currents, the offshoots of the Gulf Stream on the one hand, and the cold East Greenland Current and the Labrador Current, on the other. We have already seen how much the warmer Atlantic waters of the Gulf Stream affect the boundaries of the pack-ice. This influence penetrates farthest along the western shores of Spitsbergen and of Franz Josef Land (the branch of the Gulf Stream here sometimes being called the Spitsbergen Current) and on the west coast of Novaya Zemlya (a name used for this offshoot being the North Cape Current). We shall presently have more to say about the counterparts of the Gulf Stream, the icy currents skirting east Greenland and north-east America.

For all that, the boundaries of the pack-ice are anything but fixed. For one thing, there are the regularly changing seasons, altering the ice boundaries all the year through. For another, there is the variability of the wind which, at all seasons, greatly affects the distribution of the pack-ice. The normal boundaries at different times of the year can be seen in Fig. 36. The smallest amount of pack-ice is found in September or the beginning of October, the largest in April.

Four things may happen to a unit of pack-ice: (a) It may freeze up in the polar ice again; (b) in autumn it may become firmly fixed in the new fast ice; (c) in summer it may melt away locally; (d) it may be carried southwards with the 'ice currents'.

Two other things are clearly seen from Figs. 34 and 36. Firstly, the large strip of ice-free water on the eastern side of the Atlantic Ocean which, in winter too, passing Norway, Lapland and Spitsbergen, reaches far to the north of the Arctic Circle. Secondly, the long strip of pack-ice which, on the western side of the Atlantic Ocean, stretches far southward from Baffin Bay and along the coast of Labrador, especially in winter and spring, in the latter season even to beyond Newfoundland, i.e. to 45° N., which is the same latitude as Bordeaux!

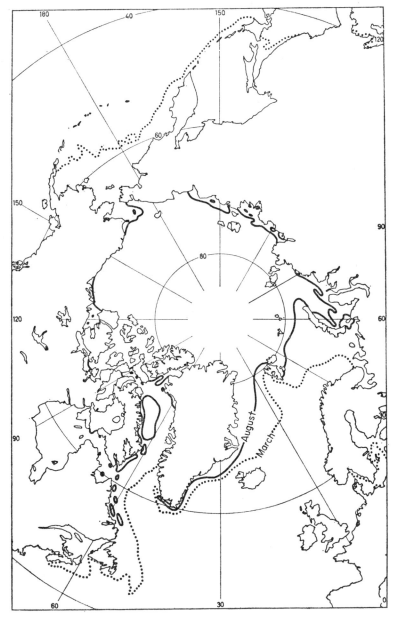

FIG. 36 Average boundaries of sea-ice in the northern seas: the most retracted position and the most advanced position (according to the Russian Morskoi Atlas).

THE GULF STREAM'S INFLUENCE

The first of the features referred to in the preceding paragraph shows at work the powerful influence of the Gulf Stream,[1] which is responsible for this outstanding contrast between the eastern and western sides of the North Atlantic Ocean. On the eastern side, along the whole coast of Norway, the sea may be free from ice in the winter as well (only the interior portions of the fjords sometimes freeze over), and excellent ports in the far north, like Tromsö and Hammerfest (71° N.) remain open; whereas on the other side, along the whole east coast of Greenland, drifting ice is still encountered even in summer. The coasts of Greenland are, accordingly, settled by little more than a small number of Eskimos.

By referring to a chart of ocean currents (Fig. 96) the reader can gain confirmation of the statement that the offshoots of the Gulf Stream to the north of Norway penetrate that far northward and eastward; but in fact the ice charts themselves furnish the most striking testimony to the empire of the Gulf Stream. Nowhere indeed is its mighty influence upon the climate of northern Europe more clearly apparent than in the ice situation along the shores of Norway, Lapland and Russia and their marginal seas. It is thanks to this comparatively warm water which the Gulf Stream carries along from the south that the sea is free from ice all along the Norwegian coast right up to the North Cape, and not only there but also further to the east, along the Murman coast. Even in cold winters the pack-ice always halts at least 250 kilometres to the north of the North Cape, which itself lies at 71° N., and 150 kilometres from the Murman coast to the west of longitude 38° E.

This is not to say, of course, that some bays and inlets penetrating inland do not freeze temporarily; but the sea remains open, as do also the principal estuaries. Petsamo Bay (Finland) is a case in point; there a fringe of ice is formed along the shore in the autumn, and lasts until well into the spring; but ships can nevertheless pass in and out throughout the winter. The Russian port of Murmansk is likewise accessible throughout the year, even though the help of ice-breakers is sometimes needed for a period.

The picture changes as we follow the coast further southward, where it encloses the White Sea. For about five months of the year this sea is covered with masses of ice, through the middle of which ordinary, strongly-built ships can usually cut their way; but along the coasts occurs heavy, fast ice which only ice-breakers can negotiate. Apparently the warm Atlantic water does not extend beyond the Kola peninsula into this sea.

The influence of the Gulf Stream is again very noticeable in the Barents Sea, which is situated between the north coast of Scandinavia (with the Murman coast of the Kola peninsula) in the south, Spitsbergen in the north-west and Novaya Zemlya in the north-east; for a large part of this sea in the south and south-west remains open the whole year through, and is as good as ice-free in late summer to just north of the northern tip of Novaya Zemlya.

[1] Chapter 6 deals with the Gulf Stream itself.

Novaya Zemlya may be said to mark the eastern limit of the region affected by the warm Atlantic water. The Kara Sea, lying between this group of islands and the Siberian continent, is covered with ice for most of the year. Only in late summer are there open areas of varying sizes, and very occasionally this sea may be entirely open for a short time; but let a north wind blow steadily and down come extensive ice-fields from the Arctic Ocean to cover the whole sea.

Turning back to the west coast of Spitsbergen, we find that here is the most northerly limit of ice-free water, namely to at least 78° N. in winter, and a little farther in summer. It is the most northerly offshoot of Gulf Stream water as demarcated by the ice boundary.

Lastly, there is another curious and somewhat conspicuous ice-free tongue stretching northward between South Greenland and Labrador, especially along the west coast of Greenland; it persists in winter, when only the fjords on the west coast of South Greenland freeze over. Here we see the influence of a current which, coming from the direction of Iceland and bending round the southern tip of Greenland, runs northward towards Davis Strait. Although this current could not, without some qualification, be called warm, it nevertheless carries much of the water of a branch of the Gulf Stream called the Irminger Current, which has turned to the west off the south of Iceland. As it runs northward between Greenland and Labrador, this flow is warmer than its surroundings, notably warmer than the Labrador Current which runs alongside its western fringe from the north.

THE ICE CURRENTS

As against the extensive lobes of ice-free area in the eastern part of the Atlantic Ocean, in the west (see Fig. 36) we saw extensions of the glacial area penetrating far southward along the whole eastern seaboard of Greenland and, in winter and spring, along the coast of Labrador right down to about latitude 45° N.

Just as the lobes of the ice-free area are no more and no less than offshoots of an ocean current (the Gulf Stream), so, in essence, the extensions of the glacial area are linked with ocean currents, cold ones in this case—true ice currents in fact. These cold currents compensate for the water flowing along the coast of Norway and Spitsbergen into the Arctic Ocean. There must, of course, be compensating relief-flow the other way; otherwise the constant supply of water from the south would cause a continual rise of sea level in the polar basin.

The main (because the most spacious) outlet from the Arctic basin passes between Spitsbergen and Greenland, besides which there is another passage between north-west Greenland and Grant Land (the northern part of Ellesmere Island). Every year, immeasurable areas of ice pass through these passages, especially the former, on their way to the south, travelling some 2500 kilometres or more towards the warmer water.

The two ocean currents which transport these ice-fields are the East Greenland and Labrador Currents (see Fig. 37 or 96). They carry icebergs as well as pack-ice; but the former come from the Greenland fjords, not the Arctic Ocean. The few icebergs coming from Spitsbergen, Franz Josef Land, North Land and other islands do not get so far.

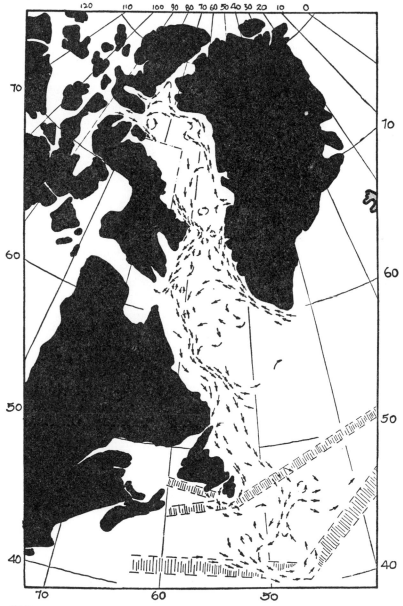

FIG. 37 Currents in the north-west of the Atlantic Ocean (after Smith). The striped lanes are prescribed shipping lanes.

ICE IN THE BERING SEA

Besides communicating with the Atlantic, the Arctic Ocean is also linked with the Pacific Ocean by the Bering Sea, but this passage is so narrow that scarcely any ice is carried through it. Hence, any ice that may be encountered in the Bering Sea has, in the main, been formed there during the winter. Small icebergs, calved by the glaciers of Alaska, are also sometimes found there.

ICE IN THE ATLANTIC OCEAN

Just to the south-east of Newfoundland, in the western part of the Atlantic Ocean at roughly 45° N. and 50° W., lies a comparatively shallow expanse of ocean, about the size of the Bay of Biscay, which goes by the name of the Newfoundland Bank or, in seafaring circles, the Grand Banks. The shortest route from western Europe to the United States traverses it. Two lurking dangers, however, conspire here, as nowhere else in the world, to make the waters unsafe for fast ships. These are not, as the reader might think, storms and shallows, but fog and ice.

FOG AND ICE

The unpleasantness of this combination need hardly be stressed. Fog by itself is a rather bad handicap at sea, slowing down navigation as it does to a speed calculated to reduce to the minimum the risk of a collision.

Fog is very prevalent in the vicinity of the Newfoundland Bank, due to the confluence here of the warm Gulf-Stream water and the cold water of the Labrador Current. The warm water comes from the south-west, the cold from the north. And, just as the water vapour of warmer air precipitates as droplets of water on a cold surface (like the misting-over of a cold window-pane), so does the water vapour of air that has come over warmer water condense to mist or fog when the air passes over the far colder water above the Newfoundland Bank which has come from the Labrador Current. The same occurs in summer, when air from the much hotter land to the west and north-west of this area comes into contact with the cold water. According to observations recorded at sea down the years, the relative frequency of fog there increases, indeed, to as much as 40 per cent. in summer (see Fig. 38). Considering, moreover, that the banks are very important fishing grounds, where a great diversity of fishing craft congregate, the nuisance value of this fog to shipping, despite the benefit of radar, with which larger ships are fortunate enough to be equipped, will be fully realized.

To all this is added the danger of icebergs. On dark nights, these can only be seen from a short distance, even with good visibility (in the case of the *Titanic*, for instance, there was no question of fog). If, then, there is fog as well, they are doubly menacing. Icebergs, brought down by that same Labrador Current from Greenland, occur frequently in these parts, particularly in spring and summer.

Fog and icebergs! No wonder many ships have foundered or been damaged here. No less than fourteen sank, and more than forty were seriously damaged in the one decade from 1880 to 1890 alone.

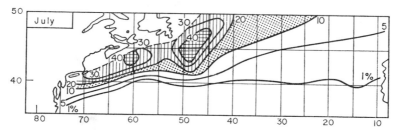

FIG. 38 Frequency of fog in the vicinity of Newfoundland in July. The numbers indicate the percentage of foggy days.

A BRIEF EXCURSION INTO HISTORY

Even at that time, however, some shipping companies took certain precautions, and defined shipping lanes in order to circumvent the danger as well as could be. Collisions between ships were formerly dreaded even more than the danger of icebergs. That was why, as far back as 1855, Matthew Fountaine Maury in his famous *Sailing Directions*, which defined shipping routes on the basis of meteorological and oceanographic experience, proposed different routes for eastbound and westbound traffic, namely a route along the southern extremity of the Grand Banks for the latter, and one running just to the south of Cape Race (Newfoundland) for the former, with the object of attempting to prevent collisions, at least between ship and ship. In 1875, the Cunard Line, the first shipping company to do so, laid down different routes for their outward bound and homebound ships, routes which now, moreover, were shifted so far south of the shortest track as considerably to reduce the danger of icebergs. The figures quoted for the period between 1880 and 1890 are there to show that many disasters occurred despite these measures. It was not until 1898 that a general international agreement was signed, in which the signatories—America and the West European countries—bound themselves to observe certain rules. Not only were 'double-track' shipping lanes laid down, but arrangements were made to shift them northward and southward in accordance with the changing seasons and, therefore, the changing ice boundaries. In all these arrangements, the dangerous Newfoundland Bank was studiously avoided.

If only the ice boundaries, changing with the seasons, were the same every year, danger from ice could effectively have been avoided by a sensible demarcation of shipping lanes. Unfortunately, however, these ice boundaries vary from year to year; and, in particular, icebergs are more numerous one year than another, and travel farther south one year than in another. It is for this reason that the international agreement did not completely succeed in warding off the menace.

This was brought home to humanity with shattering force in 1912. On 11th April of that year the *Titanic*, the latest great passenger liner of the White Star Line, sailed from Queenstown, in Ireland, on her maiden voyage across the Atlantic Ocean. With 1316 passengers and a crew of 885 aboard, she followed the route laid down for westbound ships in April. On reaching the vicinity of the ice-zone to the south-east of Newfoundland on 14th April, she received several wireless messages from other ships, reporting the presence of sea-ice and icebergs along her route. Shortly before midnight on this starlit but moonless night the *Titanic* struck an iceberg which, at her then high speed of 22 knots, was seen too late for her to take evasive action. A great length of her side was ripped open by a spur of the iceberg projecting under water. Two hours and forty minutes later the ship sank. 1513 people lost their lives in this disaster, which shocked the whole world and brought home to mankind, as little else could have done so effectively, that the forces of nature cannot, with impunity, be disregarded.

This warning was taken to heart. As a direct result, a conference of representatives of the maritime powers was convened in London in 1913 to negotiate the first International Convention for the Safety of Life at Sea, by which closely defined shipping lanes were laid down, to be adhered to by all steamers; and, moreover, an ice reconnaissance and warning service was established. All nations concerned contribute financially to this in proportion to their maritime interests, and the USA undertook the task of carrying out the service, which is known as the International Ice Patrol. Nowadays it is operated by aircraft as well as ships.

THE INTERNATIONAL ICE PATROL

The terms of reference of this body are the following: to keep watch upon the ice in the dangerous zone as carefully as possible, and to follow its movements; to keep shipping informed and issue warnings by radio, notably in the ice season; to keep a look-out for any floating wrecks or wreckage, and to sink or destroy them, lest such obstacles, drifting into the prescribed shipping lanes, should cause damage in fog; to render assistance to any vessels in distress; to study the behaviour of ice generally, if necessary throughout the year.

The Ice Patrol begins its intensive reconnaissance as soon as the presence of ice becomes a menace to shipping, which is generally in March. The dangerous season usually terminates at the end of June or the beginning of July. The year 1934 was exceptional because, for the first time in the history of the Ice Patrol, icebergs persisted into August. The Patrol vessels and aircraft are based on Argentia in Newfoundland, and the vessels operate chiefly in an area about the size of Scotland. One corvette is constantly on patrol, and another stands ready in the neighbourhood of Argentia for any emergency that may arise.

The Patrol does not only itself keep the ice under observation, but also collects reports of it radioed by other ships. (Under the terms of the Convention of 1929 it is obligatory for all ships to report the location of dangerous ice encountered.) At stated intervals the Commander of the Ice Patrol issues his radio surveys, in which detailed information on the ice situation, and on the expected movements of pack-ice and icebergs, is given to shipping. Obviously this is important, for the places where ice is stated to have been located are derived from reports which are usually several hours, or even days, old. This was certainly so formerly, when little could be discerned in fog. Although radar enables icebergs (at any rate large ones) to be 'seen' at a fair distance, even in fog, it is not an adequate detector of pack-ice or of small icebergs and growlers which, under some circumstances, are capable of sinking a ship. There is still every reason, therefore, for ships sailing these waters in a prolonged spell of fog to be on the alert.

Looking back, we are thankful to say that, since the International Ice Patrol has been in operation, there has been no major shipping disaster caused by ice in its area of surveillance.

THE STUDY OF ICE MOVEMENTS

We have already stated that one of the Ice Patrol's jobs is to study oceanic ice and icebergs, so that we shall know more about their behaviour. An important subject of study is the movement of ice in the ocean due to wind and current. Both pack-ice and icebergs have been seen to travel at a speed of 30 to 40 nautical miles a day for about six successive days, though the

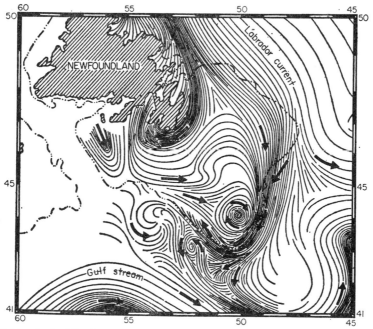

FIG. 39 Marginal eddies between the Gulf Stream and the Labrador Current (schematic representation).

average rate of travel is nearer ten nautical miles a day. After a north wind
has been blowing for a prolonged period, the speed of drift along the eastern
margin of the Newfoundland Bank is likely to be high, especially in the
vicinity of the 100-fathom line (the 180-metre depth line).

Both the speed and direction of the water's travel are very variable in
these parts, from place to place, and from time to time, and the movements
of the water follow a pattern that is anything but constant. This is due, in part,
to the fact that the Labrador Current and the Gulf Stream meet here, with the
result that the Gulf Stream turns off to the right, leaving numerous eddies
of current on its left flank. See Figs. 39 and 41. The latter shows, by the
distribution of the pack-ice, how tongues of cold and hot water intertwine.

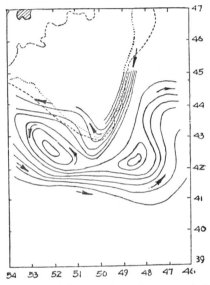

Fig. 40 A 'topographical' map of the ocean's surface around the Newfoundland Bank,
showing the deduced lines of current of the surface water (after Smith). This is a frequent
pattern there.

Every spring, therefore, the Ice Patrol has to investigate afresh the patterns
of current in the neighbourhood of Newfoundland. A useful means of doing
so is the so-called dynamic method (described in Chapter 6) by means of
the indirect estimation of horizontal pressure differences in the water, this
on the basis of temperature readings and salinity analyses, at various depths
and in a great many places in the area. That is why the corvettes of the Ice
Patrol also make oceanographic cruises into their area in spring, stopping at
selected places to allow subsurface observations to be made. These are
then converted as quickly as possible into data revealing the distribution
of pressure; and on the basis of these data line patterns are drawn. These
patterns are comparable to the isobars on a weather chart, and, like the latter,
they present a picture of the prevailing and expected currents. Figure 40 is a
specimen of such a chart for the marine area near Newfoundland.

THE ICE CURRENTS AGAIN

Let us once again look, a little more closely, at the drift of all that ice towards the neighbourhood of the Grand Banks, for it is quite clear that this locality (latitude 45°, the same as of Venice or Bordeaux) is not the birthplace of the pack-ice, either.

The East Greenland Current and the Labrador Current being the great ice-currents, we know that the ice has been brought down from the polar region. The former current comes south through the wide opening between Spitsbergen and North Greenland, and runs along the east coast of Greenland, carrying with it huge quantities of Arctic Ocean water covered with fields of pack-ice. Consequently, there is a margin of polar water with pack-ice along the entire east coast of Greenland, down to its southern tip called Cape Farewell. True, that margin narrows towards the south, and, farther away from the coast of South Greenland the coldness of the water is tempered by the Irminger Current, a branch of the Gulf Stream which, coming from the south and passing under Iceland, turns off to the west. Naturally, the ice situation is not the same every year, because the currents and the winds change from year to year. There was a great deal of ice, for instance, in 1949, when in July it stretched as far as 150 kilometres to the south of Cape Farewell.

The East Greenland Current and the Irminger Current together feed the West Greenland Current, which, from Cape Farewell, flows northward along the west coast. Being partly of Atlantic origin, this current is not very cold and is more saline than water of pure polar origin. As it travels north it gradually loses volume, because some of the water turns off to the left and crosses over to the other side of the Davis Strait, the strait which divides Greenland from Baffin Land (on the American side). There, on the western side, the strong polar current runs along the shores of Baffin Land and, farther south, those of Labrador; coming from the strait between North Greenland and Ellesmere Island and the straits along other islands of the North American archipelago, now as the Labrador Current, it drives vast quantities of ice, pack-ice and icebergs, towards the Grand Banks. From its beginning, this current keeps to the western side of Baffin Bay and Davis Strait; its axis lies above the continental slope, hence at the edge of the continental shelf; the coldest (pure polar) water lies nearest the shore.

In spring, when land-fast and pack-ice free themselves from the grip of winter, immeasurable fields of drifting ice make their way southward, and what remains of them after they have been much reduced by the sun ultimately covers the waters south-east of Newfoundland. Here, at last, a halt is called to the polar water by the Gulf Stream, which itself turns off eastward. The reader can refer again to Fig. 36 for the overall distribution of the pack-ice; that figure also shows the most advanced and the most retracted positions of the pack-ice boundary, in spring and late summer respectively.

We see, then, that the reason why the pack-ice on the American side of the Atlantic Ocean is able to advance so far south is the presence and southward flow of the icy masses of water in the regions of the American continental shelf, from Baffin Land to the Newfoundland Bank. The total surface area of the North American sea-ice region is estimated to be $1\frac{1}{2}$ million square kilometres on an average, over two-thirds of which the ice is approximately six feet thick; so that the volume of all this ice certainly comes to roughly 2500 cubic kilometres! A large part of it goes adrift, melting in the spring and early summer. And most of the warmth needed to melt the masses of ice that come south of the latitude of Newfoundland is supplied by Gulf Stream water.

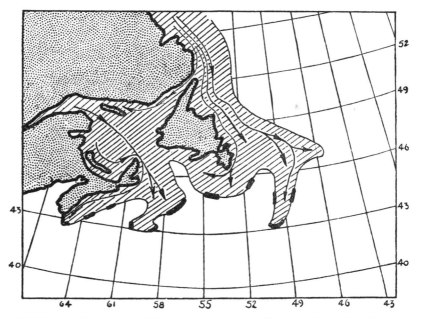

Fig. 41 Advanced boundaries of the pack-ice area near Newfoundland (after Huntsman).

Figure 41, which is drawn on the basis of observations made by the International Ice Patrol, illustrates the distribution of pack-ice in these parts, and also shows its farthest limits in spring, as observed there in the course of the years. The edge is wavy, reflecting the fact that the dividing line between the Gulf Stream and the Labrador Current is not a regular one; actually, there are great eddies at the edge of the Gulf Stream, where tongues of warm and cold water intertwine (see also Fig. 39). Such tongues must obviously affect the distribution of drift-ice, the place of which is in the cold polar water and which soon melts away if by any chance it is driven by the wind into the warmer Gulf Stream water.

The ice area is determined by the presence of the cold Arctic water, even if the ice is not formed here but is brought down by this Arctic water, and even if the ice-fields are not confined to the unmixed Arctic water of approximately 1°C but are spread out over the mixed-water region of slightly higher temperature. Also, as we have seen, the prevalence of fog is due to the presence of the very cold (Arctic) and cold (mixed) water. It may be stated as a general rule that the greater the excess of air temperature over sea temperature, the greater is the risk of fog. Whereas, therefore, the warm Gulf Stream water is not affected, this temperature difference above the very cold water and the mixed water is often so great, particularly in summer, that the frequency of fog increases to 40 in 100 days to the south-east of Newfoundland, just above the offshoot of the Arctic water. The reason why this is particularly so in summer is that, on the one hand, the water of Arctic origin is still very cold here (drifting ice does sometimes occur here right up to the beginning of summer), while, on the other hand, it is not only the Atlantic water to the south-west, south and south-east which is much warmer, but also the land to the west of these oceanic areas; hence it is more than likely that the wind brings warmer air to these quarters.

It should be pointed out that the temperature differences shown on average temperature charts of this area are generally less sharp than those between individual observations made at certain times. Let us take an instance: a chart showing the temperature iso-lines for the first half of April 1946, based on observations made by the Ice Patrol, shows that a temperature difference of 15°C over a distance of 40 kilometres was recorded, this being, therefore, an *average* drop in temperature of 3°C per 8 kilometres and continued for 40 kilometres. Locally, however, a temperature difference of no less than 10°C in 8 kilometres was found, while at the spot of the greatest drop in temperature, 3°C difference was read within a distance of 600 metres! This shows how abruptly the cold masses of water 'strike' the warmer ones. Apt indeed are the words 'cold wall'.

If we examine the fluctuations of the quantities of pack-ice in the course of the year, we find that the ice-fields on the Grand Banks reach their maximum in April or the beginning of May. Farther north, however, the maximum is attained earlier, usually in February or March. This provides clear evidence that, through drifting, these ice-fields produce the largest amounts of drift-ice near the Grand Banks a little later. But we should not forget that one year can be very different from the next, depending on the variable conditions of wind and current, which may be far more favourable to ice transport in one spring than in another.

THE GREENLAND ICEBERGS

Of the islands to the west of Baffin Bay, Ellesmere Island alone in the north has glaciers which contribute significantly to the production of icebergs. The number of icebergs calved here annually is estimated at 150.

As against this, Greenland's annual production is 12,000–15,000 individuals of sizeable dimensions. Almost as many of these are calved by the glaciers reaching the sea on the eastern seaboard as by the glaciers on the west coast, but the icebergs deriving from the east coast do not reach much farther south than Cape Farewell, the southern tip of Greenland. For, just to the south of that cape, the East Greenland Current which carries them, meets the Irminger Current (which, as we remember, is a branch of the Gulf Stream) coming from the east. With this current the East Greenland Current merges; then, rounding Cape Farewell, it turns northward.

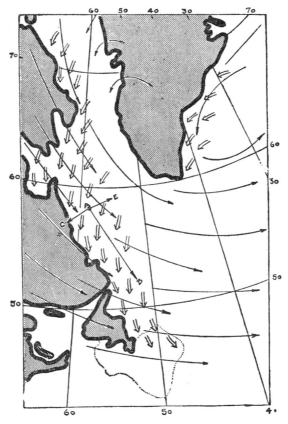

FIG. 42 Wind and current in the north-west of the Atlantic Ocean (after Smith). The predominant winds in spring are marked by single arrows and the associated oceanic currents by double ones. The line *CE* denotes the predominating air-pressure gradient. The oceanic current deviates to the right with reference to the wind.

The icebergs of the west coast, on the other hand, after travelling northward and across to the other side of Baffin Bay, are carried far south, along Baffin Island and Labrador, by the Labrador Current.

We might say, in passing, that the figures given here have, for the most part, been derived from research work carried out by the International Ice Patrol under E. H. Smith, before the war.

It should further be observed that the numbers of icebergs given here do not include the smaller glacier ice, but are individuals with a volume of not less than 1½ million cubic metres. The numbers given are, of course, approximations.

Altogether, 150–175 glaciers reach the sea along the West Greenland coast, but here the upwards of 7000 icebergs are calved by some 25 glaciers, and the most productive of those are situated between latitudes 69 and 72. Here, over a distance of not more than 300 kilometres, more than 5000 good-sized icebergs are born in North-East Bay and Disko Bay. We may safely conclude that 70 per cent. of all icebergs observed in the western part of the North Atlantic Ocean originate in this part of the west coast of Greenland. Besides these, the coastal area round about Melville Bay ranging some 400 kilometres—from northern latitude 73° to beyond 76°—supplies roughly 20 per cent.

The most productive of the fourteen important glaciers which discharge into North-East Bay and Disko Bay are the Umiamako in the north and the Jacobshavn glacier in the south; each is thought to calve something like 1300 icebergs a year.

The latter (see Plate XVIII) is one of the best known and most interesting of all Greenland's glaciers. When, in August 1928, the *Marion* sailed into the mouth of the Jacobshavn Fjord, the inner part of the fjord was literally blocked by icebergs, so much so that even a sloop could not get through. Smith relates that some members of the expedition landed, climbed the surrounding hills and had a beautiful view of all these icebergs down below. Jacobshavn Fjord is comparatively straight, 5–6 kilometres wide, and stretches some 25 kilometres inland up to the foot of the glacier, a wall 75 metres high. As far as the eye could reach there were closely packed icebergs in serried ranks, a majestic procession moving slowly towards the open sea.

It was estimated that 4000–6000 icebergs lay there in the Jacobshavn Fjord on 9th August 1928, the production of three or four years! It is in fact a not-too-rare occurrence in the Greenland fjords for icebergs to be imprisoned for a couple of years in their birthplace, either because the fjord continues to be blocked by pack-ice, if an unfavourable wind persists in the summer, or because, through their accumulation, the icebergs themselves help to block the fjord in a particular place. What Smith and his men saw in the Jacobshavn Fjord however, was apparently exceptional, for, according to information obtained from the Greenlanders of that district, the iceberg procession is commonly on the move several times a year. This is accompanied by an ear-splitting noise which can be heard far away, and sometimes goes on for days on end. The most likely time for an iceberg getaway in the Jacobshavn Fjord appears to be in the summer, notably at the spring tide.

ICEBERGS ON THEIR TRAVELS

Once the West Greenland icebergs have reached the sea (i.e. Baffin Bay), they do not immediately proceed southward because, as we have seen, the current along West Greenland flows northward. Accordingly, most of the icebergs at first 'sail' northward at the rate of 5–7 nautical miles a day, later turning off to the west. They then enter the southward current which passes along the American shores, and thus travel to lower latitudes at speeds of

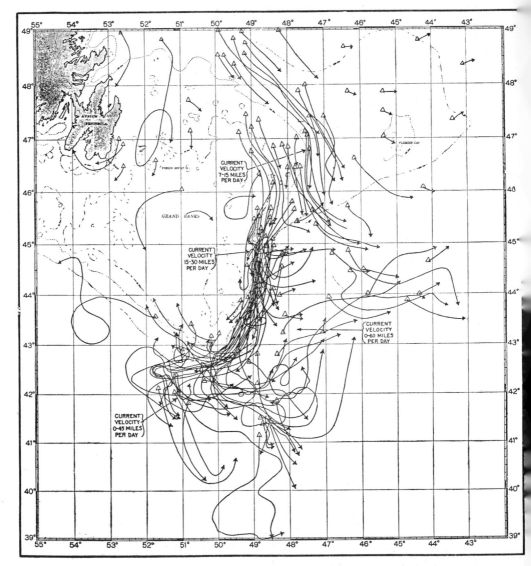

FIG. 43 Recorded drift lanes of icebergs, collected by the International Ice Patrol for a great many years and charted. The preference for the right flank of the Bank and also the frequent curving and looping will be noted.

more than 10 miles a day. Seldom do icebergs cross over Baffin Bay directly into the southbound current; in fact it is a rare occurrence for an iceberg to be encountered in the central parts of Davis Strait.

Pressure ridge photographed from the air. (Photograph WMO)

Very dense pack-ice with hummocks. (Photograph WMO)

A 'lead' or 'lane' in the pack-ice. (Photograph WMO)

Table icebergs in the Antarctic Ocean. (Photograph WMO)

To the south of Davis Strait the stream of icebergs hugs the Labrador
coast; drifting sometimes at the speed of 20 nautical miles a day, the bergs
eventually reach the waters of Newfoundland after a long voyage of roughly
3000 kilometres.

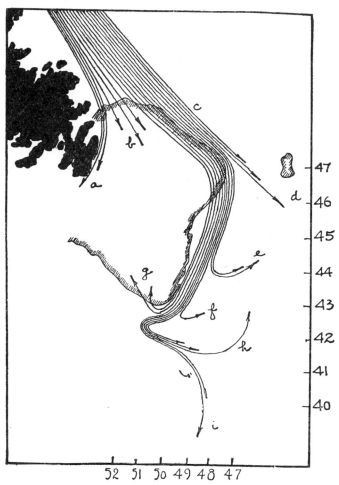

FIG. 44 The main routes of trekking icebergs around the Grand Bank (after Smith).

A voyage like this does not proceed without delays; quite the reverse!
Large numbers of icebergs often get held up somewhere, for instance in
shallows (especially at low water), against capes, or between skerries off
the shores of Baffin Island, Labrador and the north of Newfoundland. Many
an iceberg has got into a trap near Hudson Strait (along the northern tip of
Labrador) by entering with the tidal current, sometimes getting out again at
ebb-tide, but sometimes not. And not only are icebergs temporarily delayed
or forced to spend the winter in these places; many get no farther and ultimately melt away. It is estimated, in fact, that only one in every twenty

5

West-Greenland icebergs ends up south of Newfoundland. Nevertheless, all in all that makes quite an appreciable number.

An iceberg's career is something like this: it leaves the fjord in the summer, spending the winter near the shores of Greenland, say in the neighbourhood of Melville Bay or to the north of it; (there is always plenty of pack-ice or fast ice in the northern part of Baffin Bay, where icebergs are held up temporarily). In spring the iceberg begins to drift again and by autumn has reached Cape Dyer, perhaps—in the south of Baffin Island—or Hudson Strait, where it spends another winter. In the following May it can reach the Grand Bank with the main body of icebergs, the vanguard of which may have been observed there at the end of February or beginning of March.

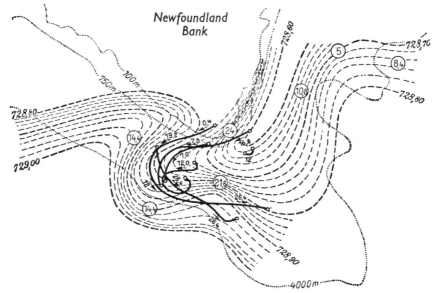

FIG. 45 Example showing the similarity between the paths of icebergs (full lines, with speeds in nautical miles per 24 hours) and the height lines of a computed 'topography' of the sea surface near Newfoundland (the stippled lines with relative heights at the extremities, in metres, and calculated speeds in nautical miles per 24 hours, within the circles). The significance of a 'topography' of the kind as indicating the currents is explained in Chapter 6. The dotted lines are depth-lines (after Smith).

Hundreds of bergs are stranded on the northern part of the Newfoundland Bank (see Fig. 44), and all through the season icebergs forgather here and melt away. Those which do not go aground here are carried farther eastward and southward by the ocean currents. Figure 43 gives an enlightening impression of the capriciousness of their paths, which often twirl and twist as a result of the great eddies of current liable to occur in the area. The illustrated paths were established by the International Ice Patrol which, in the course of many years, has been able to follow the trail of individual icebergs, or to establish it indirectly from shipping intelligence.

It has been discovered that the deep draught of icebergs forces them to follow primarily the current, not the wind; but it has also been found that a large iceberg, reduced in size by calving, and so drawing less water, later ceased to follow the current and responded to the wind.

The most dangerous icebergs in the American shipping lanes travel in the deep water along the eastern shore of the Grand Banks, roughly following the 100-fathom depth-line. In this region their average speed in the dangerous season is from 9 to 15 nautical miles a day. Figure 44 depicts the main lanes along which the icebergs 'sail'. Even if a berg leaves the Banks on its right (*c*), its further voyage may vary, as can be seen in the figure (*d, e, f, g, h* or *i*). Generally speaking, there is a definite association between the paths icebergs follow as they are carried along by the current and the 'topographical' pattern established by the Ice Patrol on the basis of oceanographic measurements. We have already referred to these patterns, and shall revert to them in Chapter 6. For an example see Fig. 45.

END OF THE ROAD

In northern waters—Baffin Bay—a moderate-sized iceberg will weigh roughly 1·4 million tons; the mass of a moderately large iceberg to the south

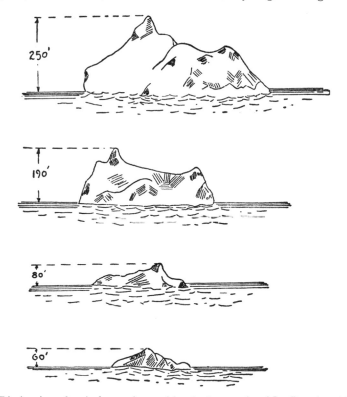

FIG. 46 Diminution of an iceberg, observed by the International Ice Patrol on 11th April, 21st April, 29th April and 12th May 1921 (after Smith). The heights are in feet.

of Newfoundland would be 160,000 tons. This implies a reduction in weight of 8 to 1, which means that, by the time an iceberg arrives south of Newfoundland it is generally half as high as it originally was; for example, it will have shrunk from 70 metres in height to 35 metres. This process of diminution accelerates, of course, occurring gradually at first and then quickly, while during a wintering the berg remains fairly stationary.

The Ice Patrol has often been able to watch an iceberg in the last stages of its life, at intervals of a few days. Figure 46 shows how quickly the ice tends to vanish at this stage. A large iceberg, 75 metres high, first seen on 11th April 1921 to the east of the Newfoundland Bank in water of 1°C, protruded above water a mere 18 metres 31 days later, and was by that time in Gulf Stream water of 17°C. In its last days it was losing height at the rate of 3–3½ metres a day. The loss of height in the waters around the Grand Bank is on an average 1½–2 metres a day.

In June 1926, to the south of Newfoundland, a large iceberg, more than 100 metres in length, was seen drifting at the northern margin of the Gulf Stream; it melted away completely within 36 hours. There is, however, an authentic report, dated the same year and month, of a block of ice being sighted at 30°20′ N. and 62°32′ W. near the Bermuda Islands!

SURVEY

Table 41 gives the average numbers of icebergs sighted to the south of Newfoundland (latitude 48° N.) in the various months, from 1900 to 1930 inclusive, and the average numbers of icebergs sighted to the south of the Grand Banks (43° N.). This table also gives the annual totals, while Fig. 47 shows separately in a graph the total numbers found to the south of the 48th parallel for a great many years. It will be noted that these numbers vary tremendously: more than 1000 in 1909, 1912, 1929 and 1945 (and even more than 1300 in 1929); merely ten or less in 1924, 1931, 1936, 1940, 1951 and 1958 (only one in 1958). The average number from 1900 to 1959 inclusive is 398.

Table 13

Numbers of Icebergs sighted to the south of Newfoundland (48° N.) and to the south of the Grand Banks (43° N.), Averaged from 1900 to 1930

Icebergs to the S. of 48° N.

Average 1900 —— 1930	Jan.	Feb.	Mar.	Apr.	May	June	July	Aug.	Sept.	Oct.	Nov.	Dec.	Annual Total
	3	10	36	83	130	68	25	13	9	4	3	2	386

Table 14

Icebergs to the S. of 43° N.

Average 1900 —— 1930	Jan.	Feb.	Mar.	Apr.	May	June	July	Aug.	Sept.	Oct.	Nov.	Dec.	Annual Total
	0	1	4	9	18	13	3	2	1	0	0	0	51

The predominating wind in the area of the paths of icebergs is the principal factor governing the differences between the individual years. Prevailing westerlies and north-westerlies will promote the southward passage of icebergs, whereas a persistent north or east wind will tend to ground them. It is not surprising, therefore, that a convincing correlation has been found between the average air pressure difference between Newfoundland and southern Greenland in spring and the number of icebergs sighted in the spring of any year to the south of Newfoundland; for, when that difference is high, it means that much westerly to north-westerly wind must have prevailed over those waters.

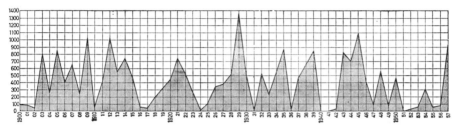

FIG. 47 Graph representing the numbers of icebergs sighted to the south of latitude 48° N. between 1900 and 1957 inclusive. The number was one in 1958 and 693 in 1959.

Exceptional conditions in the fjords of the most prolific iceberg-producing glaciers may account for the high peaks of the graph. Superabundant years may have been due to a conjunction of circumstances whereby the products of more than one glacier, accumulated for two or three years, all broke away from the fjord in the same summer. We saw above that such can happen. Conversely, a year of exceptional scarcity may be the result of the simultaneous blockage of two or more important iceberg fjords.

It is estimated, on the basis of the average total number of icebergs reaching Baffin Bay—the majority of which come from West Greenland—that the total volume of glacier ice moving southward in this way amounts annually to 30–60 cubic kilometres. If, by comparison, one calculates the quantity of pack-ice which is carried yearly along the American coast, one finds (vide Smith) something like the following: its surface can be estimated at 1,600,000 square kilometres and its average thickness at roughly 1·8 metres; thus the volume must be nearly 3000 cubic kilometres. If with this we compare the quantities of iceberg ice, we find that the icebergs do not account for more than one or two per cent. of the total amount of ice carried yearly between Greenland and Newfoundland. The pack-ice, therefore, far exceeds the icebergs in quantity, and the latter consequently chill the western parts of the North Atlantic Ocean far less than does the melting of the pack-ice. In its turn, the cooling caused by the pack-ice is only a fraction of that caused by the deep Labrador Current merely through the low temperature of all its southbound water.

A RETREAT OF ICE BOUNDARIES

We cannot conclude this chapter without at least touching on a phenomenon which has been claiming the attention of climatologists, oceanographers and glaciologists. It is a phenomenon, or rather a compound of signs, pointing to the gradual reduction of ice in the north in the recent past. We are indebted to the Swedish research worker Ahlmann for most of our information on this matter. The following are some of these trends.

At the beginning of this century, the ships fetching coal from the Norwegian mines in Spitsbergen were usually able to reach their destination without the help of ice-breakers during only 95 days of the year; after 1930 they were able to do so on an average 180 days of the year, (in 1939 it was even 203 days).

The pack-ice in those parts of the Arctic Ocean bordering Russia has also been shrinking; according to Russian investigators, between 1925 and 1942 the ice decreased by a million square kilometres. Further, where Nansen measured an average ice thickness of 3·65 metres in 1893, the *Sedov* found only 2·18 metres between 1937 and 1940.

All this coincided with a general slight increase in the temperatures of water and air, an increase which is clearly apparent from meteorological statistics, and which temporarily reached its zenith about 1940. One of the results of this increase has been the gradual migration of certain species of fish farther north in the course of the century. One such is cod, which was rare off the west coast of Greenland until 1917, but subsequently appeared there in ever increasing numbers; the area of this occurrence expanded northward from 64° to 73° and, among other things, the waters off West Greenland have become very important fishing grounds in the past fifty years. Some birds, too, have pushed the northern limits of their winter quarters farther north, and spend the winter on the north coast of Spitsbergen. A very important, and economically beneficial, consequence of the climatic change in these parts is its influence on the Scandinavian coniferous forests, which have rapidly extended beyond their former northern limits. Lastly, many glaciers in the northern hemisphere have, like the sensitive climatic thermometers they are, very decidedly retreated. The balance between snowfall on the one hand and evaporation and melting on the other, has evidently been disturbed in favour of the latter, so much so that someone suggested that the Scandinavian glaciers might vanish in forty to fifty years' time. Such a thing cannot, of course, be predicted. But, what happened in Scandinavia was even surpassed in Alaska, where the great Muir glacier retreated more than 22 kilometres within 54 years, exposing a whole system of fjords.

The fact that the general mean sea level has been steadily rising in recent history is compatible with the decrease of land ice. This is clear from a careful analysis of tidal records, according to which the rise in sea level amounts to approximately 1 millimetre a year. This is obviously associated with the intensified melting of land ice.

According to Ahlmann, the rapid ('rapid' by geological reckoning!) decline in the volume of glaciers is the end of a retraction which began two hundred years ago.

The most immediate cause of this climatic fluctuation, the recent rise in temperature, which is particularly noticeable in northern observation posts, is probably an intensification of the general atmospheric circulation, through which warm air is more persistently brought from tropical to northern regions. Such a change must undoubtedly be accompanied by reinforcement of the warm oceanic currents and, therefore, by an amplification of their influence on northern latitudes. However, it is as good as impossible to tackle this problem adequately without knowing more of the Antarctic ice, which comprises 87 per cent. of the total terrestrial mass of ice. If the climatic fluctuation about which we have been speaking has also been operative there, then it must be a phenomenon involving our whole Earth (though it does not mean, necessarily, that its effect would be to raise the temperature of tropical regions as well). Although Antarctica has been visited and studied increasingly by post-war expeditions, the series of observations made there is still of too short duration to permit of well-considered, warranted inferences.

The recent decrease of ice and its preceding increase in the Middle Ages are symptoms of a climatic fluctuation which is a repetition, in miniature, of what took place in the geological past on a far vaster scale, in the coming and going of the Ice Ages. There are signs that the Arctic ice has already been increasing again in the last few years.

Chapter Four

WAVES

Now the great winds shoreward blow,
Now the salt tides seaward flow;
Now the wild white horses play,
Champ and chafe and toss in the spray.

(Matthew Arnold)

NEVER for a moment is the sea absolutely still. That part of its movement which we perceive as an unrest of the surface we call 'waves'.

Waves are a far more general phenomenon in Nature than is commonly realized, and at first the word was used only for water waves, which were the first to be noticed. And, however accustomed we may have become nowadays to associate waves with other phenomena as well, such as sound, light and radio, all of us, as children, first learned that waves were something pertaining to water.

Few there are who are not fascinated by waves upon the water, whether they be tiny ripples which seem only just to ruffle the smooth surface and vanish almost as soon as they appear, or the mighty, towering rollers in their onward, irresistible march across the ocean, swallowing thousands of miles on their travels. We may look at a pond with weeping willows bending over it, dripping in the sun; early that morning they were white with hoar-frost, but when the sun shone, droplets and pieces of ice fell off the branches, causing a continual play of moving rings on the surface of the water—a familiar picture. Or we may stand on the beach when high breakers are rolling in from the sea, crests rising up as they approach and then curling inward and flinging themselves into a boiling mass of foam.

Waves . . .

SEA AND SWELL

The sea-surface is never at rest, even when there is a dead calm. There is always a certain, though perhaps imperceptible amount of rolling, an ever-so-slight heaving. It is felt in a boat rather than seen on the surface. And if we look at the rim of the sea on the beach, we shall notice that it is never stationary, even if the surface is as flat as a mirror. There is always some to-and-fro movement, or occasionally a tiny ripple advances, like a miniature breaker-line, and then recedes a little. We can see by that very rim that the great body of the sea is never completely at a standstill.

If anyone asks you what makes waves, you will be likely to answer 'the wind'. Certainly, if one is standing on the shore of the southern North Sea, it would seem that the stronger the wind is, the more boisterous are the waves. Those who have seen more of the oceans, however, know that it is not as simple as all that. There are coasts far less windy than some in north-western Europe, where the breakers tend to be much higher. Take the shore of southern California, for instance, with its very equable climate, where a strong wind seldom blows, yet where occasionally huge waves will batter the coast, breakers six metres or more high, without so much as a breath of wind. Indeed, one need not go especially to California. Something similar happens on the shores of Morocco, and many other coasts exposed to the ocean, especially in subtropical regions. Of course, the phenomenon is also possible at higher latitudes, but, owing to the greater prevalence of strong winds and storms there, high surf in association with calm weather is a rarer occurrence.

So where do these high waves come from, when there is little wind? The answer is that great breakers can be produced by a *swell* at sea, which need have nothing to do with local wind. By a swell we mean the long, more or less smooth waves observed at sea (or on a lake) when at the moment there is no wind blowing to which they could be ascribed, which waves, in a ship, are noticeable by a comparatively uniform and regular, sometimes rather lazy, rolling. A familiar swell is that in the equatorial zone of little or no wind, known as the doldrums or equatorial calms, where there are no significant wind-waves, for which reason the swell is all the more striking (see Plate XXIV).

By attributing the existence of high surf on windless days to a swell in the open ocean, we have shifted our problem, not solved it; for the next question immediately arises: what causes that swell?

We know that it is induced by the wind, but not by a wind blowing here and now; the wind prevailed elsewhere and earlier. A swell causing high waves to break on the shores of Morocco originated elsewhere, usually far away in a stormy area in the North Atlantic Ocean. For wind-waves do not subside the moment the storm ceases, or when they have themselves left the stormy area; they run on as a swell. And it is as a swell that the waves pursue their way upon the surface of the ocean, sometimes for thousands of miles, before they are spent, or beat upon the shore.

Contrasting with the swell, which is independent of the wind (and some-times runs against it), there are the waves corresponding to the local field of the wind and strengthened by it; we call these 'wind-waves' or 'sea' (as in the phrase: 'a high sea was running'). The Dutch word for this is 'zeegang', and the German word 'Seegang' is the same. Because a running sea depends on the wind, seamen often judge the strength of the wind by the kind of sea that is running. The overall picture of the waves is far more irregular and confused, and the crests are more pointed, than in a swell.

5*

We have an established scale for the strength of the wind from 0 to 12 inclusive (0 standing for calm, 12 for hurricane force); it is known as the Beaufort scale, after the English admiral Sir Francis Beaufort, who drafted it in 1808, using as his yardstick the surface of sail that a fully rigged warship of those days could carry in the various wind forces. In the list given below, each Beaufort scale number is followed by a brief description of the appearance of the sea, on the lines adopted by the German sailing-ship captain, Petersen. These descriptions were approved by the World Meteorological Organization for use at sea to determine the force of the wind. The Beaufort wind force is followed by the name given to such a wind at sea, and the next column gives the wind speed.

Table 15

Beaufort's Wind Scale and the State of the Sea

Beaufort Number	Descriptive Term	Speed m/sec	Appearance of the Sea
0	Calm	–	Like a mirror
1	Light air	1	Ripples with the appearance of scales are formed, but without foam crests
2	Light breeze	3	Small wavelets, still short but more pronounced; crests have a glassy appearance and do not break
3	Gentle breeze	5	Large wavelets; crests begin to break; foam of glassy appearance, perhaps scattered white horses
4	Moderate breeze	$7\frac{1}{2}$	Small waves, becoming longer; fairly frequent white horses
5	Fresh breeze	10	Moderate waves, taking a more pronounced long form; many white horses are formed (chance of some spray)
6	Strong breeze	$12\frac{1}{2}$	Large waves begin to form; the white foam crests are more extensive everywhere (probably some spray)
7	Near gale	15	Sea heaps up and white foam from breaking waves begins to be blown in streaks along the direction of the wind
8	Gale	18	Moderately high waves of greater length; edges of crests begin to break into spindrift; the foam is blown in well-marked streaks along the direction of the wind
9	Strong gale	21	High waves; dense streaks of foam along the direction of the wind; crests of waves begin to topple, tumble and roll over; spray may affect visibility

10	Storm	24	Very high waves with overhanging crests; the resulting foam, in great patches, is blown in dense white streaks along the direction of the wind; on the whole the surface of the sea takes a white appearance; the tumbling of the sea becomes heavy and shock-like; visibility affected
11	Violent storm	27	Exceptionally high waves (small and medium-sized ships might be for a time lost to view behind the waves); the sea is completely covered with long white patches of foam lying along the direction of the wind; everywhere the edges of the wave crests are blown into froth; visibility affected
12	Hurricane	–	The air is filled with foam and spray; sea completely white with driving spray; visibility very seriously affected.

When considering the descriptions, one must never lose sight of the fact that the size of the waves depends not only on the strength of the wind, but also on its duration, and the length of its path over the sea (to which we shall revert); further, it must be remembered that the waves are liable to be modified considerably by tidal currents; that the sea is affected by precipitation (rainfall, snow, hail); and lastly that, at moderate and high latitudes, at the same wind speed at observation level, the motion of the sea is higher in an air mass which is colder than the water than in one which is warmer.

So much for the general aspect of the matter. Details will be considered more fully later.

We should now be able to recognize the three types or stages of sea waves, namely, *wind-waves*, *swell* and *surf* (breakers). The wind is responsible for the wind-waves; from these comes the swell; wind-waves or swell produce the surf.

Before proceeding to discuss each of these three, it may be useful to dwell for a moment on the theory of waves generally.

SOME GENERAL CONCEPTS

Since words such as 'wavelength', and 'period' of a wave's movement, will be recurring in the following pages, we had better see what they imply. Before doing so, however, we should warn the reader that, when dealing with the more theoretical aspect of sea waves, we shall often refer to a simplified picture of their movement. The figures used to illustrate our point will generally have a more uniform appearance than that of actual wave movements in Nature, with which we are all familiar. It is only by simplifying in this way, that it is at all possible to say anything more about waves than that they are a succession of mountains and valleys. That is why we shall first of all invoke what we call *simple waves*, or a simple wave movement. The reader should be aware that this representation is never exactly reproduced in Nature, in free water; indeed, that the real picture of the wave often scarcely resembles it at first sight. Nevertheless, we can use this representation to become better acquainted with the behaviour of real waves, of which it is an idealization. Moreover, we find that we can always imagine the irregular, real waves as a merging of several such single undulations. So these have to be thought of as intermingling and co-operating, thus producing the irregular picture which corresponds to the real thing.

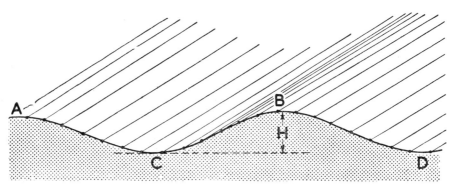

FIG. 48 Cross-section through an undulating surface of water. *H* is the height of the wave.

In Fig. 48, which represents a cross-section through the water, perpendicular to the direction of the long crests of the waves, the surface of the water is shown as an undulating line. The tops of this line correspond to crests, and the dips between them to elongated troughs. We call a cross-section of this kind 'the profile of the wave'. If this profile is perfectly uniform, in the sense that adjacent portions of the profile, from crest to crest, or trough to trough, are everywhere faithful repetitions of each other (like *AC*, *BD*, etc. of the wave-line in Fig. 48); and if the aggregate advances over the water without distortion, then we speak of a simple wave motion, or, briefly, 'a simple wave', meaning not one wave ridge but a whole row of crests and troughs.

Having got this firmly fixed in our minds, we shall easily understand the other established terms.

Wavelength: We use this term for the horizontal (straight) distance between two successive similar points of the wave profile, thus for instance the distance between successive troughs. In Fig. 48 each of the distances *AB*, *CD*, etc. is equal to the wavelength. In formulas we often abbreviate the wavelength to *L*.

Period of a wave motion: When the waves run over the water, the water itself does not follow this motion. The particles of water do not stand still, of course; but all they do is to go up and down, and up and down. (They also go to and fro, but we shall deal with that presently.) A float bobbing up and down in undulating water illustrates this. Now the time needed for one up-and-down movement is called the *period* of the wave motion; in other words we could say that the time which elapses between the passing of two successive wave crests over a given spot is called the period. Let us say that there is a stick in the water, and at a given moment a crest passes it; three seconds later the next crest passes, another passes six seconds later and another after nine seconds, and so on; the period is then three seconds, denoted by the letter T.

Rate of propagation (or wave speed or 'phase speed'): This simply means the speed at which the wave profile proceeds; hence the speed at which the crest and trough of the wave advance. The wave speed is indicated by the letter C.

Let us look again at the stick standing in the water. We saw that the second crest passed three seconds after the first one. How far has the first one got in those three seconds? Evidently a distance equal to the rate of propagation times 3 seconds. Say that rate is 4 metres per second, then the distance must be 3×4 metres $= 12$ metres. It is apparent, therefore, that the distance is generally found by multiplying the wave speed by the duration of the period. But what does that distance mean? It is the distance the first crest has got away from the stick at the moment when the next crest passes it. That, however, is exactly the same as our definition of the wavelength. Thus we get this rule:

$$wavelength = wave\ speed \times period;\ or\ L = C \times T.$$

It follows from the above simple rule that if we know *two* of the three quantities (wavelength, period and wave speed), we can calculate the third. If, for example, we know the period and the wavelength, we can work out what the rate of propagation is; for it follows from the rule that

$$wave\ speed = \frac{wavelength}{period};\ or:\ C = \frac{L}{T}.$$

Let us suppose that there is a swell at sea, the wavelength and period of which are estimated to be 40 metres and 5 seconds respectively. Then, according to our formula the speed is: 40 metres divided by 5 seconds, giving 8 metres per second.

A wave system on the water has another characteristic feature, namely, the *height* of the waves, by which we mean the difference in height between the peaks of the crests and the lowest points of the troughs (see Fig. 48, where the height is indicated by the letter H).

There is no direct connection between the height on the one hand and the wavelength or period or rate of propagation of the waves on the other. All we can say is that the proportion of the height to the length (H/L) in Nature is scarcely ever greater than $1/10$. We call this ratio the *steepness* of the waves.

STANDING WAVES

So far, we have been considering *running* waves; but *standing* waves also exist. Unlike the former, theirs is an up-and-down moving profile that does not advance relative to the water.

The simplest example of standing wave is the oscillation of water in a tank tilted slightly and then put down again. A cross-section of a standing wave is shown in Fig. 49. At one moment there is a crest at one end and a trough at the other; the next moment the position is reversed. As the distance from a crest to a trough is half a wavelength, the length of the container is equal to half a wavelength.

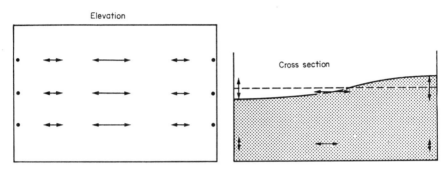

Elevation

Cross section

FIG. 49 Standing wave in a tank. The arrows indicate the to-and-fro movement of the water.

Another example of standing water-waves (see Fig. 50) is provided by the perpendicular recoil of advancing waves upon impact with a vertical wall. The interplay (called *interference*) between the advancing and reflected waves then leads to this standing undulation; the surface of the water sweeps up and down from one extreme position to the other, which is the mirror image of the former. The characteristic feature of this movement is that the water attains its greatest vertical deflection everywhere at the same moment, whether upward or downward.

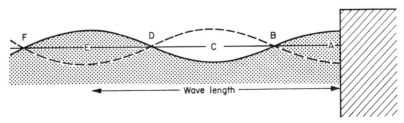

Wave length

FIG. 50 Standing waves set up by recoil from a vertical wall. The broken line indicates the position of the water's surface after half a wave period.

At the places in Fig. 50 marked *A*, *C*, *E*, etc., situated at distances of half a wavelength from each other, the water goes up and down to the maximum distance; at the intermediate points *B*, *D*, *F*, etc., it goes only to and fro, no longer up and down at all. The double-pointed arrows in Fig. 49 denote the paths of the water particles; these make rectilinear movements which may go in all directions within a vertical plane, according to the place at which we are looking. Wherever the fluctuations in height are at their maximum (at A, C, etc.), the water has a purely vertical movement; wherever they are at their lowest (at B, etc.), its movement is horizontal. At intermediate points the direction is oblique, but always rectilinear.

MOVEMENT OF THE WATER IN RUNNING WAVES

Returning to ordinary running water-waves, let us see how the water particles behave.

These movements are quite different from that of the wave profile running away at the rate of propagation. If one carefully watches small objects floating on the water, it becomes evident that the water does not only go up and down, but also to and fro; it moves forward on the crest of a wave and backward in the trough. In a vessel lying in the lengthwise direction of the waves, this horizontal movement of the water is felt very distinctly as a sideways displacement, with the crest raising the vessel, followed by a backward displacement (towards the next crest) in the trough, provided, of course, that the waves are long enough and high enough in proportion to the craft.

These forward and backward movements of water associated with crests and troughs of the waves can also be seen in plants under water, which are seen to sweep forward while a crest is passing, and backward under a trough, if the waves are not too small. It is because of this forward movement of the water in the crests that high waves (when a 'high sea' is running) have such mighty force; it is not only that the surface of the water rises with an on-coming crest, but a great mass of water is thrust forward under it and sucked back again when the trough passes.

The difference between the motion of the water in a crest and that in a trough may have unpleasant consequences, in some cases, for those who do not make allowances for it, for example when one vessel is towing another. If a fairly high sea is running, with well-developed waves, and if the distance between the tug and the tow should be, say, half a wavelength, the tow may be on a crest when the tug is in a trough, and vice versa. In that event the tow on the crest will receive an extra forward impetus at a given moment, while, through the backward motion in the trough, the tug will lose some speed, and the tow-rope will become slack. The next instant, however, it will be the tug which receives the extra impetus on the crest and the tow that is pulled back, with the result that the cable is abruptly pulled taut and may break.

It should be added that, if the water is not too shallow in proportion to the wavelength, the horizontal displacements are approximately equal in extent to the vertical ones. Visualizing a single particle of water, we shall see that these are its movements: forward in the crest, then descending when the crest has passed by and the following trough is approaching, then backward in the trough and finally upward as the next crest approaches;

then the same thing all over again. We see that the particle has described a circle in a vertical plane during one wave period; and it appears, both from observations and on theoretical grounds, that these are true vertical circles to all practical purposes, provided that the depth of the water is at least half the wavelength, and also provided that we are dealing with a simple wave motion. Figure 51 illustrates what water particles do in such a case. All the

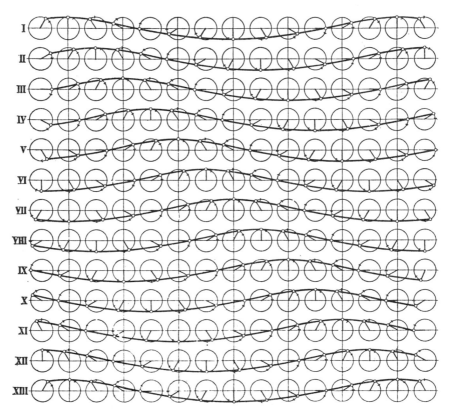

Fig. 51 Progression of a wave motion. Thirteen snapshots, each with an interval of 1/12th period.

water particles of the wave profile describe vertical circles of diameter equal to the height of the waves. During one period, each particle describes its own circle once exactly. In Fig. 51 there are thirteen 'snapshots' of a part of the profile of the wave, there being exactly one period between the first (top) and the last (bottom). The movement of a particular particle during this period can be seen by following it from the top downward in the figure. It passes through its highest point with a forward movement at the moment when the crest of the wave passes it, and goes through its lowest point with a backward motion at the moment when the bottom of the next trough passes it. An arrow shows the direction in which each particle is moving.

This picture now needs a minor correction, as it has transpired from closer study that a water particle does not return *exactly* to the starting-point of its path; instead, after every up-and-down movement, it is shifted ever so slightly forward in the direction in which the waves are advancing (see Fig. 52). It could be put this way: the return into the trough does not exactly balance the advance on the crest, so that a small net forward shift remains. In one period, for water at the surface, this amounts to roughly ten times the steepness, times the height of the waves; this is valid for waves on sufficiently deep water. With a swell of 100 metres' length and 2 metres' height, this gives a displacement of $10 \times \dfrac{2}{100} \times 2$ metres = 40 centimetres per period (at the surface). On the grounds of a law which will be discussed later, a wave-length of 100 metres on deep water involves a period of 8 seconds; so the displacement is 40 centimetres per 8 seconds, i.e. an average of 5 cm per second.

FIG. 52 Path shift of a water particle during two periods.

It will be evident that this displacement of water, in which waves are involved, could play an important part in the mechanism of oceanic currents maintained by the wind; for the very fact that the wind brings waves with it means that there is already a certain displacement of the surface water.

As this detail is immaterial to the majority of the characteristics of oceanic waves we shall usually ignore it in our further consideration of these characteristics, and regard the paths of the water particles as being closed circles.

Let us now establish the speed with which a water particle completes its path. As the circumference of a circle is 3·14 times the diameter, and the diameter of the circular paths of the surface water is equal to the height of the waves, and as, further, the circumference of the circle is travelled in one period, the speed of the water is 3·14 × *height:period*. Thus this speed is upwards of 1 metre per second for a wave 3 metres high with a period of 9 seconds. This is also the greatest forward speed reached in the crests and the greatest backward speed in the troughs. The rate of propagation is usually far greater, as this is given by the wavelength divided by the period, and the wavelength is generally far more than 3·14 times the height. Here, again, we must make a proviso, for if the waves are very steep, the circular paths are not completed at constant speed. We already know that the speed is greater in the upper segment than in the lower (backward) one. This effect is greatly magnified in very steep waves, so much so that the maximum forward speed can become, not (3·14 × *height*): *period*, but (7 × *height*): *period*. Now, should 7 × *height* be equal to the wavelength, the forward speed of the water in the crest would be equal to the rate of propagation, which is *wavelength* : *period*. There can be no greater forward speed of the

Fig. 53 Trochoidal wave profile. Here the crests project farther above the mean level than the troughs sink under it.

water, because the water would then be flung forward out of the wave; in other words the wave would 'break' (plunge over). From this it follows that, theoretically, the wave cannot attain a height of more than one-seventh times the wavelength without breaking. Meanwhile, we know that the steepness actually is seldom more than one-tenth.

At speeds like this the profile of the wave has long ceased to be the simple undulating line of Figs. 48 and 51, in which a trough is the reflection of a crest. With great steepness the crest-line takes on the character of the ridge of a two-sided roof. According to Stokes' theory, in the limiting case of one-seventh steepness the forward slope and the backward slope of the wave meet in the crest under an angle of 120 degrees (see Fig. 56).

With somewhat smaller steepness, the profile of the waves can be roughly represented by a trochoid, as shown in Fig. 53. This kind of profile has narrower crests and broader, flatter troughs than the simple line of the sinusoid represented in Fig. 48. Thus, in contrast to the sinusoid, the trochoidal profile (more nearly approximating actuality) is not symmetrical with reference to the mean water level; the level at rest (mean level) of the water surface is lower than the level which is half-way between the crests and the troughs; the distance the water sinks below the mean level is less than the distance it rises above it. The higher the waves are in proportion to the wavelength, the more pointed are the crests compared with the troughs.

Let us revert for a moment to the circular paths which the water particles describe. Up to the present, we have been discussing only the water very near the surface of the sea. But what is the deeper water doing while the surface undulates? This, too, is in motion and in the deeper layers vertical circles are also being described, but they become progressively smaller the deeper one goes (see Fig. 54). In fact, still speaking of waves in sufficiently deep water, the diameters of the circles form a diminishing geometrical series if the depth increases in arithmetical progression. It amounts to a halving of the diameter with each descent of one-ninth times the wavelength. Thus, at a depth of $1/9 \times L$, the displacements of the water particles are half the height of the wave; at a depth of $2/9 \times L$ they are a quarter, at

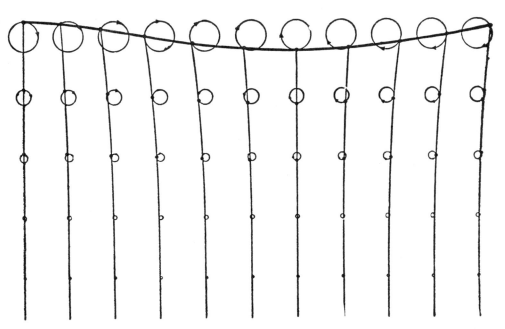

FIG. 54 Paths of the water particles at various depths in a wave on deep water. Each circle is one-ninth of a wavelength below the one immediately above it.

$3/9 \times L$ one-eighth of the height of the wave, and so on. Below the depth of half a wavelength, the displacements of the water particles are less than 4 per cent. of those at the surface.

Two things follow from what has just been said. First, the deeper the water is, the less will the bottom be affected by the waves and, conversely, the less will the motions of the waves be hampered by the presence of the bottom. Water can usually be called 'deep' without qualification so long as the depth is at least half a wavelength (so here 'deep' is a typically comparative definition). Secondly, the longer the waves are, the deeper is the range of the motions of the water. For instance, a wave of 10 centimetres reaches to a depth of 5 centimetres (for such waves, therefore, a ditch is 'deep'); but a wave 100 metres long reaches to a depth of 50 metres. It was because the motions of the water decrease rapidly as the depth increases that Vening Meinesz used a submarine for his gravity measurements at sea, since a submarine can dive to a depth at which the water is practically unaffected

by the restless movements of waves, which make gravity recordings with
sensitive instruments from a surface ship rather difficult.

The theory of the circular paths is no longer valid for water so shallow, or
waves so long, that the motion of the water ceases to be negligible near the
bottom. This is because the water at the bottom is prevented from describing
vertical orbits of significant size; its only scope is a to-and-fro movement
along the bottom. Although the water at higher levels is able to go up and
down, it does not describe circles anywhere, only flattened ellipses, as
shown in Fig. 55. The same applies to the surface, where the to-and-fro
movements are more extensive than the up-and-down ones. The nearer the
ellipses are to the bottom, the shorter are they, and also the flatter. And, as we
have said, the water along the bottom goes only forward and backward.

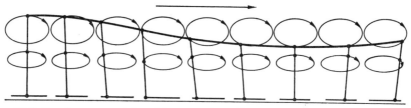

FIG. 55 Paths of water particles with a wave in shallow water (i.e. shallow compared with
the wavelength). The arrow points in the direction of the propagation.

If the water is very shallow or the wavelength very long, the ellipses, even
at the surface, are so elongated and flat, and the horizontal displacements
predominate so much, that the water performs a mainly to-and-fro movement.

THE LONGER THE WAVES THE GREATER THEIR SPEED

When we speak of 'long waves' we mean waves of great wavelength (not,
as might be supposed, waves with long crests); likewise, 'short waves'
means to us waves of small wavelength. It has been found, both theoretically
and from observation, that, given equal depth, long waves advance more
rapidly than short ones. This can be seen even on a waterway or lake, as well
as at sea, when two systems of waves are present simultaneously, e.g. fairly
long waves coming from elsewhere, and shorter ones raised on the already
undulating surface by local gusts of wind.

The relationship between wavelength and velocity in *deep water* is
definite enough to be expressed mathematically: namely, the velocity is
proportional to the root of the wavelength. Numerically: the squared speed
of propagation is equal to $1 \cdot 56 \times$ the wavelength, or $C^2 = 1 \cdot 56\,L$, provided
the speed is expressed in metres per second and the wavelength in metres
(in the number $1 \cdot 56$ the force of gravity is contained). We must repeat that
this rule, derived by Stokes more than a century ago, applies to waves in
deep water; and again we mean by 'deep water' a depth of more than half the

wavelength. So the expression does not hold for small depth, where the waves advance more slowly (about which we shall have more to say presently).

Even with deep water there are two other cases to which the above rule does not exactly apply. First, if the gradient—the ratio of height to length— is very steep (1:15 being a great steepness, for instance), the velocity is a little greater than shown by the rule. Secondly, this is also so with waves so short that they could more appropriately be described as ripples. This is because capillarity, the surface tension, comes into play with very short wavelets (a few centimetres, or less, in length) and increases the rate of propagation.

The ordinary waves we have been discussing so far are 'gravity waves', in which it is mainly gravity that causes the water to go up and down when brought out of equilibrium. The very smallest ripples, however, are called capillarity waves, because surface tension is mainly responsible for them. The rule that applies to them is: the smaller the wavelength the greater the velocity. For water wavelets this rule holds for all wavelengths smaller than 1·7 centimetres. If the wavelength is greater than 1·7 centimetres, we have the rule that the greater the length, the higher is the velocity. Wavelets exactly 1·7 centimetres long have the lowest possible speed of propagation, namely, 23 centimetres per second.[1]

The easiest way to observe true ripples is to hold a piece of string, or a twig, in flowing water, or to move it steadily in stagnant water. A very decorative pattern of ripples will then be formed around the disturbance of the water surface. If the water is flowing and we hold the object in place, the pattern of ripples will also be stationary, but with reference to the water, the ripples run at a speed which is opposite to the speed of the water.

At sea it is the larger gravity waves which predominate, and it is with these that we shall be mainly concerned. The relation mentioned for the speed of propagation in deep water applies to these gravity waves; and from it also follow relations between the speed and the period, and between the wavelength and the period. Hence if one of the three be given, the other two can be calculated. It is an easy matter to verify that *speed* (in metres per second) = 1·56 × *period* (in seconds); and that *wavelength* (in metres) = 1·56 × *period* (in seconds) *squared*; or, $C = 1·56\ T$; $L = 1·56\ T^2$. Table 16 gives a number of corresponding values of these three quantities.

It will be seen from Table 16 that, according to these relations, a wave of ten seconds is ten times as rapid as a wave of one second, but one hundred times as long. A wave of twenty seconds is twice as quick but four times as long as one of ten seconds. The waves of a swell with a period of 20 seconds (by no means rare in oceanic areas fairly distant from the main storm centres) have the enormous velocity of 31 metres per second, or 112 kilometres an hour!

[1] These figures apply only to water. Temperature and salinity have comparatively little effect upon them.

Table 16
Wavelengths and Velocities Associated with Certain Values of the Wave Period

T (sec)	L (m)	C (m/sec)
1	1·56	1·56
2	6·2	3·1
3	14·0	4·7
4	25·0	6·2
5	39	7·8
6	56	9·4
7	76	10·9
8	100	12·5
9	126	14·0
10	156	15·6
11	189	17·2
12	225	18·7
13	264	20·3
14	306	21·8
15	351	23·4
16	399	25·0
17	451	26·5
18	505	28·1
19	563	29·6
20	624	31·2

WAVES IN SHALLOW WATER

A depth of less than half the wavelength affects the propagation of the wave; with equal wavelength or period, the velocity of the wave then diminishes with diminishing depth. This will be found at sea particularly when waves advance from deep water towards the shore. Following them, we see virtually the same period everywhere but, as the water gets shallower the waves decrease in speed and length. It is fairly easy to realize why the period in shallow water is the same everywhere as in the deep water whence the waves have come, provided at least that the state of the sea surface as a whole is stationary. For if a certain number of wave crests per minute passes at a given distance from the shore, just as many waves per minute must come into the shore; otherwise some crests would have disappeared or have been created on the way, which we assume not to take place. But if the numbers of wave crests per minute are the same at those two places, this means that the period at both places is the same.

Now, with the period remaining the same, the velocity of the wave in shallow water decreases as the depth decreases, so that the foremost waves, nearest the shore, are retarded most. The succeeding waves catch them up, and automatically the wavelength diminishes.

Table 17 shows the relation between depth and velocity or length of the wave, the period remaining the same.

In this table can be found the proportion in which waves shorten compared with their initial deep-water length. The proportions are the lower row of figures; the depths to which these relations apply are found in the upper row, giving the proportion of the depth to that same initial wavelength (deep-water wavelength). We see again that, so long as the latter proportion is at least 0·5, the shortening is negligible. This table can also be used for waves in shallow water, which have not been in deep water at all, provided the period be known, from which the 'deep-water wavelength' follows. Here is an example:

There are waves with a period of 10 seconds. How long are they in water 100 metres deep and how long in water 5 metres deep? We can read from Table 16 that a period of 10 seconds is associated with a deep-water wavelength of 156 metres. Since 100 metres is more than half of this, 100 metres is 'deep' water in this case and the wavelength there is, consequently, 156 metres; obviously, the velocity is 15·6 metres per second.

Table 17

Changing Wavelength in Shallow Water

Depth Deep-water wavelength	0·50	0·30	0·20	0·10	0·032	0·010	0·003
Wavelength Deep-water wavelength	1·0	0·97	0·89	0·71	0·43	0·24	0·13^5

The picture is quite different at 5 metres' depth, where we get: *depth: deep-water wavelength* = 5/156 = 0·032. Here, Table 17 gives us the figure 0·43. This means that the deep-water wavelength has to be multiplied by this number to give the wavelength at 5 metres' depth; hence the latter is 0·44 × 156 m = 67 metres. The velocity, then, is 67 metres per 10 seconds, or 6·7 metres per second.

If the water is very shallow in proportion to the wavelength, the speed of propagation ceases to depend on the wavelength and depends only on the depth; then, *the square of the speed* (in metres per second) is approximately equal to ten times the *depth* (in metres). This generally holds if the wavelength is at least 25 times the depth. In this case we do refer to the waves as 'long waves'. At a depth of 0·1 metres, all waves which are at least 2·5 metres long have a speed of 1 metre per second. Similarly, at 0·9 metre's depth, all waves at least 22·5 metres long have a speed of 3 metres per second; at 10 metres depth those at least 250 metres long have a speed of 10 metres per second, and so on. It should be added that the exact multiplier of the depth of water is 9·8 rather than 10.[1]

TSUNAMIS

Tidal waves, so called, provide a typical example of 'long waves'. The term is used to denote waves of hundreds of miles' wavelength, so they are

[1] Actually it is: *acceleration of gravity* × *the depth of water.*

not ordinary waves raised by the wind or a swell, but certain elevations of the water surface which may be caused by a landslip under the ocean, or by the eruption of a volcano in the ocean, or by the piling-up of water under the action of a strong wind or gale. As a tidal wave caused by an earthquake or a volcanic eruption really has nothing to do with the tides, it is often called by the Japanese name 'tsunami'.

A notorious example was the tidal wave of 1st April 1946, which originated somewhere in the northern part of the Pacific Ocean near the Aleutians, where there was a submarine earthquake resulting in seismic waves in the earth and a tsunami in the ocean. This tsunami spread out in all directions, but the Hawaiian Islands, about 3700 kilometres away, suffered most from it. Roughly 4 hours and 40 minutes after the time of the submarine landslip near the Aleutians, the Hawaiian Islands were assaulted by enormous tidal waves, rolling in at regular intervals and reaching 16 metres above the average sea level in places. More than one hundred and fifty people lost their lives, and great material damage was done. Altogether, there was a score or more of these waves, the first ones of which had a period of about 15 minutes, which at once shows that they were very long waves. The great heights attained on some of the islands were due only to the fact that the successive waves were checked in the shallow water offshore, and were thus driven together and piled up. Their height in mid-ocean was estimated to be little more than half a metre.

What interests us most is the velocity of these tsunami waves. If we divide the distance given above by the difference in time, we find the velocity to be no less than about 790 kilometres per hour, or 220 metres a second. Remembering the relation existing between the velocity of long waves and the depth of the water, we can work out the mean depth of the water between the Aleutians and the Hawaiian Islands from the velocity found; namely, the square of the velocity (in metres per second) is 9·8 times the depth of the water (in metres). From this, it follows that the depth of the water on the way must have been on an average 4950 metres, according to the theory of long waves. This figure agrees with the bathymetric charts of the North Pacific.

Finally, we have to verify that this depth is far less than the wavelength was in this case. The wavelength is easily calculated from the period and the velocity, and proves to be no less than 198 kilometres (averaged). So these undoubtedly were long waves.

Another example of a 'tsunami' was that caused by the catastrophic earthquake in Chile (at approximately 39° S., 74° W.) on 22nd May 1960. It travelled to Honshu (Japan) in 23–24 hours.

ENERGY OF THE WAVES

By the energy of water waves we mean their working-power, a measure of the amount of 'work' they could perform. This energy is generally given as the mean energy present per unit water surface in the waves. Such 'work' might be the destructive work, for instance, which might be wrought by the waves. The distorted, moving water of an undulating sea has energy in the same sense as a spring under tension, a lifted weight and a material object in motion have this energy. Where does it come from? From the wind which generated the waves; it is this wind which imparts energy to the waves. It is a thousand pities that it is so difficult to convert this energy into anything useful; the destructive capacity of the waves, on the other hand, is unfortunately seen all too often.

The quantity of this energy is proportional to the square of the height of the waves; for example, waves twice as high can perform four times as much work (expressed in terms of energy). Thus a swell of 2 metres' height contains some 500 kilogram-metres, or 5 kilojoules, of energy per square metre of sea surface; a swell 4 metres high, four times as much, hence 2000 kilogram-metres, or 20 kilojoules, per square metre. (1 kilojoule = 1 kilowatt-second.)

If these energies were converted entirely to heat, 1·2 and 4·8 kilogram calories per square metre would be produced by them respectively; that is to say, amounts of heat able to warm up one litre of water through about 1·2°C and 4·8°C.

If the waves are not doing any work, the energy within them does not remain where it is; some of it runs out in the same direction as that in which the waves are advancing. We can then speak of a current of energy in the same way as we can say that a current of energy runs through the feed-wires of a burning electric lamp. We express that stream of energy in watts in the case of an electric current; we could do the same where oceanic waves are concerned, or we could express it in horse-power, as is done for engines.

We cannot here go into the physics of the transfer of energy, but we can say that it is found by multiplying the wave energy present per unit surface area by what is called the *group velocity*. This, about which we shall have more to say in another context, is, in deep water, half the propagation velocity of the wave, which is also called phase velocity. In very shallow water, however, the group velocity is equal to the phase velocity. If we apply this to a swell in mid-ocean with a height of 4 metres and a period of 16 seconds, we find the transfer of energy to be upwards of 25,000 kilogram-metres per second per metre (i.e. per metre crest length), or 250 kilowatts per metre.

If a swell like this comes rolling in, then the surf zone off the shore must cope with the amount of energy mentioned per metre and per second. The figure given signifies a supply of energy comparable to a capacity of 340 horsepower (250 kilowatts) per metre. Most of this energy is converted to heat.

THE APPEARANCE OF WAVES IN NATURE

Everyone who has seen the sea knows that waves do not really look as simple as represented by the sine line of Fig. 48. As soon as they have developed thoroughly, their profile is different from that line, and also from the trochoid of Fig. 53. The crests of high waves become more and more pointed, and ultimately, with a gradient of 1 in 7 (if it comes to that), an angle is formed (see Fig. 56) which, according to Stokes's theory, is 120 degrees. Here the limit is reached, for if the waves were to become steeper still, their crests would begin to break.

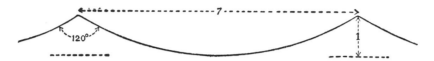

FIG. 56 Ultimate form of water waves according to theory.

Figure 48 presents other features, however, which are not true to life; and that is because simple waves are seldom actually seen. Only a swell passing through a windless area can approach the image of such a simple wave. Mostly, sea waves, and wind waves in particular, look different.

To begin with, successive waves do not have the same height. Then, the periods between the passing of successive crests are not the same, though, generally they do not vary very much. Lastly, in wind waves there are often short-crested waves instead of the elongated ridges to which reference was made at the outset. So the more common sight is that of crests separated by 'saddles', rather than very long crests of uniform height.

It can now be shown that, in a certain sense, even these irregular patterns can be thought of as combinations of simple waves; or, to put it differently, there is always to be found a number, generally a great number, of simple undulations, differing from one another in height, wavelength and direction, which, in combination, produce such an irregular pattern.

To begin with, let us consider waves which may have long, parallel crests, but which differ in height; see top curve in Fig. 57. Although this curve looks fairly regular, it is certainly no longer the profile of a simple wave, for the height is not everywhere the same, nor are the horizontal distances from

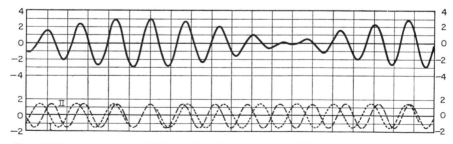

FIG. 57 The uppermost profile is equal to the sum (superposition) of two simple waves I and II, shown below. The horizontal dimensions are greatly shortened in proportion to the vertical ones.

crest to crest. This profile, however, can be represented as the sum of two simple wave profiles of slightly different wavelength; (see I and II in Fig. 57). Combining the appropriate vertical deviations of I and II at each point of the horizontal axis, we get the vertical deviation of what we call the sum of wave I and wave II. If this is done for all points, the result will be the top wave profile in the figure. Hence the latter can be *broken down*, as it were, into two simple waves of differing wavelength.

The reason why the crests are of varying height in the sum of I and II is that in one place waves I and II are 'in step', and their heights therefore add up, whereas a little farther along the waves oppose each other, so that the resulting height there is reduced.

Profiles extremely irregular in appearance can be obtained by combining not two, but several, simple waves of different lengths and heights. On the analogy of the theory of light, this is called the wave *spectrum*, by which is meant the result of breaking down the compounded wave motion into simple waves of different periods (or wavelengths, which comes to the same thing), each with its own height or energy. We shall see an example of this when we come to consider swell.

This idea of combining several simple waves serves not only to explain the differences in height and wavelengths between successive waves, i.e. the irregularities of observed wave profiles, but also the generation of waves with short crests, which hence consist of more or less isolated, short ridges or hills, and similar troughs. For when simple wave systems with endlessly long crests coming from various directions intermingle, the result is precisely those short-crested waves producing a 'landscape' of oblong, detached hillocks and valleys.

GROUPS OF WAVES AND GROUP VELOCITY

Everyone who has watched the waves of the sea with some attention must have noticed that the larger sort tend to come in groups. We are told that the ancient Romans used to think that heavy waves always came in groups of ten. Plato had it, as do many seamen of present times, that there are always three higher waves alternating with lower ones. Others speak of groups of seven. In this last case (and probably also in that of the Romans) those groups include both the high and the low waves; so by 'groups of seven' they mean that the greatest height is again attained after every seven waves. This does not necessarily conflict, therefore, with the 'three high-waves theory', for, if there should be four lower waves between three high ones, the two pronouncements would tally.

Waves, and especially those of a swell, do undoubtedly occur in groups of this kind; but it is equally certain that one 'group' by no means invariably comprises the same number of waves. It is fairly easy to watch the arrival of waves in groups wherever there is a regular, good surf, preferably in calm weather, hence the surf of a swell. While the intervals between successive breakers are fairly uniformly timed, it will often be clearly apparent that a number of high breakers are repeatedly followed by a number of lower, or even low, ones; then come high ones again, and so on and so on.

The occurrence of waves in groups like this should not surprise us if we have another look at Fig. 57. Sets of waves varying little in length have only to roll over each other in approximately the same direction to produce these groups. The phenomenon is comparable to what are called 'beats' in acoustics.

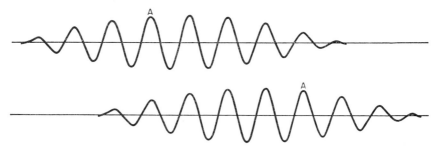

FIG. 58 Progression of a group of waves. The group as a body moves at half the speed of a single crest, A.

Let us consider a wave group like that at the top of Fig. 58 (bearing in mind that the proportions in this, and subsequent, figures are not true to nature, the wavelengths almost invariably being drawn too small in proportion to the height, to avoid undue elongation of the figure or inconveniently small heights). Now this figure could easily represent the profile of a set of waves in a swell.

In Nature, the various tops of the group are never exactly equidistant, but one can quite legitimately speak of an average distance, hence an average wavelength; and all the tops advance at a speed corresponding to the wavelength. As a coherent unit, however, the group advances at its own velocity, which is different. One has only to compare the position in the lower part of Fig. 58 with that in the upper one. These two wave lines are intended to represent two positions of the group, in between which an interval of time amounting to four wave periods has elapsed. The top marked A has advanced by four wavelengths, but we now see that the group as a whole has advanced by only two wavelengths, with the result that A, which was at first fourth from the left in the group, is now sixth from the left.

The general law applicable to waves in deep water is that the velocity of a group is only half the velocity of propagation of the individual waves. Therefore, were we, in a manner of speaking, to take a ride on a *group* at a speed called the group velocity, we should continually be finding wave tops in the group catching us up and passing us. Once it has reached the front half of its group, a wave top drops lower and lower until it finally disappears. At the same time, wave tops are constantly 'entering' the group from behind, and passing through it. If we realize that the tops of waves are not individual entities, but only local manifestations of the general movement in a group of waves, this behaviour will become more comprehensible. It can be seen, similarly, in a pond, in the ring-shaped 'group' of wavelets around the stone dropped into the water. (The circularity of the wave-crests is immaterial.)

THE FRONT OF A SWELL

The group velocity referred to is also a factor of prime importance in the propagation of a swell. When a swell coming from a stormy area passes over a more or less calm sea, there is a kind of 'front' indicating the site of the foremost waves of the swell; so the swell has not yet reached the water ahead of this front. Now the behaviour of this 'front' is exactly similar to that of the van of a wave group. This is an instance of a group which does have a front—the wave-front—but whose rear lies in the storm area, where new waves are constantly being generated. This wave-front, too, advances at group velocity. The time which has to elapse after the departure of the swell from the storm-area before the front of the swell reaches a certain place is determined, not by the wave velocity referred to earlier, but by the group velocity, which, on deep water, is half the former. The individual crests of the swell, therefore, advance at twice the group velocity, and may eventually catch up with the front; but once there they lose height, and soon vanish in the calm water ahead.

How does this come about? We can form some idea of the situation if we realize that only part of the energy moves with the wave profile—with the crests and troughs—namely, that part which is associated with the elevation and depression of the surface of the water. This part, called the potential energy, is half the total energy. The other half is contained in the motion of the water particles. In deep water, this kinetic energy remains where it is; that is to say, the water particles do not transmit any kinetic energy to their neighbours in front, nor do they receive any from their neighbours behind during wave propagation. (Remember that, as a water particle is describing its circle, its direction of movement is continuously changing, but its speed is not, and it therefore neither loses nor gains any kinetic energy.)

So, let us assume that a leading wave can be picked out in the vanguard, so to speak, at the front of the swell. After the time of one period, this wave has arrived with half its energy, namely, its potential energy (which we might call 'deformation energy'), at a place where there was no movement. But there is no such thing as a wave with potential energy only, and this wave will necessarily have had to distribute the half-energy carried along with it between the potential energy and the kinetic energy, because it has had to set in motion the water ahead of the front. So now its total energy is equal to half of what it had just been. This implies that it must have lost height; and that continues progressively as it marches into the calm water ahead.

It will be seen at once that this leading wave will soon have disappeared, and that the waves coming behind it will come to the front and also disappear in their turn. That is how the front of the swell—not, of course, as sharply defined as represented above—moves forward at a rate which is half the velocity propagation of its crests, as discussed earlier and expressed as a formula. To distinguish it from the group velocity, we alternatively call that velocity *phase velocity*.

GROUP VELOCITY IS PROPAGATION VELOCITY OF ENERGY

The reader may remember that, when we began to discuss energy, we had earlier mentioned group velocity in connection with the energy of the waves. We may, in fact, also call group velocity 'propagation velocity of energy'.

This can again be clarified by the example of waves induced by a stone thrown into a pond. At every moment, the energy of those waves is contained in that extending circular band, and it apparently moves at the rate at which the band expands. That band, however, is a group, and that rate is not the velocity of the individual waves (the phase velocity), but the group velocity.

The statement that the group velocity is half the phase velocity is valid for deep water. In shallow water, the group velocity is more than half. In very shallow water, or, which comes to the same thing, in the case of very long waves, there is no difference between the two velocities.

SIGNIFICANT WAVES

After all that has been said about the irregular appearance which is often, though not always, presented by waves in the ocean, it may reasonably be asked whether, in many cases, it is feasible to attribute a given wavelength and a given period to the undulation of the sea surface. In some circumstances it is clearly evident that two entirely independent systems of waves, each of which can easily be picked out, are running through or over each other. For instance, there may be quite a heavy swell on the one hand, and small, wind-driven waves slipping over the backs of the swell, on the other. (See Plates XXIV and XXVII), or else quite a heavy sea may be running from one direction, and a swell from another; or perhaps two kinds of swell may be running from different directions (see Plate XXIX, lower part), in which case two (or three) individual wavelengths and periods can be attributed to the total picture of the undulation, while, moreover, each has a certain height and a certain direction of advance.

In a case like that represented by Fig. 57, while it is true that there are two intermingling trains of waves of slightly different wavelengths, they are visually indistinguishable; nor are they any less so in the even more irregular wave profiles often occurring in Nature. Now, in that case one simply takes the average distance between a large number of successive crests and calls that average 'the' wavelength.

Similarly, there is an average period. Were one to construct a graph of the height of the water at a given place, as some instruments do automatically (see Fig. 61), the mean time interval between the crests in the graph could be taken as the period which is characteristic for the prevailing irregular undulation.

Now, how are we to tell what is the height? No two tops are equally high, nor two troughs equally deep; and the wild motions of the sea in a storm are extremely irregular. So if we repeatedly refer to 'the' wave height in a wind field, this must be based on a prearranged agreement. There are several alternatives. One might be the average of the differences in height between successive crests and troughs, which would include the occasional fairly low waves, like the low crests and shallow troughs in the flat part of the group in Fig. 57. Accordingly, this average is really too low to represent a true picture of the actual situation. One could, of course, take the greatest height observed; but that would give an exaggerated picture, especially if it happened to be that of just one wave seen only once.

We shall adopt the definition suggested by Sverdrup and Munk. This is arrived at by taking the average, not of all wave crests, but only of the most important ones, the 'most important' being the highest 33 per cent. of all waves observed. Thus, if we were to register a great number of passing waves, and make a note of the heights, we should have to consider that third part of the total number which had the greatest heights, and then find the average of their heights. We call these the 'dominant' or 'significant' waves, and the height according to this agreement is the 'significant' wave height.

This definition has had to be inserted to make meaningful the figures we shall mention later.

OBSERVATIONS AND MEASUREMENTS

Before proceeding to consider how sea waves (wind-waves) develop, we must dwell briefly on the ways and means of observing and measuring them. The reader will realize that this is by no means easy, for what could be more volatile than a passing water wave? In many cases mere approximations have to suffice.

THE WAVELENGTH

The length of waves can be measured by paying out an old-fashioned log[1] so far from the stern of the vessel that it rests on a crest just when the stern is riding on the next crest. If the ship is sailing at right-angles to the direction of the crest, the length of paid-out line is equal to the wavelength; if not, the former length has to be multiplied by the sine of the angle made between the direction of navigation and the direction of the crest.

If the wavelength is not too great compared with the length of the vessel, then it can be estimated by comparison with the length of the ship, or with a known distance between two fixed points on it.

Another method is to compare the intervals at which successive crests reach the ship with the time required for a crest to pass from stem to stern

---

[1] A log is a speedometer. The oldest method of measuring the speed of a vessel is by a log, a block of wood, which floats upright on the water, attached to a paid-out line.

or vice versa. For example, suppose the ship is sailing at right-angles to the direction of the crests, and a crest catches up with the vessel every 15 seconds, whereas it needs 10 seconds to pass from the stern to the stem; if, then, the length of the ship is 80 metres, the wavelength is apparently 15/10 times the ship's length, hence 120 metres. If the vessel is not sailing at right-angles to the direction of the crest, then the angle between the sailing direction and the crest direction has to be accounted for by multiplying this result by the sine of the angle.

The wavelength can be estimated or measured from the shore or from an aircraft, if the distance between the wave crests can be compared with known distances along a breakwater or mole, jetty or pier, or with the length of a passing ship. From an aircraft flying near the shore the wavelength can also be compared with distances along the coast or on land.

THE VELOCITY OF PROPAGATION

To measure the speed of the waves from a ship under way, it is necessary to take into account the speed of the ship through the water. If the ship is stationary in the water, and at right-angles to the direction of the crests, the times are recorded at which one particular crest passes two fixed points on her side; and the velocity is then found by dividing the distance between these two points by the recorded time difference. This can best be done by two people.

If the ship is not stationary, but is sailing in the direction of the waves, the speed of the ship has to be added to the above result. And if the vessel is sailing into the waves, her speed must be subtracted from the result. If the direction of the vessel forms an angle with the direction in which the waves are propagated, this angle should, again, be accounted for in the calculation.

One observer by himself can measure the wave velocity by paying out a log over a known length from the stern, and recording the time required by a crest to advance from the log to the ship, or vice versa; and he must also take into account the speed and direction of the vessel.

The velocity of waves can be measured from the shore or an aircraft, if there are suitable fixed points against which the motion of the crests can be measured.

THE WAVE PERIOD

This, the easiest feature to measure, is found by recording the time that elapses between the passing of a fixed point by two successive crests. This may be aboard a stationary ship; but if the vessel is sailing, the simplest method of measuring is to watch something (if necessary, thrown overboard for the purpose) drifting in the water, or else a conspicuous patch of foam; and to record by stopwatch the times at which the object is on the summit of a wave.

If waves are breaking regularly on the shore, the period is fairly easily measured by recording the times when successive waves break, or by

Aerial photograph of T3 ice-island in the middle of pack-ice; taken in May 1951 from a height of 600 metres. (U.S. Air Force photograph.)

A corner of T3 ice-island in which the undulating structure is clearly visible. (U.S. Air Force photograph.)

PLATE XVIII

The Jacobshavn glacier. A very large iceberg, estimated to be a mile in length has just been calved. The fjord is partly frozen over. The 'lumps' in the white ice are icebergs, not ice-floes. (U.S. Coast Guard photograph.)

counting a number of breakers and measuring the total time interval between the first and the last one.

THE HEIGHT

This may be the most difficult to measure, at any rate in mid-ocean. If the waves are so short that the length of the ship is at least a few times the wavelength, the height of the wave can be conveniently observed on the ship's side, where the profile shows up; this on the assumption that the vessel is cutting through the crests at a wide angle (preferably at right-angles, because there is then little rolling), and that there are some clear marks for measuring on the ship's side.

Height is difficult to observe if the waves are long, because there is no available yardstick for comparison. With little height, the slopes on the water surface are likewise unobtrusive, and there is little to catch the eye. The observation of high waves is badly hampered by the pitching and rolling of the ship. Mistakes are very easily made when heights are being estimated, and we know that the figures thus given are often unreliable.

FIG. 59 Measuring great wave-heights from a vessel.

Without mechanical aids, the best way to observe anything like high waves aboard a vessel is to find a place from which the crests are seen at the same level as the horizon when the upright vessel is in the deepest part of a trough; the height of this observation point above the waterline is then the height of the wave. (See Fig. 59.) Beware of watching distant waves, for, owing to the curvature of the earth, these may project above the horizon, although actually they are below the level of the observer.

This warning applies equally to the observation of the height of waves or breakers from the shore. There, too, one can follow a similar procedure by seeking a place where, at eye-level, the tops of the waves or breakers just seem to touch the horizon. One has then to know the height of one's position above the average waterline, and thus find the height of the crests above the average water level. This height is somewhat different from what we have defined as the 'height of the wave'; to find the latter, the depth of the troughs (below the average water level) has to be added to the former; with breakers and with waves just about to break, this depth is only about one-third of the height of the tops above the average level.

It is easier, of course, to measure the heights of waves advancing alongside a pier or breakwater, or something similar, if one places certain clear marks on the object against which they are gauged. There is no need to enter into further details.

6

INSTRUMENTAL AIDS

Froude's floating seamark is a comparatively simple appliance for measuring waves reliably, even in mid-ocean, provided that no excessively high seas are running. This instrument (see Fig. 60) is a tube with a scale division at the top and a weight underneath to keep it upright. To check bobbing, a fairly large, round disc is fitted near the bottom of the instrument, which keeps it at a depth where the vertical movements of the water are expected to be slight, and so at a more or less constant level, despite any up-and-down movement there may be of the surface of the water. The differences in height of passing waves can then be read from the scale.

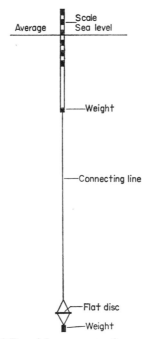

FIG. 60 Froude's wavemeter for use at sea.

Taking stereophotographs is also a way of measuring waves. It was used, for example, by the German Atlantic expedition of 1925–27 with the *Meteor*. Two cameras are set up, one on each end of a 'yard', high above the water surface; together, the two exposures taken simultaneously produce a stereoscopic image. The topography of the water 'landscape' can be established accurately by measurement of the differences between the two photographs.

Aerial photographs also provide a useful means of exact observation of waves, less for the estimation of their height than for that of their length, and possibly also velocity (for which only a fixed point on the film is required), also for studying the pattern made jointly by the crests. As we shall see, they show up interesting facts, especially in shallow water.

Waves, of course, can also be measured from the shore with an optical instrument, like a theodolite with graduated scale or a camera, perhaps a ciné camera; but we shall not enter into the details.

Finally, there are the recording *wavemeters*, of which there are four principal types, based on the following four principles: (1) the principle of the tide-gauge, in which the up-and-down movements of the water surface are transmitted mechanically by one means or another to a pen recording on a slowly-revolving drum; (2) the principle of the underwater pressure gauge; in this the waves passing over the instrument are recorded by means of the variations in pressure which they induce,[1] these variations being electrically transmitted to a recording instrument elsewhere; (3) the principle of echo-sounding in reverse; the instrument takes continuous upward echo-

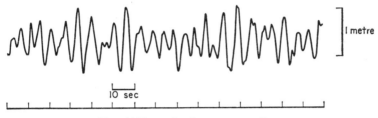

Fig. 61 Example of a wave recording.

soundings from below to the surface of the sea, thus registering the changes in height of that surface; (4) the principle of the acceleration gauge. During wave motion an object (say a float) drifting on the water, undergoes upward and downward accelerations which are transmitted to an attached gauge as downward and upward forces respectively (in the same way as we, when travelling in a lift, experience an increase in our weight during upward acceleration and a reduction in our weight during downward acceleration); these changing forces are converted into an electric signal which can be transmitted by a floating connecting cable to a ship, where the signal is converted electronically into a registration of the wave motion. The great advantage of this method (i.e. with a floating wavemeter which is an acceleration gauge) is that it does not require a fixed point. The wavemeter can be used anywhere in mid-ocean, and is used by some lightships.

A different version of the same sort of instrument is the 'ship-borne wave recorder', which has been developed at the (British) National Institute of Oceanography. This apparatus records the up-and-down movements of a point of the ship's hull somewhere under water, and at the same time, also

[1] Note: These changes in pressure are *not* identical with the changes in the weight of the water column above the instrument and are therefore *not* a direct image of the changes in height of the sea surface. They are proportional to the horizontal movements of the water at the depth to which the instrument is immersed. At increasing depth the variations in pressure diminish in the same way as these movements of the water. Hence at great depths only the longer waves will be recorded.

the pressure variations at that place, these two records together telling what the up-and-down movements of the water surface are.

A wave record is shown in Fig. 61; the undulating line represents the changing height of the water surface, or perhaps the varying water pressure. The horizontal co-ordinate, running from left to right, is the time.

WIND-WAVES

GENERATION AND DEVELOPMENT OF WAVES

In this, as in so many other matters, it is the elementary questions which are the most difficult to answer. How are waves generated? How does their life begin on water initially as smooth as a sheet of glass? A breath of wind brushes its surface, and suddenly there is a dark path of wavelets. And, soon after the wind drops, the wavelets subside; but if the wind continues to blow with enough force, the wavelets increase both in height and in length.

There are minor irregularities in every current of air that passes over the water, and these are associated with small wave-like irregularities in the pressure, pressure disturbances, which will be imported to the water surface as tiny depressions and elevations. It now remains to be seen whether these are viable enough to persist and grow, or will soon die away. For, to begin with, those wave-like rufflings of the water's surface will not stand still; they will spread in all directions, like the rings produced by a falling stone. The wind, however, has a different effect, in that it apparently maintains, 'feeds' and strengthens only those wavelets which run with it. The wavelets need that supply of energy, for without it they would soon vanish as a result of internal friction, which acts very strongly on short wavelets in particular.

Apparently the wind 'feeds' only those waves which advance approximately in its direction. Yes, but how?

Jeffreys (1925) has suggested an explanation which, although it is not the last word on the problem, would seem to account for the normal growth of waves. If we look at Fig. 62, we shall see some stream lines, but they are not symmetrical in relation to the crests and the troughs. This asymmetry is due to inevitable turbulence of the air current over the uneven surface of the water, a turbulence which is responsible for, among other things, an eddy of air to leeward of a crest. The important thing about this is that excess pressure is created to windward of a crest, and a pressure deficit to leeward. It will now be evident that waves running in the direction of the wind are strengthened by it; for, looking at the arrows indicating the motions of the water in Fig. 62, we shall see that, in the windward parts of such waves, where excess pressure prevails, the water is descending, so that there the movement of the water is promoted. A pressure deficit—one could call it a slight suction—prevails to leeward, but here the water is ascending; so here, too, the motion of the water is being stimulated. But any stimulation of up-and-down movements of the water means a heightening of the waves.

The wind has another effect on waves advancing in its direction. Where it skims over the crests, it boosts the forward movement of the water by a kind of sweeping action—by 'pull'. True, the water slithers back in the troughs, against the wind; firstly, however, this backward movement does not wholly balance the forward one in the crests (as we have already seen), and, secondly, the movement of the air along the bottom of a trough has a far weaker forward impetus than has that along the crests; indeed, it may even be directed backwards if the eddies to leeward of these crests are large enough.

The first of these two wind effects is called the 'pressure effect' and the second the 'pull effect'. Both reinforce waves running with the wind, that is, with the wind at their backs. In this way, the wind feeds the waves from their very inception.

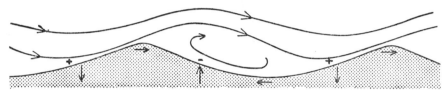

FIG. 62 How the wind reinforces the waves. Excess pressure and pressure deficit are indicated by the + and − signs. The waves are advancing towards the right and the motions of the water are arrowed.

There is one more condition, however, upon which the growth of 'newborn' waves depends. That is that the supply of energy by the wind shall not equal, but shall exceed, the amount of energy used up by the wavelets through *internal friction*.

This, too, was studied by Jeffreys. On the basis of a theoretical estimate of the amount of energy supplied by the wind, and the internal consumption of energy, he deduced that waves can only develop if the wind speed is above a certain limit; further, that wavelets with a velocity of propagation approximately one-third of that of the wind have the best chance of developing. Measurements by Jeffreys showed that this limiting wind speed is roughly 1·1 metres per second. According to this theory, the first waves to be formed would have one-third of this velocity, hence approximately 35 centimetres per second, which corresponds to a wavelength of about 8 centimetres. Observations made by others have fairly well confirmed this order of magnitude, though some investigators have measured wind-wavelets of 5 centimetres wavelength.

In recent years, a more refined theory of the growth of wind-waves has been developed by various investigators, in which a sort of 'resonance' between wind and water surface plays a role. We shall not, however, enter into the details of this theory.

We have so far considered only increased height of the waves through accretion of energy, but it is a known fact that the wavelength likewise increases with the length of time the wind has been operating upon the waves. This is fairly comprehensible, since the wavelength could scarcely remain unchanged while the height was increasing from a couple of centimetres to, say, one metre; the steepness would then be far too great. Then, again, internal friction also comes into play.

Although this matter is not yet fully understood, it can be said that, so far as energy consumption through internal friction is concerned, the longer waves live more 'economically' than do the shorter. So, if the wind supplies as much energy to short waves as to long ones, the latter retain more of it for their growth. If both are present simultaneously, eventually the longer ones will predominate. As we have already seen, waves of various lengths are always involved in that irregular interplay which accompanies the wind. We then speak of a *spectrum* of the waves, in which larger and smaller wavelengths occur, even if the small waves dominate at first. Owing to this effect, whereby the longer waves are favoured, greater and greater wavelengths begin to *dominate* the total picture in proportion to the length of time the wind has been acting on the waves. This is what happens when we see 'the' wavelength increasing.

OIL ON THE WAVES

Is a drop of oil capable of subduing the fury of the waves? This might appear to be a preposterous question, but it is no fairy tale.

Clearly, oil is not able to dissipate those giant oncoming rollers. Where could the accumulated energy in them suddenly go to? But a film of oil *can* calm them down, can make the sea less rough; the undulating surface of the water becomes smoother, so the wind loses some of its grip upon it, hurls less of it about; the sea becomes less chaotic and ships have a respite from their tossing.

By quickly spreading out into a thin film, the oil poured upon the turbulent waters subdues them. The arrangement of the molecules in this very thin skin of oil gives it a certain toughness, which strongly counteracts the rippling of the surface. That is how the roughness of the sea abates.

THE HEIGHT ATTAINED BY THE WAVES

The height of waves at a given place, like their length, is determined by two factors, namely, the velocity of the wind and the length of time it has acted upon them. As long as the wind is operative, the height and length of the waves increase with time. At first height increases quite quickly, but later on much more slowly. Table 18 gives an example with a wind velocity of 15 metres a second.

Table 18

Duration (hours)	2	6	12	24	36
Height of waves (metres)	1·4	2·9	3·8	4·3	4·5
Wavelength (metres)	26	60	90	120	140

Two things have to be borne in mind to understand fully the implications of a table like Table 18: firstly, that the heights given are invariably the *significant* heights mentioned earlier; secondly, that 'duration' in the table stands for the time during which the wind has acted upon the waves. This is not as simple as it seems. If we consider some particular spot on the water, the waves there need not necessarily increase in size the longer the wind blows. The waves of this instant are, admittedly, being increased by the wind, but they are moving on; so their greater height is observed elsewhere, not at the spot we are watching. If, nevertheless, the height increases here too, it is because the newly-arriving waves are higher than the previous ones which have passed. However, it may not be like this, but rather that the new waves here are just as high as the previous ones, although the wind has continued to blow and the height of the waves has by no means reached its maximum at that particular velocity. A simple example will at once make this clear.

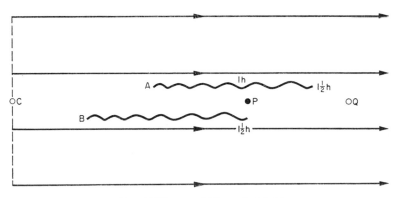

FIG. 63 Waves within a wind field.

Imagine a lake or coastal area of the sea, and an offshore wind, and that you are watching the waves at a definite spot near the shore. However long the wind continues to blow, the waves there will always be comparatively small, for the very good reason that they come from the shore and have been exposed to the influence of the wind for, at most, the time it has taken them to reach the spot you are watching. Its distance from the shore being small, that time must be short; therefore, even if the wind had been blowing for a hundred hours, the waves would not be high.

It is because of this complication that we defined the second factor affecting the height and length of waves as being, not the time during which the wind has blown above a given place, but that during which it has acted upon the waves. This time may depend upon the expanse of water, which is called the *fetch of the wind*.

In the example just given, the distance to windward of the spot under observation to the shore was the *fetch*. Let us clarify the general aspects of the matter by considering Fig. 63, in which *P* represents a particular place on the water. The groups of waves which have reached the vicinity of P in, let us say, one hour, have travelled a given distance, AP, and have been exposed to the wind over that distance. Half an hour later, other groups reach P, namely, those which have travelled one-and-a-half hours from a remoter point, B. They have been exposed to the wind from B to P. As time goes on, therefore, waves driven along a greater distance reach P. This does not go on endlessly, however, as there is a limit somewhere (at C in the figure), either because it is the boundary of the water with land to the left of C, or because the dominion of the wind ends there. (This is not to say that it is calm to the left of C; the fact is rather that the wind is so much milder, or is blowing from a totally different point, and therefore has little effect upon the waves running towards P.) The distance from C to P is the fetch for P, by which is meant the distance to windward from the point of observation, either to the edge of the effective wind field (in the sense described above) or to the shore, if that comes within the wind field.

It will be clear from the foregoing that, with increased duration, there comes a moment for every point when it is no longer the duration, but the path of the wind which determines wave height. In Fig. 63, this will be so after, say, two hours for P. From this time—which we shall call the 'duration limit' for P—onwards, the height of the waves is governed by the path of the wind, and it ceases to lengthen locally. The duration limit for point Q, to the right of P, will be longer than for P, because Q has a longer fetch (CQ) than P. The longer the fetch, the longer is the duration limit. On the other hand, the duration limit also depends on the velocity of the wind, for the stronger the wind, the faster are the waves it generates; but, the faster the waves, the sooner is reached the duration limit for a given point.

Returning for a moment to our example of a wind velocity of 15 metres a second, let us now assume that the fetch is 200 kilometres; growth will then cease at the end of 12 hours, and the duration limit will have been attained. Hence the dominating height will still be 3·8 metres after 15, 20 or 30 hours. To reach a height of 4·5 metres, the fetch would have to be at least 600 kilometres (duration limit 30 hours).

Two questions which are asked over and over again are: what height can waves attain at sea, and what is the greatest height ever recorded?

The latter question is difficult to answer, because heights reported cannot all be taken at their face value. It is not the good faith of the reporter that is in doubt, but rather the reliability of the method adopted for gauging the height. The highest wave ever recorded by a method acceptable in this sense was one of 33 metres, which was encountered by the American ship *Ramapo*, in the middle of the North Pacific on 7th February 1933, after a prolonged period of stormy weather. That this was unique, however, is evident from the fact that a number of heights of about 20–25 metres appear in a subsequent list of giant waves seen.

We now know that the conditions for the generation of very high waves are winds of gale or hurricane force raging over a great expanse of water for a very long time. These conditions are most frequently met with in the broad belts of predominating west winds, both in the northern hemisphere, comprising the North Atlantic and the North Pacific Oceans, and (especially) in the southern hemisphere, where this belt almost entirely encircles the three oceans. Very great wavelengths also occur in heavy seas, particularly in the so-called Southern Ocean, on the way from South Africa to Australia for instance, where seas of 200–250 metres' wavelength in gales are not uncommon. Wavelengths of more than 350 metres are sometimes reported (that is, in wind-waves; in a swell they can easily be greater). Exceptionally high waves can be formed when two high waves of different origin, or propagated from different directions, meet and pile up as it were. It is quite certain, however, that the very great heights mentioned above are not only rare, but quite exceptional.

COMPUTATION OF WIND-WAVES

During and after World War II, much work was done in several countries on devising, from known facts about the wind, notably its velocity, duration and fetch, means of calculating the dimensions of oceanic waves. This information was needed during hostilities more particularly, in connecton with landing operations, but it is also obviously valuable to the peaceful pursuit of navigation and coastal protection.

The simplest way of tackling this problem is an empirical one which enables us to derive from the above three wind data (velocity, duration and fetch) the significant height and period of the waves. To do this, graphs are constructed from the largest possible number of observations of waves and the associated wind fields, to show, as nearly as possible, the relation between the waves and the particulars about the wind. These methods were first worked out by Suthons in England, and by Sverdrup and Munk in the United States, *inter alia*, and were later improved by others.

The following two tables were extracted from the graphs used by the Meteorological Institute in the Netherlands; in reading them it should be borne in mind that the figures given for wave height and period are averages taken from many recordings. Table 19 shows the expected wave height in metres (upper row) and wave period (lower row) at the prevailing strength and fetch of the wind. Table 20 enables us to find the distance travelled by the waves at the given duration of the wind (see p. 153). If this is shorter than the fetch, then it is not the latter, but the former, that must be used in the first table.

The relationship between oceanic waves and wind is far more complicated than such graphs or tables would suggest. The best procedure is always to consider the waves as compound, and thus to study the *spectrum*. There are, indeed, a few methods of calculating a wave spectrum from the wind field, but, although the approach is promising, these methods are still somewhat hypothetical.

Table 19

Expected wave heights (metres, upper row) and periods (seconds, lower row, italics) associated with various velocities and fetches of the wind, assuming that the duration is long enough. See what is written in Table 20.

WIND	\multicolumn{7}{c}{FETCH of the WIND}
	20	50	100	200	500	1000	1500 km
5 m/sec	0·4	0·5	0·5	0·5	0·5	0·5	0·5 m
	$2\frac{1}{2}$	3	3	$3\frac{1}{4}$	$3\frac{1}{4}$	$3\frac{1}{4}$	$3\frac{1}{4}$ sec
10 m/sec	1·1	1·5	1·7	1·9	2·0	2·0	2·0 m
	$3\frac{1}{2}$	$4\frac{1}{2}$	$5\frac{1}{4}$	$5\frac{3}{4}$	$6\frac{1}{2}$	$6\frac{1}{2}$	$6\frac{1}{2}$ sec
15 m/sec	1·6	2·5	3·2	3·8	4·3	4·5	4·5 m
	$4\frac{1}{4}$	$5\frac{1}{2}$	$6\frac{1}{2}$	$7\frac{3}{4}$	9	$9\frac{1}{2}$	$9\frac{1}{2}$ sec
20 m/sec	2·2	3·4	4·7	6	7	8	8 m
	5	$6\frac{1}{2}$	$7\frac{1}{2}$	9	11	12	$12\frac{1}{2}$ sec
25 m/sec	2·7	4·2	6	8	10	12	12 m
	$5\frac{1}{2}$	7	$8\frac{1}{2}$	10	$12\frac{1}{2}$	14	15 sec
30 m/sec	3·1	5·0	7	10	14	16	17 m
	6	$7\frac{3}{4}$	$9\frac{1}{4}$	11	14	16	17 sec

Table 20

Distance of wave travel (in kilometres) corresponding to a given duration of the wind. If shorter than the wind fetch, it, not the latter, determines the dimensions of the waves. Where no figures are given, further prolongation of duration or wind fetch makes no difference to the waves (see Table 19).

	\multicolumn{7}{c}{DURATION}
	2	6	12	18	24	36	48 hours
5 m/sec	8	35	85	140			km
10 m/sec	13	60	145	240	340	550	km
20 m/sec	20	90	230	400	580	1000	1400 km
30 m/sec	25	120	300	520	750	1300	1800 km

SHIFTING STORM FIELDS

There are occasions when a storm springs up at sea, and in no time huge seas are running, far higher than could reasonably be expected by merely taking account of the short time the gale has been raging there. But if one realizes that the heavy seas did not grow just there, the occurrence ceases to be puzzling.

This is the case of a storm area moving in the same direction as the wind, in the direction, therefore, in which the seas are running. Generally, however, the speed with which the wind field shifts is different from (usually lower than) the velocity of the wind. Now, if the wind-waves which advance at the forefront of the storm area keep more or less in step with the shift of that area, the effective time during which the foremost waves (wave group) are exposed to the wind may be very prolonged. The storm field takes its own waves with it and, as soon as it arrives at a certain point, huge seas run there as a result of this confluence. A case of this kind is most likely to occur in the southern sector of atmospheric depressions passing from west to east in the northern hemisphere and in the northern sector of similar depressions in the southern hemisphere.

Figure 64 represents a tropical cyclone, a severe storm depression of limited range which drives its waves in all directions. As the longest waves advance faster than the cyclone shifts, they can get ahead of the cyclone (as a *swell*), and thus herald its coming elsewhere.

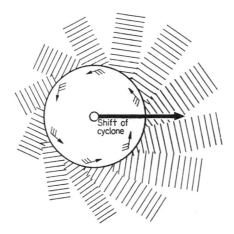

FIG. 64 Swell proceeding from a moving tropical cyclone. The size of the strips is intended to provide a measure of the height of the swell. As the swell comes from within, its direction at the edge of the cyclone does not coincide with the direction of the wind, which is indicated by small arrows.

LIMITATION AND FORCE OF STORM WAVES

We have already seen that in strong winds the waves do not generally reach those maximum heights which the theory assigns for the wind forces involved. As a rule, this is because either the duration or the fetch of the wind is not long enough. These limiting factors apply first and foremost to the severest of all storms that scourge the ocean, tropical cyclones (typhoons, hurricanes), because their range is smaller than most of the storm depressions of higher latitudes and the waves therefore have no time to grow to their largest dimensions.

Another limiting factor on the height of the waves is the squally character of these cyclonic winds, because the highest crests are often smashed and blown away in the worst gusts. It is these disrupted and far-flung masses of water which do such terrible damage to shipping. Anyone who fondly imagines that severe damage to ships in a storm is a thing of the past is grossly mistaken; modern ships, however seaworthy, may equally fall prey to it. We have only to think back to the American heavy cruiser *Pittsburgh*, breasting a typhoon in the western Pacific in June 1945, when a huge sea ripped off thirty metres of her bow. And half a year earlier, in December 1944 three United States destroyers were lost in a cyclone between the Philippines and the Marianas.

Naturally, waves develop their greatest violence while they are still exposed to the activating impetus of the wind; for all that, their force is by no means spent when they leave the wind behind them and proceed on their way as a *swell*. As such they are capable of carrying their energy along with them for thousands of miles. Before we enter more closely into this, however, we must consider another phenomenon by which storms at sea can be detected at remote distances, and this on solid ground.

MICROSEISMS

It has long been known that seismographs—those sensitive instruments which register the vibrations and tremors of the earth's crust—record not only earthquakes but also, very often, a certain unrest, a constant shuddering, of that crust, which does not derive from a particular landslip or 'quake, but goes on unintermittently, now faint or imperceptible, now very pro-

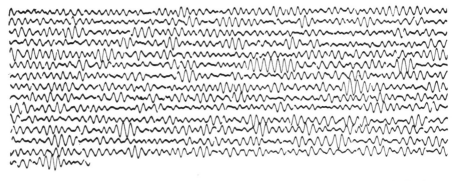

FIG. 65 Fragment of a seismogram read by the Meteorological Institute at De Bilt, Netherlands, on 17th December 1945. The microseisms (clearly in groups) are seen here with periods of approximately six seconds.

nounced. A seismogram (the registration of a seismograph) on which these *microseisms* can be seen very clearly, is reproduced in Fig. 65. They look like tiny undulations; their period seldom exceeds six seconds.

It soon became apparent that the microseisms were stronger in winter than in summer, and the obvious inference was that winter storms at sea were responsible for the difference. At first, it was thought that the pounding of the breakers on the shore set up vibration in the earth's crust, and that this vibration was propagated as microseisms, but in recent years it has become increasingly apparent that the microseisms very often stem from the middle of the ocean, and that they issue from the heart of a storm area. In fact, the recognition of this occurrence has led to the setting up along (*inter alia*) the Caribbean shoreline of a number of warning stations for the approach of tropical cyclones from far out at sea.

The question which at once comes to mind is how waves can excite vibrations in the sea-bed under a storm area if the water is a thousand metres deep; for it is known that the variations in pressure involved in running water-waves do not penetrate far down into the water. As, with increasing depth, these pressure variations diminish in exact proportion to the abatement of the movements of the water themselves, the pressure of the wave field can scarcely vary at all at a depth equal to the wavelength. Then how can microseisms be induced at depths of thousands of metres?

The properties of standing waves provide the answer. A fluctuation in pressure takes place under such waves (Fig. 50), which is *not* confined to the topmost layer of water, but is perceptible at great depths. That standing waves do occur in the area of a storm, notably a travelling storm, is beyond question; for wherever waves of equal, or nearly equal period tumble over each other from contrary directions, standing waves are produced. (The fact that they are not pure standing waves is neither here nor there.) And these colliding waves are all the more likely to occur in a shifting storm area because a given place across which the centre of the storm passes is battered first, let us say, by a south-east wind, and later on by a north-westerly one.

Where a fairly large expanse of water is subjected to standing undulation, the centre of gravity of the whole undulating mass goes up and down rhythmically (this does *not* occur with running waves alone), twice in one wave period, for whether the water is in one extreme position or the other (the reflection, see Fig. 50) the centre of gravity of the aggregate is slightly lifted with respect to the position at equilibrium. As this up-and-down movement of the water's centre of gravity acts by reaction upon the bottom, the latter undergoes a fluctuation of pressure with double the frequency of that of the waves, or with a period which is half the wave period. This fluctuation of pressure is then propagated with a high velocity as microseisms in the sea bed. It must be repeated that it is by no means necessary for purely standing undulation to prevail upon the sea-surface; in fact, during a storm, it never will. Any large, progressive waves passing through the area will not disturb the effect at all.

Thus it is that even seismographs on land remote from the coast receive signals, which are transmitted through the solid earth, of storms raging in mid-ocean. That the recorded periods do not usually exceed six seconds accords with the fact that the wave periods *in* a stormy area seldom exceed twelve seconds.

It should be added that microseisms can be generated not only in the field of storm waves, but also where a swell beats upon a steep shore, reflections of the waves there giving rise to standing waves.

SWELL

A swell, as the reader will remember, consists of waves which started as wind-waves but are no longer exposed to the wind which generated them, either because the wind has dropped (in many cases it would be more to the point to say that the wind, or the gale has departed), leaving the waves behind, or because the waves have got beyond the wind's range. The latter will occur, for example, if an extensive north-west gale is blowing somewhere near Iceland in the North Atlantic, the area of the storm stretching at a given moment in a south-easterly direction to a certain limit, which might be a cold front where the wind abruptly changes direction. Whether or not this limit is sharp, the waves running north-west to south-east do not come to a standstill there, but run on into the quiet waters beyond the range of the storm. Here we get a swell.

A swell soon looks different from an ordinary running sea. The ridges of the waves are smoother, and have a more rounded contour and, often, long crest lines; also, their wavelength—the distance from crest to crest—increases with the 'age' of the swell. As, moreover, the height decreases with age, the steepness of a swell is smaller than that of wind-driven waves. The overall appearance of a swell is more regular, and it makes an entirely different impression from wind-waves of the same height, especially if there is little wind. To an observer standing not far above sea-level, the approaching ridge of a swell of sufficient height may, with its long crest-line, form a mock horizon, behind which the hull of a vessel disappears. See Plates XXIV and XXV.

A swell is easily detected on an aerial photograph, if the light is not too bad. In the photograph, taken from the air, of the coast of South California, which is reproduced in Plate XXVII, one sees the long ridges of a swell right across the small, irregular wind-waves, like folds in a curtain.

One typical feature of a swell is the occurrence of waves in groups of alternately increasing and decreasing height, so that, every six to ten waves, a couple or so of the highest come along. This occurrence of wave groups was discussed in an earlier section.

WORLD TRAVELLERS

The waves of a swell are certainly well travelled, for they visit places thousands of miles from the area of their origin. As they are particularly conspicuous in districts where there is commonly little wind, these are the best-known places for a big swell. Such a one is the west coast of Morocco, where oceanic swell occasionally causes such terrific surf that communication between the sea and places along the coast is virtually paralysed, and ships moored in the harbour of Casablanca have much to endure. When we come to discuss the deformation of oceanic waves in coastal waters and above shoals, we shall also see why it is that an oceanic swell develops such overwhelming force in the shallow water along the coast. What we now have to consider is the origin of that swell. A glance at the map will show that north-west or northerly gales between Newfoundland and Iceland are the prevalent sources. A big swell off the Moroccan coast then, depends on whether the fetch of that distant storm is long, and points in the right direction.

In this case, the distance the swell travels is something like 2000 kilometres. If we wish to calculate the time it takes to do so, we must remember that, as we had occasion to note before, the front of the swell moves at *group velocity*, i.e. half the propagation velocity of the individual waves. For example, if we are dealing with waves of a swell having a period of 15 seconds, then the associated wave velocity is 23·4 metres per second, or 84 kilometres an hour. Therefore the speed at which the front of the swell progresses is 42 kilometres an hour; hence in this case the time taken to travel a distance of 2000 kilometres is 48 hours. This does not imply that the individual waves take this time—one can never follow individual waves that far, for they soon lose their identity. What it does mean is that, 48 hours after the storm waves have reached their full development at the end of the gale's fetch, the associated swell is beating the Moroccan coast 2000 kilometres farther to the south-east with a period of 15 seconds.

A swell can travel far greater distances than this. On the islands of St. Helena and Ascension, both situated in the Atlantic far to the south of the Equator, a very long swell with high breakers is occasionally seen rolling in from the north; it comes from a storm area, far away in the North Atlantic, some 6000–7000 kilometres' distant. If we take the wave period to be 20 seconds, we find a group velocity of 56 kilometres per hour; that is a voyage of $4\frac{1}{2}$–5 days.

So there is always a swell on the oceans of the world, somewhat more so here, a little less there. Stormy areas are constantly sending their harbingers to remote places, making their impact upon shores that have rarely, if ever, experienced a gale.

WAVE SPECTRA

We know that waves at sea consist of a mixture of waves of varying wavelengths, and we compared this mixture with light, in which various wavelengths occur.

Just as compound light can be broken down into the individual colours by means of a spectroscope, so instruments have been devised for analysing wave registrations in such a way as to provide an image of the 'spectrum'. Figure 66 shows a successive series of such spectra, obtained from wave registrations recorded in England. Each spectrum is represented by a curve with a series of peaks. Those peaks are associated with certain wave periods which can be read along the horizontal axis; the higher the peak (it could be compared with a line or band in a light spectrum), the stronger are the waves of (approximately) that period in the mixture.

A wave spectrum of this kind reveals all sorts of interesting facts. One can, for instance, pick out some very long, but weak swell which is not visible to the eye because it is covered by many shorter waves. These low, long waves of a swell are usually the first fast messengers of a far-distant storm, because the longest waves are the fastest, and the higher, shorter waves do not come until later. An illustration of this is to be seen in our figure. At 13·00 in the spectrum of 14th March we see, at the extreme right, a wave component of roughly 24 seconds. In the later spectra these long waves become more and more pronounced as a clearly coherent band, which obviously derives from

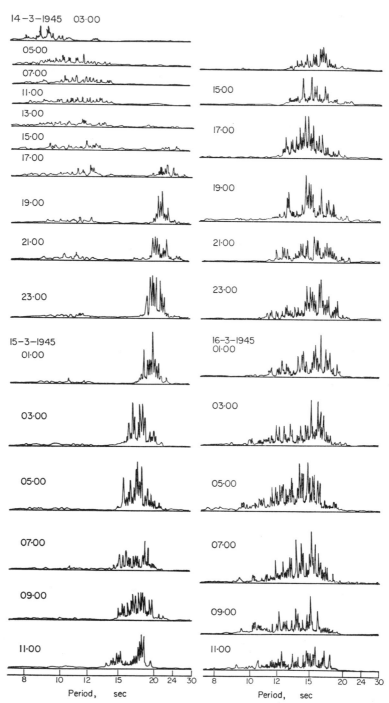

FIG. 66 A series of wave spectra obtained by analysis of registrations of waves on the Cornish coast (after Deacon). At 1 p.m. on 14th March the first indication appears of a very long swell (period 24 seconds), which comes from a remote storm to the south-east of Newfoundland. The following spectra show gradually decreasing periods of this swell, while the height increases. (As from 03.00 on 15th March, the heights are drawn to three-fifths the scale.)

a storm. The height is seen gradually to increase, but the centre of the band shifts to shorter waves; in time, the shorter waves of the swell arrive.

It has been found possible to ascribe particular groups or bands of this kind in wave spectra to well-determined storm areas apparent on a weather chart. The time taken by these groups to travel has then been found to tally with the time calculated from the distance of the storm and the group velocity associated with the existing wavelength. Usually the storms detected by analyses of waves off the British coast were in the North Atlantic, but very occasionally, when that ocean was very calm (in the summer), some weak, very long swell has been correctly ascribed to storms in the southern hemisphere, 10,000 kilometres away!

A swell gradually loses height, but the farther it has travelled the more does its length increase. It is not difficult to see why it loses height; friction— internal friction and the resistance of the air—gradually deprives the waves of energy, while at the same time the swell fans out as it proceeds, since not all the waves passing beyond the range of the wind are propagated in exactly the same direction, if only because the wind itself does not blow rigidly in one direction. As the swell advances, the total wave energy spreads progressively in breadth owing to this fanning out. It also spreads lengthwise through what is called 'dispersion': a field of swell which has a given length in the propagating direction gradually spreads out in that direction, because the longer waves get ahead of the shorter ones. Both the fanning-out and the dispersion bring about an expansion of the total energy of the swell over a larger surface, and so a diminution of the average wave energy per square metre, and, therefore, a loss of height. This loss is added to the loss through internal friction (due to turbulence), and resistance of the air. It should be pointed out, with regard to these latter factors, that a strong cross-wind or contrary wind can considerably upset a swell and cause it to lose height.

How is it, however, that, besides becoming lower, a swell also becomes longer at increasing distance?

To understand this, we must remind ourselves that, when we speak of 'the' wavelength, we mean the dominant, or significant, wavelength. The waves which pass beyond the range of the wind consist of a complex of components of varying wavelengths. The wavelength, or period, which we observe visually is the dominant wavelength or period in this complex. Now the internal friction of the water and the resistance of the air have a damping effect on all combined single undulations of the complex, but more so on the shorter than the longer ones. We could compare the phenomenon to light, which is a mixture of colours, i.e. a mixture of light rays of differing wavelengths, but in which a certain colour—say green—predominates. We can also call the corresponding wavelength the 'dominant wavelength', and we say that the light is green even if there are other wavelengths, violet, blue (the shorter wavelengths), yellow, orange and red (the longer ones) in it. If this light passes through an intermediate substance in which all components are absorbed to some extent, but in inverse proportion to their wavelength, then green will cease to dominate after passing a certain distance through this substance, as it will have been weakened more than yellow, which has a longer wavelength. Thus this intermediate substance causes a shift of the dominant wavelength towards red, which has the longest wavelength of all.

The distance passed through acts in a similar manner upon the dominant wavelength of the swell. The ultimate cause is, therefore, the unequal weakening effect of friction and resistance upon waves of different lengths. The mechanism of wave motion is such as to make the longest waves advance the most economically.

An essential point in this argument is that the long wavelength observed at the end was inherent from the start. That is why, to calculate the time taken by a swell to travel a certain distance, it is necessary to account for the velocity (group velocity) associated with the dominant wavelength or period at the end of that distance (hence not a kind of average).

Table 21 represents an excerpt from the results of a careful study of the behaviour of a swell in the open sea. It is assumed that the swell does not encounter any appreciable wind. This table does not lay down any hard-and-fast rule, as it merely illustrates an average case; there can, of course, be certain deviations.

Table 21

Distances (in kilometres) along which a swell of different initial periods suffers certain losses in height, and the associated increasing periods (in italics). The losses in height are represented by the row of figures along the top of the table.

DIMINUTION OF HEIGHT OF WAVES

Initial Period	0·8		0·6		0·5		0·4		0·3
3 sec	15		45		70		125		230 km
		3		*3¼*		*3¼*		*3½*	*4 sec*
6 sec	65		170		280		500		900 km
		6¼		*6½*		*6¾*		*7*	*7¾ sec*
10 sec	175		475		775		1400		2500 km
		10¼		*10½*		*11*		*11¾*	*13 sec*
15 sec	400		1075		1750		3150		5700 km
		15½		*16*		*17*		*18*	*19½ sec*

Let us take an example. Suppose the initial period of the swell is 10 seconds (wavelength 156 metres), the height 4 metres; then, after a distance of 1400 kilometres, the height is still 0·4 × 4 metres = 1·6 metres, while the dominant period has become 11¾ seconds (wavelength 215 metres).

We see by the row of figures at the top of the table that the height actually does decrease with increasing distance, but that the period increases. If we read down one column of distances, hence from smaller to larger periods, we shall see that the greater the period, the greater is the distance within which the same loss of height occurs. This accords with the fact we have mentioned, namely, that long waves are tempered less than shorter ones travelling the same distance.

DEFORMATION OF WAVES ALONG COASTS AND SHOALS

When we were dealing with the tsunami of 1946, we mentioned, in passing, that long waves undergo a tremendous change when they come into shallow waters, a change which may ultimately become a transformation, turning what was a smooth swell in mid-ocean into pounding breakers.

We must now take a closer look at this deformation of waves in coastal and shallow waters. We shall find that nearly everything about them alters, their velocity, length, height, direction and shape, with only the period, as we have already said, remaining approximately the same. For the period is determined by the number of crests per unit of time—say per minute—passing a given place. The obvious primary assumption is that, as the waves travel from a point A towards the shore past a point B (situated in shallower water), just as many pass point B per minute as point A. That is tantamount to saying that the period at B is the same as at A.

All the other characteristic quantities of waves, however, change sooner or later, when they reach shallow water. With declining depth the wave velocity diminishes and, as the period remains the same, the wavelength likewise decreases. This change is described in Table 17.

Now if the waves do not advance squarely upon the coast, or if the crests are not exactly parallel to the lines of equal depth in the shallow water, something else occurs.

DEFLECTION OF THE WAVES

In optics, the word refraction denotes the bending of light rays. An analogous phenomenon occurs when oceanic waves enter upon shallow water. The analogy is valid because light, too, is a phenomenon associated with waves; it is, in fact, an electromagnetic wave phenomenon. The wave theory of light speaks of wave-fronts perpendicular to the rays of light, moving at the speed of light. These wave-fronts of light are comparable to the crests of water-waves (thus not to what we have already called the 'front of a swell', but to the crest lines of the ridges of the waves). Now, refraction occurs when the speed of light changes, for example when light is passing from air into water or glass, thereby losing velocity, or vice versa.

We know that light is refracted when it impinges obliquely upon an interface. This also occurs when light reaches us from the atmosphere, but in this case the rays are bent gently rather than sharply, because they pass so gradually from the rarer to the denser layers of the atmosphere that there is no abrupt change in the speed of the light anywhere, hence nowhere a sharp change in the direction of the rays.

The resemblance between this and the behaviour of sea waves in shallow water becomes evident when we consider the wave fronts of light. These are everywhere perpendicular to the 'rays', so when they bend, it can only mean that the wave fronts swerve. If we look at Fig. 67, in which the three long, curved lines with arrows represent three bending rays, while the line-sections cutting these rays at right-angles are sections of wave front, we have to realize that the deflection of the wave fronts is not the result of the curvature of the

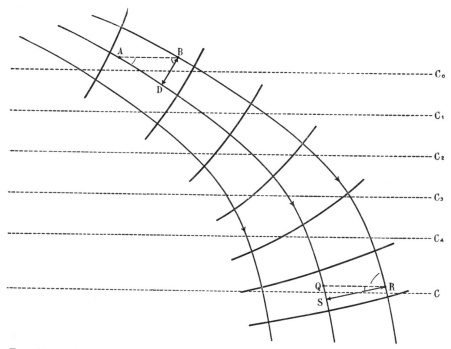

FIG. 67 Gradual deflection of wave-crests in shallow water with straight parallel depth lines. The three arrowed lines are rays.

rays, but the other way about. And if we now turn our thoughts to water-waves, it is easy to see why their crests have to swerve.

Let the horizontal dotted lines in Fig. 67 be lines of equal depth and, therefore, if the period is constant, lines of equal wave velocity. Suppose we are accompanying a crest from the top left in the figure to the right below. The right wing of that crest is continually nearer the coast (which we shall imagine as being at the bottom of the diagram) and, consequently, is in shallower water than the left wing. This being so, the crest must inevitably swerve, just as a rank in a column of men swerves in a bend, the man on the outside taking longer steps than the man on the inside. In the same way the crests in shallow water will be deflected so that their direction approximates to the lines of equal depth.

The word 'rays' is also used in sea-wave parlance to represent the lines which everywhere intersect the crests at right-angles; so they have to curve, as the figure shows. Fundamentally, this phenomenon is the same as the refraction of light, and the word is also applied to waves.

The crests, naturally, begin to swerve only at the point where the velocity decreases, i.e. at a depth which is half the wavelength. Therefore, whereas short waves advance in a straight line until they get close to the shore, the refraction of long waves begins a good way off the coast.

SNELL'S LAW

There is a law for the refraction of light, called Snell's law, which says that, for light passing through a surface separating two media, there is a definite relation between the direction of the ray on one side and that of the ray on the other side of the interface. This implies that the sine of the angle of incidence (i.e. the angle formed by the incident ray with the perpendicular to the interface) and the sine of the angle of refraction (i.e. the angle formed between the refracted ray and the perpendicular) stand in a mutual fixed relation, which is called the *refractive index*. This ratio is equal to the ratio of the velocity of propagation prevailing on the side from which the ray comes, to that velocity on the other side.

Snell's law applies to water-waves as well as to light waves, with the proviso that in the former case there is no interface at which the ray is abruptly bent; instead, there is a gradual change of wave velocity. A simple way of adapting Snell's law to this state of affairs is found, provided the wave period be given, if the lines of equal depth run parallel as in Fig. 67, where the horizontal dotted lines represent lines of equal depth and, therefore, lines of equal wave velocity (C_0, C_1, etc.). Here we get the perpendicular to the lines of equal depth replacing the 'perpendicular to the interface' required for the formulation of Snell's law.

Now, the angle formed between the 'ray' at a given place and this perpendicular is equal to the angle between the local crests and the depth line (e.g. angle ABD). Accordingly, we can define Snell's law for sea waves as follows: If waves of a given period pass over shallow water with straight parallel depth lines, the sine of the angle between the crests of the waves and the depth lines changes in ratio to the velocity of propagation.

Hence, if the velocity diminishes—which it does near the shore—the angle between the crests and the shore must likewise decrease. Quantitatively, with reference to Fig. 67, we would write: sin angle ABD : sin angle $QRS = C_0 : C$, or $(AD/AB) : (QS/QR) = C_0 : C$. Suppose that at B the waves come from deep water. If the direction there (hence angle ABD) is known, and the period given, then we can calculate from the depth at R and S the direction in which the waves will be advancing there, because the velocity in deep water, which we call C_0, follows from the period; from the depth further along follows the velocity C there (see Table 17). The ratio given above then enables us to calculate angle QRS from angle ABD.

It is evident from the foregoing that the refraction can only be computed if the period (or the wavelength in deep water) is known. The easiest way to work it out is with the help of a graph, from which C/C_0 can be read if D/L_0 (i.e. the depth divided by the wavelength prevailing in deep water) is given.

REFRACTION PATTERNS

If the depth lines are not straight and parallel the matter becomes more complicated, and the deflection of the crests can no longer be calculated from a simple formula. The general reasoning, however, remains the same, namely that, owing to the differences in velocity, the ridges of the waves are deflected in such a manner that the rays curve towards the shallow water. Starting from straight crests of a certain direction in deep water, we get a pattern of crests in shallow water which is governed entirely by the topography of the sea-bed. A pattern of this kind can also be constructed, provided the particulars of the waves in deep water and the topography of the bottom in the shoals be known.

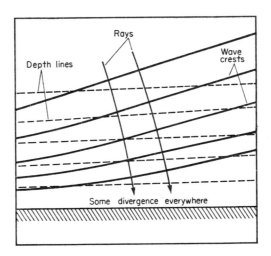

FIG. 68 Refraction of a swell over an evenly sloping bottom near a straight coastline.

Figures 68–74 show some types of refraction patterns. Figure 68 is the simplest, and most nearly resembles the case of straight parallel depth lines.

Although there is a straight coastline in Fig. 69, there is a dip in the bed of the shallow water; so there is greater depth here than alongside, and the waves are therefore faster. If the waves are advancing squarely upon the coast, those crests which are above the dip will get ahead of those to right and left of them, and will therefore bend outward, as shown in the figure.

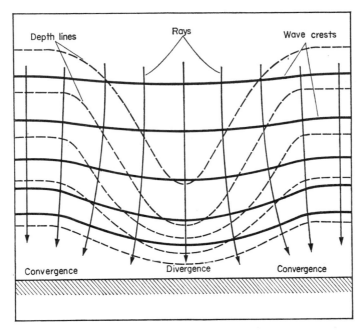

FIG. 69 Refraction above a submarine dip.

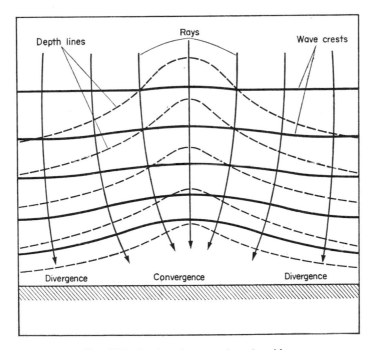

FIG. 70 Refraction above a submarine ridge.

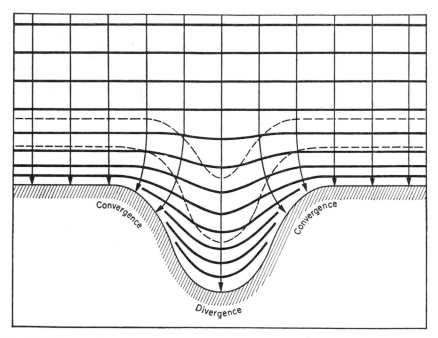

Fig. 71 Refraction above and in a bay (the arrowed lines are rays and the crests are at right angles to them).

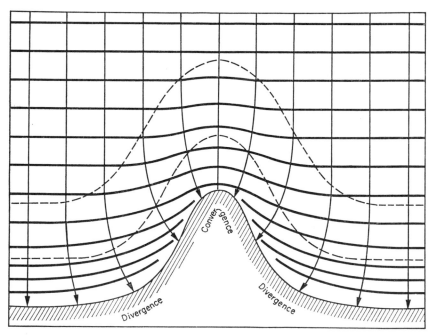

Fig. 72 Refraction before a peninsula or cape; swell approaching straight ahead. (The arrowed lines are rays, with the crests at right angles to them.)

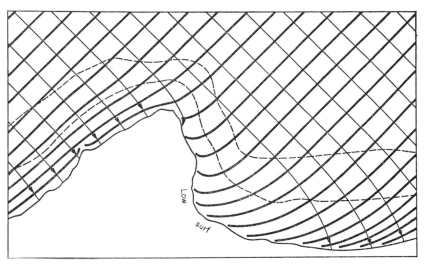

Fɪɢ. 73 Refraction of a swell approaching a peninsula or cape sideways.

The associated curvature of the ray is also conspicuous; a submarine valley acts, so to speak, like a concave (divergent) lens. The reverse occurs above a submarine ridge, or rise, in shallow water; see Fig. 70.

The next figures are more or less self-explanatory. Everywhere the crests are seen ultimately to stretch out more or less in the direction of the shore, swerving widely, if necessary, in order to do so. The greatest swerve takes place in cases like that of Fig. 73, where the waves also advance towards the shore on the right-hand side (the sheltered side) of the cape, though much weakened, as we shall see; and Fig. 74, which shows how waves coming from above swerve right round an island and, after a sweeping turn of 180 degrees, also advance upon the coast at the back of the island. As in this case a swell is able to sweep around both sides of the island, a crosswise pattern of waves is formed at the back, which is perceptible at a great distance behind the island. We learn about seafaring Polynesians in the Pacific Ocean, that they are so familiar with this cross-swell that they depend upon it, under certain conditions, for finding their way home.

It should be pointed out that in diagrammatic wave patterns as in Figs. 67–74, the drawn crest lines might equally represent successive positions of an individual crest line as simultaneous positions of several of them; and that in the latter case by no means all the crest lines are shown. It would therefore be wrong to suppose that the wavelength can be measured from the diagram.

Wave patterns can be studied very rewardingly from aerial photographs, a few of which are reproduced in Plates XXVII–XXIX. The reader is referred to the legends.

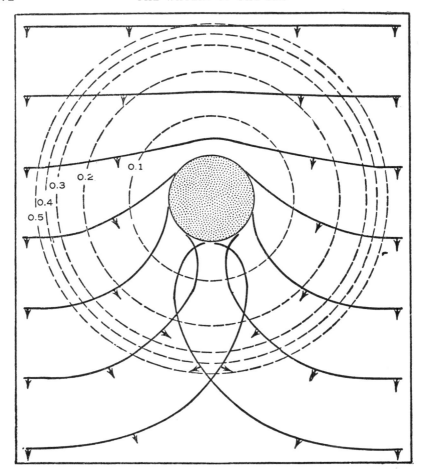

FIG. 74 Refraction around an island. The figures on the circular depth lines are the depths divided by the wavelength found in the deep water. 'Rays' have not been drawn in this illustration.

EFFECT OF REFRACTION ON THE HEIGHT OF THE WAVES

The introduction of 'rays' into the description of the phenomena of waves, to complete the analogy with the theory of light, might be taken to imply that these lines, defined as the, generally curved, lines intersecting the crests at right-angles, were of no more than formal significance. But there is more to these 'rays' than that.

First, they are used for the construction of a refraction pattern or diagram, since they indicate everywhere the direction in which the crest is being propagated. Starting from a definite initial position of a crest line, one can erect perpendiculars at a number of its points, and from each point proceed that distance along it which corresponds to a definite lapse of time and to a definite local wave velocity determined by the depth. Thus a new position of the crest is constructed, and if one continues this procedure the whole pattern can be built up.

The 'rays' in this pattern now acquire physical significance, by virtue of indicating the tracks along which the energy of the waves advances. Looking again at Fig. 70, we see that the rays in the middle distinctly *converge*. In optics, something similar is found behind a convex lens. We know that a bundle of parallel light-rays passing through such a lens converges behind it towards a certain point, the focal point, in which all the energy of that bundle is concentrated.

In our case, likewise, the wave energy is concentrated at places where the rays converge, and this increases the height of the waves. Where the rays do just the opposite, that is to say, *diverge*, the reverse will take place; the energy of the waves will be spread out laterally over a widened 'front', and the waves will become lower than they were elsewhere. This is illustrated in Fig. 70, to the left and right of the area of convergence, and in Fig. 69, in the middle, above and opposite the submarine dip.

This explains the long-known fact that sometimes at one place along a fairly straight coastline, the waves coming in produce far higher breakers than they do at another nearby place, for no visually apparent reason. This is usually due to the topography of the bottom under the shallow offshore water.

Divergence or convergence is also clearly visible in the other patterns of waves (Figs. 71–74). In Fig. 73, for instance, there is very pronounced divergence on the right-hand side of the projecting cape. This means that, although the waves swerve round the cape, thereby also reaching the shore on the lee side, they are greatly weakened by divergence.

Reverting briefly to the simplest case, that of straight parallel depth lines, we see from Figs. 67 and 68 that there is always a certain amount of divergence, except when the waves advance perfectly straight into shore. The more obliquely the waves come in, the greater is the divergence and, therefore, the weakening of the waves in their swerve towards the shore. It can be calculated that waves whose crests in deep water form an angle of 50 degrees with the shoreline may lose 14 per cent. of their height through divergence; if that angle is 70 degrees, the height may drop by as much as 33 per cent.

The effect of convergence and divergence through refraction, which we have been discussing, however, is not the only factor affecting the height of the waves.

SHORTENING OF THE WAVES INCREASES THEIR HEIGHT

Let us return for a moment to a swell coming straight into shore, and again let us first suppose the depth lines to be straight and parallel; there will then be no refraction. For all that, something is happening, for, as the velocity decreases so also does the wavelength as the waves approach the shore; so the distances between the crests become smaller. Concurrently, the height of the waves also changes, although there is neither divergence nor convergence.

Once the waves begin to 'feel bottom'—that is, when the depth has declined to about half the wavelength—they first lose some of their height, and then begin to grow. If they do not then break all too soon, they are liable to become considerably higher than they initially were. This continues up to the place where the surf begins.

The cause of this change is a slight initial increase in the velocity with which the wave energy is propagated, followed by a rapid decrease. This subsequent deceleration of the stream of energy should not surprise us, because the propagation velocity of the waves also diminishes as the water becomes shallower. The slight initial increase in energy speed is associated with the change from deep-water waves to shallow-water waves, whose mechanism of energy displacement is somewhat more 'economical'. Acceleration of the propagation of energy must, obviously, reduce the height of the waves, and a slowing-down of the propagation of energy must raise it. To confine ourselves to the last (and most important), if the stream of energy towards the shore is slowed down in front, there must ensue some form of concentration of energy, just as the water level in a river bed must rise if the flow is slowed down somewhere though continuing from behind (which is what also happens to the supply of energy of the waves).

The waves begin to grow beyond their initial height approximately at the place where the depth is 0·06 of the original wavelength; where the depth is 0·01 of this wavelength, the height of the waves is more than 1·5 times their initial height (in deep water); with the depth at 0·003 that wavelength, the height is more than twice the initial height; all this is on the assumption that the waves get so far without having broken; we shall deal with this presently.

The figures given in the preceding paragraph are only valid if the waves are not affected by refraction. If they are, the additional effect of divergence or convergence, which, as we have seen, likewise influences wave height, comes into play. In the presence of convergence, (e.g. above and opposite a submarine ridge, see Fig. 70), the waves will begin to gain height at greater depths than those mentioned, and on the whole the heights, too, will be greater than those given. All this can be worked out mathematically, but we shall not enter into details.

EFFECT OF CURRENT UPON WAVES

All we have so far said about the behaviour of waves applies equally to water in uniform motion and to water at rest, provided the motion of the water throughout the area under consideration be uniform, and provided we understand by 'period', 'velocity of propagation' (and, possibly, velocity of the wind) those quantities which an observer drifting with the water would measure.

Matters change when the speed of flow is not the same everywhere, so that the waves encounter different currents. Seamen know only too well how boisterous tidal inlets can be when a tidal current runs against the waves. Well, what goes on?

The main thing is that out at sea, where the current was weak, the waves did not feel it; but later on they do. Owing to the mechanism inherent in the energy propagation of waves, the stream of energy is checked at the place where the countercurrent strengthens, and this raises the level of energy, in the same way as the water level rises in a watercourse when its velocity is slowed down somewhere. Any increase in the energy of waves entails an increase in their height. A countercurrent therefore heightens oncoming waves; moreover, it tends to make the crests approach one another, or, to put it differently, it shortens the wavelength. That means shorter, higher waves. This can reach a point where the waves break in the countercurrent, as though it were a shallow place. (Calculations show that a countercurrent, running at one-quarter the speed which the waves had beyond the reach of the current, is always enough to make them break.)

A current flowing in the same direction as the waves has, of course, the opposite effect, and steadily reduces their height. Two aerial photographs, reproduced in Plate XXX, show in a striking fashion the difference between these two cases, and more particularly the effect of countercurrent. In both cases the periods and heights of the waves way out to sea were virtually the same. Contrasting markedly with the quiet scene while the tide is coming in, however, the waves in the outgoing tide become so steep that they break and throw up spray wherever the current is strong enough (especially in the middle of the inlet).

We learn from this that waves break, thereby losing energy, not only over shoals but also when they meet a countercurrent. And waves may be subjected to refraction by differences of flow as well as by differences of depth, when it is not merely a question of countercurrent or following current, but also of sideways currents in which waves are caught. Much more could be said about this, but it would take us too far afield.

SURF

Of all the magnificent scenes presented by the oceans, surf, the finale of that great drama enacted by wind and waves, is surely the most impressive.

Along the southern coasts of the North Sea, very high storm waves only occur in a long-persisting N.N.W. wind, because in other directions the stretch of water along which the waves can advance before they reach the coast is not very long. But just think of the western coasts of Scotland, Ireland and southern England, where the huge waves of the open North Atlantic bear down with full force; and where the coast is, moreover, rocky and steep, the furious, thunderous breakers send boiling masses of water soaring cliff-high.

Watching breakers in a gale, one naturally infers that it is the high wind itself which is playing this boisterous game with the waters, forgetting that a devastating surf can likewise play havoc, without much wind. In actual fact, once the waves are formed their mechanism itself forces them to break when they reach the coast. Admittedly, the energy released in these breakers originally owed its existence to the wind, but it accumulated in the waves in the course of a long journey before they reached the shore.

The climax in the career of waves is best illustrated by the breakers of a swell. In the breakers of storm-waves we hear the resounding symphony of wind and sea; but it is the roar of the sea alone that booms out in the breakers of a swell. Do not imagine, however, that these breakers are not as high as those of storm-waves; if it is long enough, a swell approaching the shore up a steadily-sloping sea-bed is ultimately capable of rising to twice the height it had in deep water.

Standing on the shore, one sees the waves rolling in with impressive regularity, the first visible sign of the approaching swell being a dark band produced by the difference in reflection of light between the front and rear slopes; it is the front which appears to be the darker. The long ridge approaches quickly, rising higher and higher, the crest becomes sharper, the front slope becomes ever steeper and finally more or less concave; then the crest-line leaps forward, a curtain of water, and a veritable cascade comes tumbling down in front of the hollow face of the breaker. That is the end; nothing remains of the whole ridge but a whirling, foaming mass of water which runs on for a short distance but has soon spent its strength and, in an uncoordinated retreat, evacuates the invaded strip of beach, boulders or crags.

But then the next ridge comes rolling in, and behind it yet another, and so it continues with impressive rhythmical regularity.

Such breakers are more or less of the ideal type, of which that shown in Plate XXVI is a classic example. We describe them as 'plunging breakers'. Their characteristic feature is a curtain of water which is poured down, so to speak, from the crest, and is at first detached from the front of the ridge. The crests are often long, and of uniform height.

Plunging breakers are formed when the evolution of the ridges in the shallow waters is little disturbed by other effects, such as wind, crossing waves, current and irregularities of the bottom. Their development is favoured by a moderate (not too small) gradient of the slope of the bottom in shallow water—by virtue of which the evolution from a deep-water wave to a breaker is accomplished in a fairly short space of time—and by a small steepness of the waves in deep water, which promotes eventual greater elevation of the crest.

A plunging breaker loses its energy in a comparatively short time after plunging; this is a true collapse. The other type of breaker, which we call a 'spilling breaker', is quite different in this respect. Breakers of this type can run on for quite a distance, losing energy continuously through the breaking ('spilling') of their crests. They are less objectionable on landing than is a plunging breaker.

The factors promoting spilling are wind, irregularities of the bottom, crossing waves, countercurrent and also pronounced steepness of the waves while still in deep water.

THE DEVELOPMENT OF BREAKERS

We must now consider how the evolution of waves results in surf.

We have already referred to the slowing-down of waves, the shortening of the wavelength and the change in height. Together with these changes there is a change in shape, which in this case tends to invalidate the classic theory applicable to sinusoidal waves; for, if the initial wave steepness is not too great, the wave-ridges come to resemble 'solitary waves'.

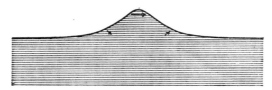

FIG. 75 Solitary wave

A pure solitary wave consists of one single ridge, the slopes of which gradually run down on either side to where the water is virtually flat and horizontal (see Fig. 75). The characteristic features of these waves are the concentration of practically all the energy in the crests, and the water's forward movement only; as there is no true trough, nor is there any returning movement. The whole mechanism of such waves is different from that of the waves we have hitherto been considering. Another important difference is that the energy of solitary waves is not proportional to the square, but to the third power of their height.

The waves of a swell in shallow water do not, of course, become perfect solitary waves, because they are not entirely solitary; but their energy is ever more concentrated in the crests; the ridges become progressively narrower and the troughs in between ever flatter (see Plate XXVII).

This is how the process of breaking might be described: when the water finally becomes very shallow, it is noticeable that there is less depth under the face of the ridge than under its back, as a result of which the face progresses more slowly than the crest, which overtakes it. This is why the face becomes concave and the crest then plunges over it (see Fig. 76). Put somewhat differently: the moment of breaking is that at which the forward velocity attained by the particles of water at the top of the wave form exceeds the steadily declining speed at which the form moves forward, with the result that the water shoots out of it. Theory and observation have shown that this takes place when the depth is approximately 1·3 times the height of the wave.

Let us now study a swell with a long period, i.e. great wavelength in deep water. Let it be 300 metres, and the height 1·5 metres. Such waves already begin to feel the bottom where the depth is still 150 metres; they start exceeding their initial height where the depth is 0·06 × 300 metres = 18 metres. True, the wavelength has then decreased to about 0·6 of the length in deep water, and the steepness has increased to about 1·7 times its initial value, but as the latter was very slight, the present steepness is likewise

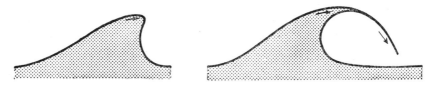

Fig. 76 A breaker just before and while plunging.

small. Consequently, the waves are able to advance much farther without hindrance. Where the depth is 3 metres, that is, 0·01 of the deep-water wavelength, the height of the wave has grown to more than 1½ times the original figure, hence to 2¼ metres. Meanwhile, here the swell has in very large measure assumed the character of solitary waves; as the depth is a little more than 1·3 times the wave height, they will be able to advance a short distance further before breaking. By that time their height will have increased by more than 50 per cent.

Now let us consider waves of the same initial height, but of much shorter wavelength, say, 30 metres in deep water. Where the depth is 0·06 of their deep-water wavelength, these waves, too, would rise above their initial height; this depth is now only 1·8 metres, but this is already less than 1·3 times the height of 1·5 metres. In other words, these waves do not even get so far, and the height of the breakers they produce is something less, even, than their initial height of 1·5 metres.

The rule that emerges from the foregoing two examples can be formulated as follows: the greater the wavelength or period of the waves of a certain height in deep water, the higher the breakers they produce (if the height of the waves in deep water is fixed).

This rule can be further clarified with reference to the energy which the waves carry towards the coast. Practically all the transported energy is discharged in the individual breakers following each other at intervals of one period. We have already seen that the transmission of energy per second is proportional to the square of the height in deep water, and to the group velocity, which is there half the wave velocity, and is itself therefore proportional to the period; or, put differently: with equal height in deep water, a doubling of the wave period doubles the transport of energy towards the coast. So, per period this gives us four times the amount of energy. In other

Above: Huge iceberg in the N.W. Atlantic Ocean. The surface is smooth along the waterline and partly hollowed out by the waves (on the left of the photograph). Higher up there are faces of rupture. The aircraft belongs to the International Ice Patrol.

Below: Two earlier waterlines run obliquely across this iceberg; it had obviously capsized twice. (Photograph U.S. Coast Guard.)

PLATE XXI

Large, horseshoe-shaped iceberg. Its interior has melted away above water, save only the projecting point in the middle. (Photograph U.S. Coast Guard.)

words, breakers of the swell with twice the period have four times as much energy; or, again, the energy of the breakers is proportional to the square of the period, hence proportional to the wavelength in deep water (which, we remember, is also proportional to T^2); all this provided the height be the same in deep water. Now, as we know, the energy of solitary waves is proportional to the third power of the height; hence the height is proportional to the cube root of the energy. According to the foregoing, therefore, the height of the breakers is proportional to the cube root of the wavelength in deep water.

Table 22

Ratio of breaker height to the initial wave height with varying initial wave steepness if the waves are parallel to the shore

Initial steepness	$\dfrac{1}{500}$	$\dfrac{1}{200}$	$\dfrac{1}{100}$	$\dfrac{1}{50}$	$\dfrac{1}{20}$	$\dfrac{1}{10}$	$\dfrac{1}{7}$
Elevation factor	2·4	1·8	1·46	1·22	1·0	0·92	0·93

All this holds for waves whose initial steepness is *sufficiently small* to enable them ultimately to develop into true solitary waves before producing plunging breakers. If the steepness is already great in deep water—say, 1 in 10 or more—they break fairly soon after 'feeling bottom', but then as spilling breakers. In that case, not all the energy is discharged at once; the waves continue to advance some distance, constantly breaking at the top, and thereby steadily losing height. These breakers cannot be defined as solitary waves, which is why the above calculation and the rule applying to the height of the breakers—namely, that this is proportional to the cube root of the deep-water wavelength—do not hold for steep waves like these. Nor is the law valid in this case which says that the depth where the waves break is 1·3 times the height of the breakers. What does apply is the general qualitative rule which declares that, the less steep the waves are in deep water, the higher will be the breakers they produce.

Lastly, we have Table 22, which is based partly on theory and partly on observations, showing how the height of the breakers is related to the height of the waves in deep water (lower row) when the steepness in deep water (upper row) is given, always on the assumption that the waves are squarely facing the shoreline. If they are not, reference should be made to Table 23.

CURRENTS ASSOCIATED WITH THE WASH OF THE WAVES

Waves—especially the 'solitary' ones of surf—involve not only an up-and-down movement of water, but also a net forward transportation, so that water does indeed come undulating towards the shore with the surf. This water has, however, to drain away again, so there is a constant back-draught at the same time. Some of this back-draught takes place along the whole

7

shore, some in well-defined runlets which flow outwards, more or less at right-angles to the shore. It is these 'rip currents' which are most dangerous to foolhardy bathers and inexperienced swimmers. They arise where the configuration of the coast favours their release, for if the waves do not come in exactly perpendicular to the shore, the water they bring may first escape sideways, in which case a current will run along the coast. Where, however, its configuration and that of the offshore shoals hamper the sideways flow of the water, a thread of current will detach itself from the shore and a rip current will run out to sea.

Table 23

Height of breakers for various values of initial steepness at 30°, 50°, 70° and 80° angles of incidence

Initial Steepness

Angle of Incidence	$\dfrac{1}{500}$	$\dfrac{1}{200}$	$\dfrac{1}{100}$	$\dfrac{1}{50}$	$\dfrac{1}{20}$	$\dfrac{1}{10}$	$\dfrac{1}{7}$
30°	2·3	1·7	1·4	1·16	0·95	0·89	0·91
50°	2·1	1·55	1·25	1·05	0·86	0·81	0·85
70°	1·7	1·25	1·0	0·84	0·68	0·62	0·64
80°	1·35	1·0	0·8	0·65	0·52	0·46	0·45

Wherever the undertow is spread along the whole coast, it carries away loose material lying there—from boulders down to pebbles, fine sand and silt—which either originated from the abrasion of rocks by the sea itself, or was brought down by rivers. While this loose material is being displaced by the wash of the waves and their back-draught, it is at the same time being sifted and sorted. The largest fragments do not get far, but the more finely-divided material is borne off with the minimum of agitation and flow. The carrying current need not necessarily be caused by the waves themselves; they may merely churn things up, while current initiated by some other cause operates the transport service. So, the farther one goes out to sea, the finer will be the material one finds on the bottom. Some of the very finest, the particles of clay, ultimately come to rest at a remote distance from the shore.

Reverting for a moment to the flow along the coast. Where an obliquely approaching swell predominates, the advancing, undulating water will set up a current mainly in a definite direction along the coast. This current is naturally limited to a narrow strip of shallow water, but it is precisely there that its effect is highly important, because it is constantly carrying sand, and perhaps silt, along with it. The existence of such uni-directional currents can sometimes be inferred from the oblique shape of a river mouth. And there have been occasions when they have made their presence felt in a most unpleasant manner; when a breakwater had been made with insufficient forethought and after a time a considerable stretch of the shore on one side of the breakwater was found to be gradually denuded of sand, with encroachment of the sea as the result. How had this come about? The breakwater had interfered with the flow of sand along the coast, but the transport of sand continued nevertheless; consequently, the sand was carried off on the downstream side, but none came in to replace it.

This shows that a beach is not just static; at best one could say that there is a dynamic balance, a balance which Man cannot, with impunity, upset.

INTERNAL WAVES

DEAD-WATER

There is a Norwegian saying, 'lying in dead-water', which means that one cannot get on. It is, of course, a nautical term. When one is rowing a boat, sailing a yacht or a small motor-boat in Norwegian fjords or other waters situated not far from land, it may all at once become very difficult to make any headway; it is as though the craft were being held back by some mysterious force. Nor does she respond well to the helm. This is doubly troublesome in a sailing vessel, because she keeps falling away to leeward. One may spend hours in dead-water struggling to get out of it. Then, suddenly the vessel 'breaks away' when, for instance, the wind gets up a little, or if another craft, unaffected by the dead-water, passes at full speed nearby; sometimes, however, this can happen for no apparent reason at all.

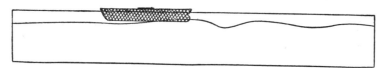

FIG. 77 Internal waves induced by the boat at the interface between heavier and lighter water.

It is generally agreed that this strange phenomenon occurs only where there is a layer of fresh or brackish water overlying the heavier sea-water, a frequent condition along Scandinavian coasts because they are protected by many islands and peninsulas; furthermore, as the tides are not very active, the layers of fresh and salt water are slow to mingle, slower than along most other coasts. Conditions in summer off the Siberian coast are likewise favourable to dead-water; in the channel between the coast and the ice, the sea-water is often covered with river-water and melt-water. It was there that Fridtjof Nansen's heavily-built and poorly-powered ship *Fram* had much to endure from dead-water. On his return, Nansen urged Ekman to study the phenomenon both theoretically and by experiment. On the evidence of this research the phenomenon was shown to be due to the action of *internal waves*, which occur at the interface of the lighter, overlying water and the heavier water underneath. (See Fig. 77.)

We must look into these special kinds of wave before considering dead-water in greater detail.

INTERNAL WAVES

Waves do not occur only on the surface of the sea, but also at an internal interface where the upper water is less dense than the water below it. Now we know that ordinary surface waves have an effect in the layers of water beneath the surface, as well as in those on it. If the surface is undulating, an internal interface will therefore undulate with it, but more faintly in proportion to its depth. In the case of internal waves, however, the carrier of the waves is not the surface, but the interface down below, within the waters, while the surface above remains practically level.

Internal waves behave differently from surface waves in two ways. First, as far as the motions of the individual particles of water are concerned, although these also describe elliptical or circular orbits, the water above the interface rotates in the opposite direction to that of the water under the interface. Under the interface the water advances (i.e. moves in the same direction as that in which the wave is being propagated) where a crest is passing, and retreats where a trough is passing—just like surface waves. But the reverse happens above the interface, where the water retreats as a crest passes and advances during the passing of a trough (see Fig. 78). The water performs up-and-down as well as these to-and-fro movements, which together produce orbits which the water particles above and below the interface describe in contrary directions. If both layers of water are deep enough, these orbits are circles that become smaller, both above and below, the farther they are from the interface. So the most pronounced movement is found at the interface. The same happens when neither layer is at great depth; but the orbits then become elliptical, as in the case of surface waves in shallow water.

The other important difference is the far slower propagation of internal waves, given the same wavelength. This is due to the fact that the internal interface is far more easily distorted than is the surface, because there is comparatively little difference in density between the upper and lower water. Therefore the forces in an internal wave of given length are weaker than in a surface wave of the same length and height, and the water consequently reacts more slowly to an internal wave; its period is longer, its velocity of propagation smaller.

If both water layers are deep, i.e. if their depths are at least half the wavelength, a formula bearing a strong resemblance to that of Stokes for surface waves is valid for the wave velocity. For the square of the velocity is a certain factor times the wavelength, yet this factor is far less than 1·56, being 1·56 *times* the difference between the specific gravities of the water layers, divided by their sum. For example, if the specific gravities are 1·025 and 1·015, then we get 1·56 × 0·01/2·04, or, roughly, the two-hundredth part of 1·56, which means that the wave velocity is approximately fourteen times lower than that of surface waves of the same length.

In the sea the upper layer is seldom deep, at least if it is a question of fresh or brackish water on salt water; then different rules for the velocity of propagation come into force. For all that, it remains a fact that the greater the wavelength the higher the velocity, though it is always much lower than that of equally long surface waves. If the wave is long compared with the thickness of the upper layer, and if the lower layer is deep enough, the velocity approaches a maximum depending only on the thickness of the upper layer.

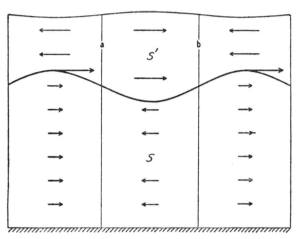

FIG. 78 Diagram of internal waves between two liquids having s and s' specific gravity. The arrows at the tops of the waves indicate the direction of propagation, the others showing the motions of the liquid particles.

The square of the velocity is then 9·8 times the thickness of the upper layer *times* the difference in specific gravity divided by the specific gravity of the upper layer (which, in the sea, always differs little from 1).

Examples: Let the salinity below the interface be 35‰ and the upper layer be 1 m thick, with salinity 30, 20, 10, 0‰ respectively, then (with the temperature at 0°C) the maximum velocity of the internal waves would be 20 cm/sec, 34 cm/sec, 44 cm/sec and 53 cm/sec respectively. If the thickness is, say, four times greater or four times less, the velocity is twice as great, or twice as small.

EXPLANATION OF 'DEAD-WATER'

A vessel travelling through stratified water of this kind excites internal, as well as surface waves. These internal waves follow the vessel at its own speed, and must therefore become steadily longer if the vessel gathers speed. But this means increasing loss of the ship's energy to these waves, a loss reaching its maximum when the waves approach their maximum velocity. As a result, the vessel is unable to exceed this maximum velocity of the waves, unless it has enough energy to 'escape'. Nansen's ship *Fram*, normally making 4·5–5 nautical miles an hour, was therefore able to make, in dead-water, only 1–1·5 miles (i.e. 0·5–0·8 metres per second) at best.

A vessel in dead-water loses this energy because, as may be seen in Fig. 77, she is situated above the front slope of the first subsurface wave, hence with her stern in a region where the waters of the upper layer are running back, and therefore have a braking effect. If, furthermore, the crest of a sufficiently high internal wave reaches the rudder, the latter will be in the forward-running water and will not be able to operate properly; a sailing vessel will then generally go off course and fall to leeward. But if, for a shorter time, the vessel can be given only a little more speed than the maximum velocity of the internal waves, she will 'escape' and make greater headway with less consumption of energy. Subsurface waves are then no longer able to run along with the ship.

THE INTERNAL UNREST OF THE OCEANS

The only necessary condition for the production of internal waves is the existence of layers of water of different densities, the lighter water overlying the heavier. Now a difference in specific gravity may not only be due to a difference in salinity, but equally well to a difference in temperature. We know that warm water lies on colder water nearly all over the oceans, and in principle internal waves can occur anywhere. Usually, however, they are situated at greater depth than in the case described above of dead-water; and they seldom plague small vessels, because they draw too little water, or large ones, because they are more highly powered. These internal waves can nevertheless be detected by recording with a thermograph the temperature fluctuations at some certain constant depth.

The phenomenon is most evident in a layer where there is a steep lapse of temperature in a short vertical distance. We saw earlier that this often happens under an isothermal upper layer several tens of metres or more in thickness; see Fig. 28 for an example. It is easy to see why the undulation of internal layers of water can be detected by temperature readings. Suppose that the lower layer in Fig. 78 is, not more saline, but colder than the upper one, and that the temperature is registered at a depth where the thermometer is under the interface while a crest passes, and above it when a trough passes. Obviously, the temperature will then go up and down, as we can see from Fig. 79. As there is, in reality, no sharply defined interface with an abrupt jump of temperature, but a transitional layer, there are no up-and-down jumps in the temperature recording, but simply an undulating line.

Just as the surface of the sea is seldom at rest, but is almost ceaselessly undulating, so likewise are the internal transitional layers between the warmer upper waters and the colder waters below almost constantly in undulatory movement; it is the internal unrest of the oceans. There is little scope for these internal waves only in places where the temperature above and below is approximately the same, such as the Arctic and Antarctic in the cold season, and in the shallow oceanic parts of the moderate zones.

The periods of these internal waves in the oceans vary from a couple of minutes to a day. It has been found that the period of internal waves at a given place cannot decrease beyond a certain minimum, which increases as the gradient of specific gravity in the transition layer concerned is less steep.

To a certain extent the long-period internal waves—of the order of half a day or a whole day—are associated with tidal forces; indeed, they may be termed *internal tides*.

Long internal waves are liable to produce enormous vertical displacements, especially at some considerable depth. Soundings taken by the *Meteor* and the *Snellius* showed that some layers of water in the depths went up and down as much as 60 metres.

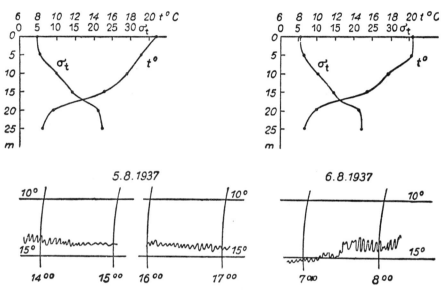

Fig. 79 *Below* Temperature recordings at a depth of 17½ metres in the Fehmarn belt in the Western Baltic (after Neumann). The fluctuating temperature betrays an up-and-down movement of the sea-water along the recording thermometer.
Above The associated vertical distributions of temperature (*t*) and specific gravity, the latter having 1 subtracted and the result multiplied by 1000.

Chapter Five

EBB AND FLOW

The tide comes, turns, stays never still;
It waits upon no Prince's will.

(*After a motto on the lift-lock*
at De Lemmer, Friesland.)

I T has long been known that the water level at places along the banks of
Lake Geneva sometimes strangely rises and falls, with a period of roughly
an hour and a quarter; the name given to this phenomenon in those parts is
'seiche'. The greatest changes in level usually occur at the extremities of the
lake, where they may amount to more than one metre.

SEICHES

A Swiss doctor called Forel studied the phenomenon closely between
1870 and 1880, and showed that an oscillation of the whole mass of water was
involved, like that of water in an oblong tub tilted briefly at one end. We
touched on oscillation of this kind in the preceding chapter; see Fig. 49.
A seiche—now a generally accepted term—could also be described as a
standing wave, its wavelength being equal to double the length of the
swinging mass of water. When the water, at one end of the lake which for the
moment we shall suppose is shaped like an oblong tank, rises, it goes down
at the other end, and goes mainly to and fro in the middle (see arrows in
Fig. 49). Seiches occur in other lakes of some size, besides Lake Geneva.

Disregarding the causes of seiches for the present, let us consider the fact
that the period of the oscillation is independent of the force with which the
water has been made to swing. Considering lengthwise oscillation, we know
that the length of the lake is half a wavelength; now, as the depth of all lakes
of any considerable size is incomparably smaller than their length, our
standing wave takes on the character of a long wave or 'tidal' wave, for
which there is a very simple relation between period and wavelength, the
same as that for long, progressive waves, namely

$$wavelength = period \times velocity = period \times (9 \cdot 8 \times depth)^{\frac{1}{2}}$$

or

$$period = \frac{2 \times length\ of\ basin}{(9 \cdot 8 \times depth)^{\frac{1}{2}}},$$

the period expressed in seconds, the length and depth in metres. We see
that the period increases with increasing length and diminishing depth.

This representation is, of course, unduly simplified, since no lake is shaped exactly like a rectangular tank. Generally, therefore, the period of oscillation will depend not only on the length—in so far as any one particular length is demonstrable—and the (average) depth, but also on the shape of the lake; and that is liable to be very complicated, but we shall not enter further into the details of this matter.

Here is a numerical example. If the lake is 7 kilometres long, the numerator of the above formula becomes $2 \times 7000 = 14,000$. With the depth at 5 metres, the denominator therefore is $(9 \cdot 8 \times 5)^{\frac{1}{2}} = (49)^{\frac{1}{2}} = 7$. The result is $14,000/7 = 2000$, i.e. 2000 seconds, or 33 minutes.

We have already noted that the period of Lake Geneva is approximately $1\frac{1}{4}$ hours. Lake Balaton in Hungary is about as long, but far shallower; accordingly the period there is 10 hours. The great Lake Erie in America has a period of 14 hours; Lake Baikal in Asia is twice as long, but is also much deeper, and its period is only $4\frac{1}{2}$ hours.

SEICHES IN OPEN BAYS AND ADJACENT SEAS

This kind of fluctuation to which water is sometimes subject—known internationally by the French–Swiss word 'seiche'—is likely to occur, not only in lakes or almost isolated basins like the Black Sea, but also in open bays and marginal seas, the only difference being that, to an open bay there

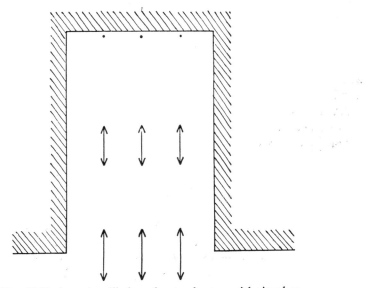

FIG. 80 Horizontal oscillation of water due to a seiche in a bay.

is only one closed end where the water chiefly rises and falls. As the other end is open, the greatest oscillation is not in the middle of the basin, but at the mouth; see Fig. 80. When the water level in the bay rises, the water at the mouth runs inward; when it drops, the water at the mouth runs outward. The maximum up-and-down movement is found at the farthest end of the

7*

bay; in this case there are practically no differences in level at the opening, where the to-and-fro movement predominates. All this is on the assumption that there is *free* (unforced) oscillation.

It will be evident that, in this case, the length of the basin is not half, but a quarter of the wavelength to be assigned to this oscillation, if it is regarded as standing wave; for the fluctuating water profile of Fig. 80 corresponds to the AB section of standing wave motion shown in Fig. 50. To find the period of oscillation in a rectangular basin, we now have to write in the numerator of the previous formula four times the length of the basin instead of twice that length, viz.,

$$period = \frac{4 \times basin\ length}{(9 \cdot 8 \times depth)^{\frac{1}{2}}}.$$

The period of either a closed (first formula) or open (second formula) basin is often called the *intrinsic*, or *natural*, *period* of that basin.

Seiches are very common, both in fairly narrow bays and in open marginal seas, like the North Sea.

THE ORIGIN OF SEICHES

Among the possible causes of seiches is a strong wind driving the water towards one end, which makes the water surface as a whole slant a little. If the wind then abates rather abruptly, the force responsible for the aberrant level will likewise drop, and the water level will seek to regain its equilibrium, continuing to oscillate however, owing to the inertia of the mass of water. This produces an oscillation similar to that found in a tub of water. Friction will eventually restore equilibrium. Seiches are as likely to be caused in this way in a closed as in an open basin.

A second possible cause is difference in barometric pressure between the ends of the basin. If the centre of a low-pressure area (a depression or cyclone) passes over, or close to one end, the water will stand a little higher there than at the other end (a pressure difference of 10 millibars corresponds to a difference of 10 centimetres in the height of the water). If this pressure difference is then extinguished fairly abruptly, the water mass will start to oscillate. This cause, too, may prevail in either closed or open basins; chiefly in long basins, as these offer the best scope for pressure differences.

The observation of such oscillations in bays and inlets in open communication with the sea is rendered difficult, of course, by the ebb and flow of the tides, which in themselves involve a rise and fall of the sea level. In order to perceive the special effects with which we are now dealing, we must subtract the normal tide heights from the observed change in water level in the course of time. This has been done for the North Sea, for instance, in connection with the study of *storm surges*. A gale blowing from the north-west or north is capable of raising the water in the southern North Sea far above the normal tide-marks; the result is called a storm surge (to which we shall revert more fully at the end of this chapter).

If the (known) normal tide levels are subtracted from the measured water levels rising and falling with the tides, it will often be found that there is also a rise and fall in the difference itself. Such an inertial oscillation occurs when the wind quickly subsides or turns after the moment of maximum extra surge. The period of this oscillation, of course, has nothing to do with the tidal period; in the North Sea it is 35–40 hours in the case under discussion, namely surge from the north-west. After a certain time (say, half a period, or a period and a half), the water level, owing to this oscillation, falls below the normal tide-mark. We repeat, a clear picture of what is going forward can only be obtained by unravelling these two types of oscillation, namely the tidal and the inertial oscillation (seiche).

There is a third possible cause of seiches, but it is only of practical significance in bays and marginal seas which are in communication with the open sea. This is the tide on the open sea, which works its way in through the opening of such a basin. We shall revert to this when we come to discuss the ebb and flow of the tides.

THE TIDES

THE PHENOMENON

Ebb and flood, the regular rise and advance, followed by the fall and retreat of the water lapping the shore, like the rhythmical breathing of the sea, has been known to Man from time immemorial.

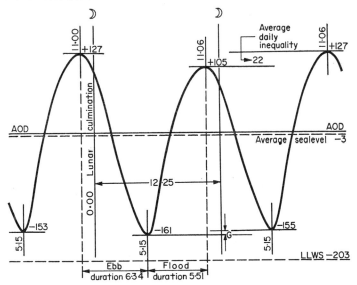

Fig. 81 Average tide curve at IJmuiden (from *Tide Tables for the Netherlands* issued by Dutch Department of Waterways). The figures alongside the vertical lines stand for the times in relation to culmination of the moon. The levels with reference to the Amsterdam ordnance datum (Amsterdam water-mark) and the differences in level are given in centimetres. LLWS stands for the average 'low low-water spring' (the lowest spring low water of every month and those then averaged over a number of years).

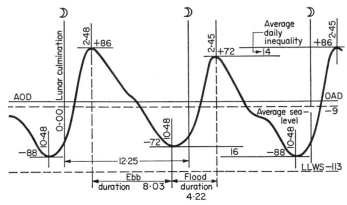

F<small>IG</small>. 82 Average tide curve at Delfzyl (after *Tide Tables for the Netherlands*) (see legend under Fig. 81).

This 'breathing' usually consists of two inhalations and exhalations a day, for the times of high-water have intervals of approximately 12 hours and 25 minutes, as do the times of low water. Hence together two complete rises and falls last 24 hours and 50 minutes. This means that every day the high-water mark is reached roughly 50 minutes later than on the previous day, but in between there has once again been high water. The same rule applies to low water. This is a semi-diurnal tide; but there are some places (the Gulf of Mexico, for instance), which have a diurnal tide, that is, one high water and one low water in 24 hours and 50 minutes. Examples of tide-graphs are given in Figs. 81–84.

Tides manifest themselves in various ways. In some places the rising-and-falling movement predominates, when the sea creeps up and up, only to retreat again some six hours later. This rising-and-falling movement will be most conspicuous on steep shores. Elsewhere, the dominant movement is an advance (flood-tide) and retreat (ebb-tide), the conquest and evacuation of stretches of ground. The Wadden Sea comes naturally to mind, where, in continuous alternation, the sea encroaches upon miles of land and then falls

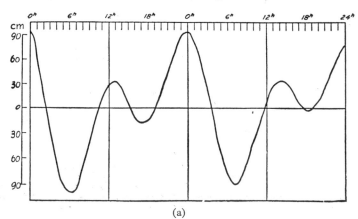

(a)

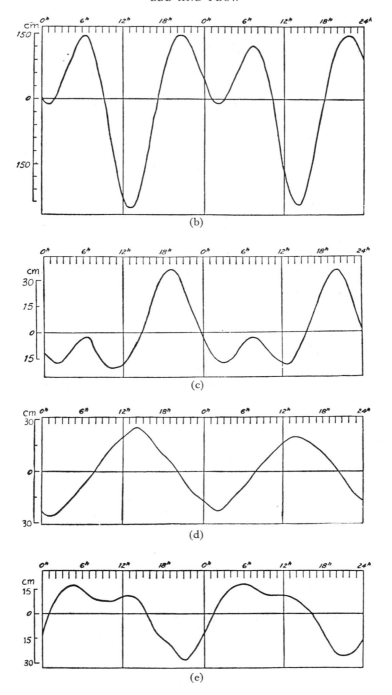

FIG. 83 Examples of different kinds of tide graphs (from H. A. Marmer, *The Sea*, Appleton, New York). (*a*) San Diego (California); (*b*) Seattle (Washington); (*c*) Honolulu (Hawaii); (*d*) Pensacola (Florida); (*e*) Galveston (Texas).

back again. Elsewhere again it is less a matter of sea-water's rising and falling, or advancing and retreating, than of a rapid current flowing longitudinally in one direction and being followed by an equally rapid flow in the opposite direction. These tidal currents predominate in straits and estuaries.

The strange thing about tides is that they are most noticeable in certain open bays and adjacent seas, and least so in lakes, on the one hand, and the open ocean on the other.

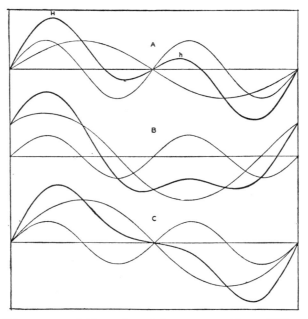

FIG. 84 How different types of tide graph result from superpositions of different semidiurnal and diurnal tides: *A* is the most common mixed type with two different high waters (*H* and *h*) and two different low waters. *B* has unequal high waters but approximately equal low waters (the opposite may also occur). *C* has one high and one low water every day (every 24 hours and 50 minutes, to be more precise).

Taking the last first, it is, of course, difficult to discover, in the open ocean, whether the level of the water rises and falls in a certain interval. This rise and fall is best seen on the shores of islands situated in the middle of the ocean. Readings on true oceanic islands have rarely shown a difference in level of much more than half a metre. Even so, it seems quite likely that the topography of the sea-bed around the island, where the water gradually becomes shallower, may tend to reinforce the tidal differences, in the same way as it amplifies a tsunami and a long swell. Hence the up-and-down movement of the water level in the open ocean is generally not conspicuous.

In lakes, tides are far less perceptible still; the amplitude here—and that only in large lakes—is a mere matter of centimetres. The amplitude in Lake Erie is 8 centimetres, but that of Lake Baikal, which is larger, is only

$1\frac{1}{2}$ centimetres. The tides are also comparatively small in the Mediterranean (30 cm) and the Black Sea (10 cm).

In the areas of bays and adjacent seas, however, the ebb and flow phenomenon assumes truly majestic proportions in many places. The immense amplitudes along the Channel Coast are well known. They reach their maximum on the French coast, in the Bay of St. Malo (Brittany), where the amplitude at spring tide may be as much as $15\frac{1}{2}$ metres. Fundy Bay, on the east coast of North America (between New Brunswick and Nova Scotia), where the spring-tide sometimes has an amplitude of 18 metres, holds the world's record.

The average tidal amplitude along the Dutch coast varies from 3 metres in Zeeland to $1\frac{1}{2}$ metres in the middle of the coast of Noord-Holland Province. Further north and east it increases again to about 2 metres.

Another point is that high and low water are not always equally pronounced in one and the same place. The tidal amplitude varies from day to day, but even this is to a certain extent rhythmical, as the tide is at its highest approximately every alternate fortnight, when it is called the *spring tide*. In between two spring tides comes the smallest tidal range, i.e. *neap tide*.

Although the times of high and low water on any given day are different in every place, so that even along the shores of so small a country as the Netherlands there is high water at one end when there is low water at the other, the spring and neap tides occur at approximately the same time all over the world, notably spring tide one or two days after new and full moon, and neap tide one or two days after first quarter and last quarter.

THE MOON AND THE TIDES

The fact that the spring-tide comes at about the time of new and full moon gives food for thought. It signifies that the strongest tides prevail when the sun and moon are approximately in line, or stand opposite each other. Both heavenly bodies apparently affect the tides; but the moon's influence is dominant, which is obvious from the interval of 24 hours and 50 minutes between the high water of today and the corresponding high water of tomorrow, because this is exactly the same interval as there is between two successive passages of the moon through the meridian of a particular place. Every day the moon above any particular place passes the south 50 minutes later than on the previous day. This is because, owing to its own movement around the earth, the moon is constantly shifting with respect to the (apparently) revolving celestial dome, notably in a contrary direction to that of the daily rotation of the heavens.

It is the moon, therefore, which determines the tidal periods, the sun playing second fiddle to her; so let us, for the time being, concentrate on the moon.

It is sometimes said that ebb and flow are produced by the gravitational pull of the moon. It would be more correct to say that they are due to the rotation of the moon and earth around their common centre of gravity, coupled with a different degree of attraction experienced by various points on earth. This is what happens: Suppose for a moment that the earth were to cease revolving around its axis for a time; in that event it would not yet stand still in relation to the moon, since both bodies rotate about their common centre of gravity. This is situated within the body of the earth, at 4630 kilometres from the centre; and the earth, without the rotation about its own axis, now makes a small circular movement comparable with that of a teacup turned gently to stir the contents. Hence each point of the earth describes its own circle (see Fig. 85), and is subjected to two forces besides the gravity of

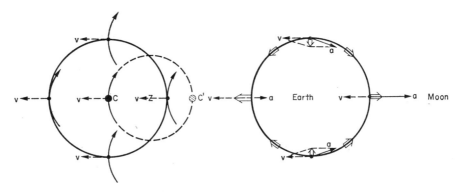

FIG. 85 The origin of the tides. *Left.* The centre of the earth (C) rotates about the common centre of gravity (Z) of the earth and moon. All points of the earth describe equal arcs of a circle (drawn as though the earth were seen from the South Pole); so there are equal centrifugal forces (*v*). *Right.* The interaction between the centrifugal force (*v*) and the gravitational force of the moon (*a*) produces a tidal force at each point of the surface. The tidal forces are double-arrowed in the figure.

the earth, namely, the pull of the moon, and the centrifugal force resulting from this rotation. As the circles of all points on the earth are of equal size (in so far as such a point does not shift relative to the earth), namely, having a radius of 4630 kilometres, the second force (*v*) is consequently everywhere equally large and also equally directed. This, however, cannot be said of the first force, which is greater on the side of the earth facing the moon than on the other side; and, as it is directed everywhere towards the moon, its direction varies slightly from place to place (see Fig. 85). Now, in the centre of gravity of the earth, the gravitational pull of the moon and the centrifugal force balance each other, but they do not do so exactly at points of the surface. The pull of the moon predominates a little on the side facing the moon, so that a small surplus is directed towards the moon; on the opposite side the gravitational pull falls slightly short, and a surplus, about equally small, is therefore directed away from the moon. In both cases there is thus a small surplus, a residual force directed upward (outward), also on the side turned away from the moon. The magnitude of this residual force is a mere 1/9,000,000 of the force of gravity of the earth.

At those points of the earth's surface which, as seen from the moon, are situated on the margin of the earth (above and below in the figure) and where, from the reverse point of view, the moon is seen standing on the horizon, the two forces are approximately equal in magnitude, but not exactly so in direction; there remains a very small downward (inward) resultant. At places in between the latter and the former points, resulting forces are usually generated which are not directed vertically.

The small resulting forces are called the *tidal forces*. Supposing the earth to be encased in a liquid sheath, a global sea covering the whole earth, these tidal forces would cause a very slight ovate deformation (see Fig. 86). The reader will realize that the ranges in this figure are greatly exaggerated.

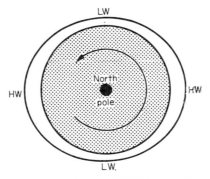

FIG. 86 The rotating earth in a water-jacket with high water (HW) and low water (LW).

Letting the earth again rotate about its axis, this means that, with its water-jacket, it will, as it were, revolve under this ovate profile. The water revolves with it of course, but the profile does not, and a certain portion of the water alternately passes high and low parts; hence the water surface will go up and down there, reaching a highest level twice in the time of one revolution plus 50 minutes and a lowest level twice in the same time. The extra 50 minutes are added by the slow rotation of the ovate profile itself, together with the moon, in the same direction as the earth's rotation, notably once in about four weeks.

If we consider the whole of this cycle as seen from the earth, it is as if two water elevations and two subsidences circumnavigated the globe every 24 hours and 50 minutes.

The matter would be simple enough if the moon always stood above the Equator. In that event the two elevations passing there in a lunar day (which is what we shall call the period of 24 hours and 50 minutes) would be equally high and the subsidences equally low at every point of the earth; this is called a pure semidiurnal tide. But that is not the case. Suppose the moon stands above the Tropic of Cancer. At any random point of it, she will then pass through the zenith in her upper culmination, but in her lowest she will go through the north and will not drop more than 43 degrees below the horizon.

Consequently, the corresponding high waters will also be unequal; the low waters may also vary. This inequality might be described as a tidal course resulting from the superposition of a pure semidiurnal on a diurnal tide; see Fig. 84.

For the time being we shall concern ourselves with the semidiurnal tide. Before we do so, however, there are further complications to consider.

THE INTERPLAY OF SUN AND MOON

The first complicating factor arises from the fact that the sun as well as the moon induces tidal forces. At first sight it may seem strange that the sun should not have greater effect than the moon. Although the sun is 389 times farther from us than is the moon, its mass is 26 million times greater and its gravitational force (which is in inverse ratio to the square of the distance) is still 172 times stronger than that of the moon. As we have seen, however, it is not gravitation itself that counts, but the difference in gravitational pull between two sides of the earth. The tidal forces are proportional to this difference, and the latter is now in inverse proportion to the distance from the attractive body, raised to the third power. It is for this reason that the tidal forces derived from the sun are only 0·46 of those coming from the moon. But the effect of the sun is by no means negligible. The sum of the lunar and solar effects at spring-tide (one or two days after full and new moon) is more than twice the residual difference when they counteract each other at neap tide (one or two days after first and last quarter).

THE GLOBAL TIDE AS A FORCED WAVE

There is another important complication, not an astronomical but a hydrodynamic one, proceeding as it does from the mechanism of water movements with which the tides are associated.

Instructive as the idea is of the deformed surface of the global ocean (Fig. 86) under which earth and water rotate—and it is an idea derived from Newton himself—it is not an exact representation of the facts, even when we temporarily adhere to the notion of a global ocean encasing the whole earth.

It has already been stated that, from a terrestrial view, the tides in that global ocean may be regarded as two waves running with the moon around the earth. But we have to remember that waves have their own laws, too. Not only the vertical but also, and chiefly, the horizontal motions of water associated with such long waves, which must necessarily occur as the waves advance, bring their own mechanism of forces into operation. Thus, for instance, if there were no moon or sun to dictate the velocity at which such waves advanced, these would have their own propagation velocity, determined by the depth of water; and it would be the same as that at which tsunamis are propagated, that is, for instance 196 metres per second or 706 kilometres per hour, given an average depth of, let us say, 4000 metres. (For the moment we are ignoring the fact that the spherical shape and rotation of the earth influence these waves, as in actual fact is the case with waves having the length of half the circumference of the earth.) The actual velocity with which the tidal wave hastens across our imaginary global ocean however, is determined externally, namely by the time of 24 hours and 50 minutes within which it has to circumnavigate the earth. Along the Equator, for instance, this gives a velocity of more than 1600 kilometres an hour.

A wave of this kind, the speed and period of which are determined by external forces (in this case chiefly by the moon), is called a *forced* wave. So this wave is 'not allowed' to move as it might 'wish' (if it were a free wave).

All the same, its internal mechanism does affect the course of the undulation and the picture therefore is different from that suggested by our former highly simplified representation of the facts. More especially, the character of the wave affects the height of the oceanic tide, and the phase, i.e. the difference between the time of high water and the time of the moon's culmination at any particular place; for, now that the moon is towing the tidal wave, so to speak, these times will no longer coincide.

We shall not enter further into this dynamic theory of the tides (Laplace). It involves very complicated mathematics and, moreover, has not yet been completed. All we would say is that, although the earth is not completely encased in water, there is nevertheless one region where the tide actually can circumnavigate the globe as a wave, and to which this theory therefore applies. It is the region of the great Southern Ocean.

COMPLICATION CAUSED BY ALTERNATION OF SEA AND LAND

The third complication is the most radical of all, and is caused by the alternation of sea and land. What do the tides do in the Atlantic Ocean, for instance, or the North Sea?

Let us first take the Atlantic. We have seen that the tidal waves in the Antarctic Ocean circulate from east to west. Therefore, where the Atlantic communicates with the Antarctic Ocean, elevations of the sea-level constantly pass twice every lunar day and night; but, in the Atlantic Ocean, they will then be propagated towards the north. A tidal wave is thus formed, which progresses as a *free* wave, the period obtained in this way being the same as that at the source, namely, in the Antarctic Ocean, hence a semilunar day; the velocity here, however, is not dictated by the moon, but by the depths of the ocean.

Let us follow the high water along the meridian of 20° W., beginning at latitude 45° S. If there is high water here at a certain time, it prevails six lunar hours later at about 13° S., in the neighbourhood of Ascension; twelve lunar hours later at 22° N., to the south of the Canary Islands; eighteen lunar hours later at Iceland. (We mean by a lunar hour the twenty-fourth part of a full lunar day, i.e. of 24 hours and 50 minutes. Hence a difference of twelve lunar hours in the arrival of high water between two points means that the next high water has just arrived at the first point when the high water we are following has reached the second point.)

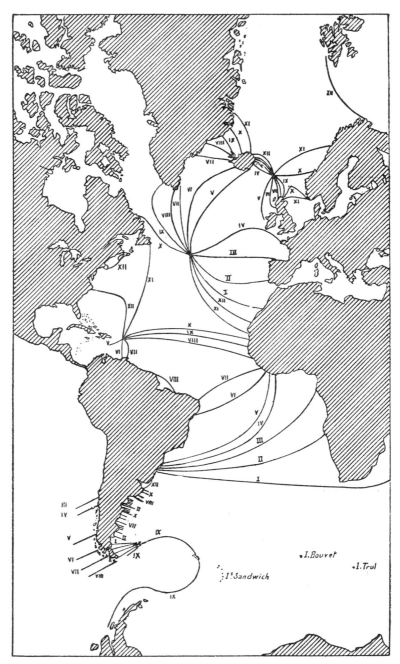

Fig. 87 Cotidal lines on the Atlantic Ocean (according to Villain).

The points of simultaneous high water can be connected on the map by lines. One such line will give the position, as it were, of the crest-line of the tidal wave at a given moment, making visible the progress of the tidal wave. Figure 87 shows these cotidal lines, as they are called, for the Atlantic Ocean; the adjacent Roman figures represent time differences in lunar hours.

It is clearly evident from this map that the course of our tidal wave, which runs mainly from south to north over the ocean, is anything but regular. That is because far more is involved than just a regular wave running from south to north. To begin with, the tidal wave rebounds from the coasts, generating crossing, or counter-running, tidal waves, which complicate the picture by interference. Furthermore, our implication so far has been that the tide in the Atlantic is only a derived one, a free wave advancing from the the Antarctic Ocean, whereas actually the Atlantic Ocean, like every enclosed sea, also has its 'own' tide, a forced tidal oscillation; that is to say a tidal oscillation which the Atlantic would also have if it were closed at its southern end.

Finally, there is one more complication, quite independent of that created by the alternation of land and sea. This is the effect of the earth's rotation upon horizontal movements. This is the factor primarily responsible for those remarkable turning-points of the tide-lines, several of which are to be seen on the map in Fig. 87 and which are called 'amphidromic points'. We shall return to these presently, but let us first consider the natural tides in basins bordered on the east and west.

Think of a basin of limited dimensions in the vicinity of the Equator, where the moon passes through the zenith. At every instant a small tidal force, changing with the position of the moon, is added to the force of gravity (we are now only considering the lunar tide). Figure 88 illustrates this tidal force for five moments of half a lunar day. When the moon rises, the tidal force (1) is directed straight down; when it has climbed about halfway to the zenith, the tidal force (2) points to the east; when it is in the zenith, the tidal force (3) points straight upward; when it has descended again about halfway westward, the tidal force (4) points to the west; and when it sets, the tidal force (5) is again directed downward. The resultant of the force of gravity and the tidal force together fluctuates slightly owing to the change of the latter. If we represent this resultant by an arrow, its point describes a small orbit, as can be seen in the figure. Now if, at every moment, the water-level is to stand perpendicular to the operative total force—which a water-level tends always to do—it, too, will have to fluctuate, as shown in the right-hand illustration of the figure. We see that a kind of seiche, a standing wave, is induced, but it is a *forced* standing wave. The period is half a lunar day, hence 12 hours and 25 minutes.

Now we know that every basin has its own period for a given kind of oscillation, this being determined by the dimensions and shape of the basin. The hydrodynamic forces operating in the mass of water will therefore come to bear, inasmuch as the water-level will not be so 'obedient' as to assume, at every moment, exactly the position of equilibrium, i.e. a position perpendicular to the resultant of force of gravity and tidal force (positions 1, 2, 3, 4 and 5 on the right of the figure). If, for instance, the instrinsic period of the basin should be greater than half a lunar day, the enforced oscillation will become too fast for the mass of water, and the position of the water will always lag behind the (changing) position of equilibrium.

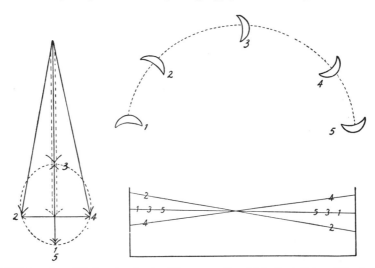

FIG. 88 Tides of equilibrium in a basin. The arrows 2 and 4 in the left-hand illustration do not yet give the extreme ranges of the tide.

As to the amplitude of the tidal oscillation, the larger the basin the greater will this be, since it is primarily the gradients of the water's surface which are determined by the tidal forces. Apart from this, however, the amplitude depends largely on whether the intrinsic period of the basin differs much or little from the tidal period. If they agree well, *resonance* prevails, and the amplitudes are greatly increased. There is some degree of resonance in Lake Balaton, mentioned earlier, with a period of 10 hours, and Lake Erie, with a period of 14 hours. Accordingly, the tidal range of Lake Erie is 8 centimetres, whereas that of Lake Baikal (which is twice as long and, owing to its far greater depth, has a period of $4\frac{1}{2}$ hours and therefore exhibits no resonance) is only $1\frac{1}{2}$ centimetres.

Figure 88 related primarily to a water basin above which the moon was passing through the zenith (or the nadir). This never occurs at higher latitudes, where the tidal force will not continue to revolve in a vertical plane. Neither will the resultant of the force of gravity and the tidal force therefore fluctuate in a vertical plane; instead, it will swing around slightly, producing a circulating tidal wave such as obtains in basins which are not too elongated, like the Black Sea.

Where a basin as wide as the Atlantic Ocean is concerned, it must be borne in mind that, contrary to the basic supposition of Fig. 88, the position of the moon, and, therefore, the tidal force, at the western end are different every instant from those at the eastern end.

The intrinsic, or internally generated tide (in the above sense) of sea areas of limited size resembling bays or adjacent seas, is usually less important than the oscillation induced externally (by a progressing tidal wave, for instance). This is due to the effect of reflection, mentioned earlier. This is a factor to be reckoned with, particularly where this wave enters a more or less enclosed adjacent sea. To some extent, the northern part of the North Atlantic (including the Arctic Ocean) is such an adjacent sea, into which the tidal wave enters from the south. Two other examples are the North Sea, into which this tidal wave runs around Scotland, and the English Channel. Lastly, there are the smaller bays.

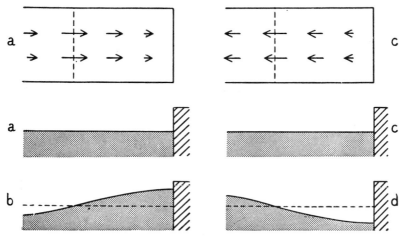

FIG. 89 Standing tidal wave in a bay. *a*, *b*, *c* and *d* are four successive moments of a tidal period. The figure also shows a plan of *a* and *c* with arrows pointing the direction of flow. In *b* and *d* the tide is just turning.

Through interference, the invading wave and that reflected from the extremity (which does not have to be entirely closed to reflect it) together produce a standing wave similar to that depicted in Fig. 50. There ensues a seiche in the bay, induced by the tide outside it. The profile of the oscillating water surface (Fig. 89) now may well have a very different appearance from that of a free seiche (Fig. 80); notably, the nodal line—that is, the line of maximum inflow and outflow (and of the minimum up-and-down move-ment)—may now be situated inside the bay instead of at its mouth. This depends on how the tidal period compares with the intrinsic period. Again, the strongest tide occurs in the bay when these two are equal, that is to say when the bay is in 'resonance' with the tide. The notorious tide in Fundy Bay, the amplitude of which is sometimes as much as 18 metres at spring-tide, is one example of such resonance; the natural period of that bay is probably upwards of twelve hours.

The production of two nodal lines by interference between the incoming and the reflected wave is illustrated by the Red Sea, which receives its tide, for the major part, from the Indian Ocean. At its mouth, at Perim, in the south, the amplitude is 40 centimetres; at Assab, some 100 kilometres to the north, the motion of the water is mainly horizontal; at Kamerau there is again a rise and fall of 30 centimetres, but here there is a rise when there is a fall at the mouth, and vice versa; purely horizontal motion prevails again at Port Sudan; finally, the Gulf of Suez, too, has an amplitude of nearly 30 centimetres, once more in unison with that at the mouth.

DIURNAL TIDES

Up to the present we have been considering semidiurnal tides. As we know, when the moon is not standing exactly above the Equator, an inequality exists between two successive tides. This could just as well be described as the result of the interaction of a diurnal and a semidiurnal tide (see Fig. 84).

The question of resonance of certain seas with the tides, which we considered in relation to semidiurnal tides (period 12 hours and 25 minutes) can now also be considered for the diurnal tide component (period 24 hours and 50 minutes). And we shall find that, under certain circumstances, notably when the moon is far beyond the Equator, in certain seas—for example the Java Sea and the Gulf of Mexico—the diurnal tide is reinforced by resonance to such an extent that it predominates, producing tide curves with one high water and one low water in 24 hours and 50 minutes; examples are to be found in Figs. 83(d) and 84(c).

THE CORIOLIS FORCE AND THE TIDES

We come now to the last complication strongly affecting the course of the tide in many seas. It is the Coriolis force, that is, the action of the rotation of the earth upon horizontal movements. Without it, certain features of the overall picture, notably that of the tide-lines, of which Figs. 87 and 91 furnish examples, would baffle us completely.

Consider first a progressing wave in a sea area shaped roughly like a channel. In the crests, the current flows in the same direction as the wave. As the Coriolis force in the northern hemisphere causes a deflection to the right, relative to the direction of the current, the tide on the right-hand side will be higher than on the left (the reverse being the case in the southern hemisphere). As the water runs back in the troughs, there will be a deflection towards the other side; that is to say, the low water on the left-hand side is less low than on the right. (Left-hand and right-hand here are from the point of view of someone looking towards the propagation of the tide.) The greatest total amplitude is, therefore, on the right-hand side. This is one of the reasons why the tidal wave entering the English Channel from the ocean produces greater amplitudes along the French coast than the English coast.

With standing tidal waves in fairly wide bays, the Coriolis force is responsible for amphidromic points, so called. These are the centres of rotation of the tide-lines, some of which are seen in Figs. 87 and 91. In so far as the Coriolis force is responsible for them, they arise in the following manner.

Suppose that the standing tidal wave formed in the bay or open marginal sea has a nodal line where, at every moment, the tidal current is greater than elsewhere, and where, on the other hand, the height range is smallest, while on either side of this line the tides are running in opposite directions; see Fig. 90. Assuming that we are in the northern hemisphere, the Coriolis

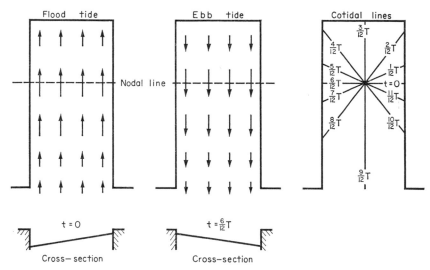

Fig. 90 Explanation of an amphidrome. The times are in twelfth parts of a tidal period (lunar hours).

force, which deflects flowing water to the right, causes a transverse slope of the water surface in the bay as long as the water is flowing. The currents are strongest at those moments when there is no gradient in the long axis of the bay, and the greatest strength of current is then found in the nodal line. The greatest transverse slope must also be along this line if equilibrium with the Coriolis force is to be established. If it is then flood tide, the drop must be from right to left (left-hand drawing in Fig. 90), and high water will be to the right of the nodal line. A quarter of a tidal period later, the water's steepest gradient is in the longitudinal direction; high water will then be at the end of the bay, whereas the current is practically zero and, therefore, the Coriolis force is inoperative. Yet another quarter tidal period later we have the strongest ebb; there is no drop in the lengthwise direction, but the Coriolis force produces a transverse one, now from left to right, with high water to the left of the nodal line. Another quarter tidal period later high water is in the mouth of the bay.

Thus we see that high water circulates round the bay and the cotidal-line swings around the middle of the nodal line. This centre of rotation is an amphidrome.

Summing up the foregoing facts in a very few words, we might say that the Coriolis force produces a transverse oscillation, besides the existing lengthwise oscillation, and that these two standing waves produce a rotatory tide.

The above was only a simple example. Where there are several nodal lines there are also several amphidromic points. Moreover, the transverse fluctuation may or may not be in resonance, a factor upon which the tidal levels and the position of the cotidal lines largely depend.

Lastly, friction is another potent factor, generally responsible for some displacement of the amphidrome from the centre. The chart of the cotidal lines in the North Sea (Fig. 91) illustrates the complexity of the matter.

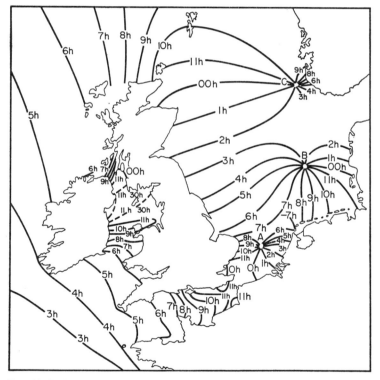

Fig. 91 Cotidal-lines in the North Sea. *A*, *B* and *C* are amphidromic points.

TIDAL CURRENTS

In the cases we have been considering, the earth's rotation also generates currents at right angles to the direction in which the primary tidal wave is propagated. If we follow the direction of the current, we shall find that it rotates anti-clockwise in one tidal period within the basin. An essential condition for the existence of this type of rotating tide is the presence of transverse slopes which balance the Coriolis force.

Rotating tidal currents are not only induced by the Coriolis force. For example, in the western part of the English Channel, where a running tidal wave enters and the sea-bed slopes down gently from the coasts, the currents which run lengthwise at high water and at low water alternate with currents running towards and away from the coasts during rising and falling water respectively. Consequently, there are tidal currents, rotating counter-clockwise along the French coast of the Channel, and clockwise along the English coast. Figure 92 shows an example.

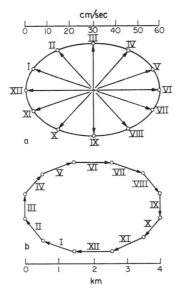

FIG. 92 *Above* Rotating tidal current (diagrammatically). The current arrow describes a 'current ellipse'. *Below* Alignment of the current arrows gives the track of a parcel of water.

Wherever water is free to swerve to right or left in the open ocean, and provided there are no transverse slopes, the Coriolis force always deflects it to the right, relative to the direction of flow at the moment. The water will therefore rotate to the right and the velocity arrow will now revolve clock-wise. (The reverse will be true in the southern hemisphere. It could be said with equal truth that the velocity arrow revolved with the sun, and that would apply to both hemispheres.) This is the most common type of tidal current found in the open ocean and in large seas.

Direct measurements, with current meters, of tidal currents in the ocean are not easy to take (for the technique, see Chapter 6). They have been taken by various expeditions, including the *Michael Sars* expedition in 1910, in the vicinity of the Azores and the Canary Islands; the *Meteor* expedition, mainly in the South Atlantic; the *Snellius* in East Indian waters, and several later expeditions. Velocities in the open ocean appear to be no more than 30 centimetres per second, or thereabouts.

Tidal currents in oceanic regions near continental coasts, in adjacent seas and especially in bays and straits, are far stronger. Velocities in the North Sea off the Dutch coast reach from 1–1·5 metres a second and as much as 2·5–3 metres a second in the English Channel and the Straits of Dover. The strong currents in the Messina Strait, liable to attain to 3 metres a second, have long been well known. In the narrows of Chalkis, between the island of Euripos and the Greek mainland, the tidal currents are very capricious, now and then reaching velocities of 4–4·5 metres a second, or 9 nautical miles an hour.

Tidal currents are very strong indeed at the north-eastern tip of Scotland, notably between Scotland and the Orkneys (in Pentland Firth), where velocities of 4·5–5 metres a second have been recorded at spring-tide. Lastly, there is that enormously strong current between the islands of Taliabu and Mangoli, to the East of Celebes, which likewise reaches 5 metres a second, or 10 nautical miles an hour (10 knots). (*Note:* number of knots = 2 × number of m/sec., approx.)

Navigators need to know about tidal currents in certain maritime areas, especially in channels and straits, not only on account of their possible adverse effects, but also because they can be very useful under certain circumstances. If a vessel sailing through the English Channel towards the North Sea passes through the Straits of Dover just before high tide at Dover, she will have benefited for a whole six hours by the tidal current running towards Dover, and will again be sailing with the tide in the southern North Sea after the tide has turned, because the current there, as well as in the Channel, then runs out from Dover.

BORE

Near some river mouths the incoming tide (especially at spring-tide) rushes up the estuary like a wall of water. This is the 'bore', which the French call 'mascaret'. Another word for it is 'eagre'. It does not occur in all estuaries, only if the tide comes in very swiftly at a certain time, and the mouth of the river narrows too much to be able to cope with the inrushing tide. More and more water comes in from the tide, catching up with that which has already entered. It therefore piles up to form a steep wall over which water keeps plunging, like surf. It is therefore sometimes called 'tidal surf'.

Bores occur in several French rivers, like the Seine (where formerly heights of 4 to 5 metres used to be seen), in the Orne, the Couesnon (where it is called 'barre') and in the Gironde. The shoals at the mouths of the Seine and the Gironde have been dredged out, and nowadays the mascaret has almost disappeared. The English rivers Severn and Trent have bores. At present, scarcely any German rivers have one. The Codiac River, and the mouth of the Colorado in North America have them, and the famous bore in

South America is that called the 'pororoca', which is found in the mouth of the Amazon, and which sometimes reaches 5 to 6 metres.

The phenomenon is far more common in Asiatic rivers, such as the Hugli (near Calcutta) and the Megna; East Sumatra has bores in the Rokan and in the Kampar; and on the north coast of Borneo there is one in the Sadong and another in the Batang Lupar.

Lastly, the most famous bore of all is that of the Tsien-Tang-kiang, occurring at its wide mouth as a waterfall miles long and often 8 metres high, thundering upstream at a speed of sometimes 6·5 metres per second.

STORM SURGES

At the end of this chapter on the ebb and flow of the tides, let us dwell for a moment on a phenomenon which, although deriving from a totally different origin from that of the normal tides, which we call the 'astronomical tides', is yet in the nature of a 'flood' followed by an ebbing away. We are referring to the phenomenon of storm tides or storm surges and, more generally, that of the *effect of wind upon the water levels.*

We must, however, look at some historical facts before considering storm surges as a natural phenomenon.

SOME HISTORICAL FACTS

Outside our little quarter of the globe, tropical cyclones have caused terrible inundations by whipping up a surge of water and flinging it down on the shore. Take hurricane 'Hazel', in the autumn of 1953, for example. That particular disaster was not catastrophic, but in many other cases the damage caused by the hurricane was increased tenfold by the inrush of water. It was so in 1943, when the water claimed two thousand five hundred human lives in Cuba; and in 1900, Galveston in Texas was destroyed by a hurricane flood rising out of the Gulf of Mexico. Greater still were the disastrous tropical cyclones in the Gulf of Bengal, such as that of 1876 in the mouth of the Ganges (one hundred thousand victims).

An early storm flood in the history of the Netherlands was that called the St. Elizabeth flood, which, in 1421, engulfed seventy-two villages and killed ten thousand people. Then there was the All Souls' flood of 1570 and, nearer our own times, those of 1825, 1894, 1916 and 1953. In 1916 the Zuyder Zee dykes were breached in numerous places and the storm flood gushing through the gaps inundated vast areas of the Provinces of Noord-Holland, Gelderland and Overijssel. It was this storm which hastened the decision to enclose the Zuyder Zee. Similarly, the flood of 1953 put on the priority list the plans to shut off the inlets in the south-western part of the Netherlands. Actually, this was not the last exceptional storm surge to date. In December 1954 the North Sea coasts were to experience something even more rare, namely a twin storm surge.

We also remember the great storm surge of February, 1962, in the German Bight, which flooded part of Hamburg and its surroundings.

THE ACTION OF THE WIND

Let us define a 'storm surge' as a situation in which a storm whips up the level of the sea to a great height; this is the result of the combined action of the wind and the astronomical tide. To understand the part played by the wind, we must detach it in our minds from the astronomical tide, pretending for a moment that the latter does not exist. What is it, then, that the wind does?

In common parlance it is sometimes suggested that the wind piles the water up into a heap; but this might seem to imply that the level of the water would rise higher and higher if the wind continued to blow, and this inference is wrong. The fact is that the wind primarily causes the surface of the sea to slope and, if it continues to blow long enough with constant force and in constant direction, that slope will become stationary by getting into balance with the force of the wind.

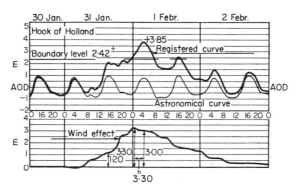

FIG. 93 The great storm flood of 1953. *Above* The registered water levels at the Hook of Holland and the normal calculated tide graph. *Below* The differential graph, representing the elevation of water levels caused by the storm.

For the North Sea, wind blowing from the north-west, i.e. along its long axis, is the most menacing. Assuming that the sea-level at the northern end, where the North Sea is in open communication with the enormous volume of the Atlantic Ocean, is more or less constant, a slope from north-west to south-east would present to the Dutch coast a rise in sea-level proportional to that slope and to the length of the tract of water subject to that gradient. Now, in equilibrium this gradient is approximately proportional to the square of the *wind's velocity*, and in inverse proportion to the average *depth* of the sea. For example, if a severe gale is blowing at 25 metres a second across the North Sea and we take the average depth to be 65 metres, this gradient is 1 in 300,000, i.e. 1 centimetre in 3 kilometres, which is very little. But if the wind blows over the whole length of the North Sea, and this gradient therefore also stretches across the full length from Scotland to the

Dutch coast, which is across, say, 900 kilometres, the elevation at one end is 300 centimetres. Thus, if the Dutch coast should happen to be that end, there will be a 3-metre rise above the levels of the tide table. This is what happened during the disastrous flood of 1953. In most places the maximum elevation then even exceeded 3 metres. Figure 93 illustrates the course of this storm surge at the Hook of Holland. The bottom curve shows, from hour to hour, the course of the additional elevation which is called the 'wind effect'.

COMPLICATIONS

It will be evident that something is calculable in the above situation; but, for all that, matters are not as simple as they may seem, for the formulated rule regarding the association of the gradient of the water surface on the one hand, and the wind and the depth of the water on the other, is valid only under very strict limitations—it might, indeed, be said, under model conditions. First of all, we have assumed that a condition of equilibrium has been established, as when the wind is stationary, or at any rate changes very slowly. Secondly, the rule applies only if there is no transport of water in the area of sea involved. Let us take the latter first.

Even if equilibrium has been established, there are three reasons why a significant constant transport of water may well take place. First of all, in the North Sea, there are the Straits of Dover, which act as a leak through which a current will be running, even if a stationary condition prevails, and draining water from the North Sea during a storm surge. Consequently, the levels along the coasts will be lower than if there were no such 'leak'. Given the postulated stationary condition, this does not mean that the water is falling owing to the leakage; such a leak will also drain a stationary current running from the north through the whole of the North Sea and bringing the levels of equilibrium along the coasts—especially in the south—lower than they would be without this 'leaking current'. Secondly, a transport of water in the sea may be due to differences in the strength of the wind above various parts of the sea. Imagine a north-westerly wind above the southern North Sea, blowing more fiercely along the British than the Continental coast. This will cause a general counter-clockwise circulation of the waters; that is, they will run southward *with* the wind along the British coast, but northward, *against* it, along the Continental coast. Finally, a current can also be induced by differences in depth of the sea affected.

Now every significant current, however induced, affects the water levels, owing to friction along the bed, which sets up a counterforce, and the rotation of the earth, which, through the Coriolis force, causes a gradient at right-angles to the current. Such currents, therefore, greatly complicate the relationship between wind and water levels.

As has been said, these complicating factors operate even when equilibrium prevails, but because of rapid changes of the wind field, it very often does not prevail. The sea is always trying to approach the equilibrium compatible with the momentary wind field; this theoretical equilibrium is, as it were, the aim towards which the sea is striving. But the aim is continually changing; evading the sea, if you will. This is a case, not of something 'lagging behind the facts', but of the 'facts' lagging behind something, namely behind that constantly changing equilibrium position. This is allowed for in the practice of forecasting water-levels. For the Dutch coast the Royal Netherlands Meteorological Institute reckons that the actual elevations arrive on an average three hours after the calculated (equilibrium) elevations. In extreme cases the time lag may exceed three hours, as can be seen in Fig. 94. This figure shows the course of the twin storm floods of

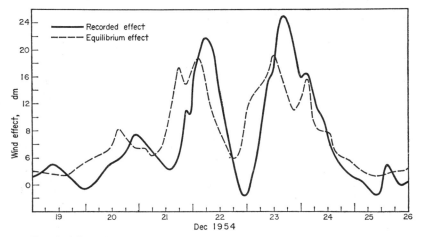

FIG. 94 The twin storm floods of December 1954 near the Hook of Holland.

22nd and 23rd December 1954, again off the Hook of Holland, by means of two curves. One curve shows the equilibrium levels calculated for every period from the wind field (the weather chart), and the other the actual elevations that occurred. In this case the lag was roughly six hours.

Another fact, besides the lag, is clearly evident from these graphs. Taking the first of the two peaks, we see that it is even higher than the maximum level of equilibrium. Because of its 'inertia', the rising water does not at once cease to ascend when it has reached the maximum equilibrium level, but overshoots the mark. This 'overshooting' effect is likewise allowed for in the practice of forecasting.

This, however, was not all, in the case of the twin storm. There were two successive storms, on 22nd and 23rd December, each causing a storm surge with an interval of roughly 36 hours. Now this interval is approximately the same as the period of the North Sea's *own oscillation*, by which we mean the kind of oscillation to which the waters of the North Sea will be subject if their equilibrium is disturbed in a certain way (there are various ways, as there are many directions, in which that equilibrium may be disturbed), and they are then 'left to their own devices'. As the interval between these two

PLATE XXII

Stranded iceberg in the evening of its life. (U.S. Coast Guard photograph.)

PLATE XXIII

Giant waves of the Antarctic Ocean. (Photograph Larisch.)

storm floods was approximately the same as such a period of natural oscillation, the inference is that a kind of resonance occurred, a phenomenon well known from the theory of harmonic oscillations.

On both 22nd and 23rd December, the peaks of the theoretical rises (hence those which would have corresponded to a balance of forces) at the Hook of Holland were approximately 1·90 metres; but the rises actually recorded were 2·30 metres in the morning of 22nd December, and 2·50 metres in the afternoon of 23rd. So, not only were they considerably higher than the equilibrium elevations, but they exhibited a kind of upward swing, indicative of resonance.

A subsequent theoretical analysis has shown that the rise associated with the second storm surge had practically reached the attainable limit at the strength of the gales. This means that, had other storms of the same strength followed, there would scarcely have been any further increase in the peak elevation owing to the internal friction of the oscillating water.

In the foregoing we have been referring consistently to the additional elevations, not to the actual water levels. This is because we were considering the effect of the wind independently of the tidal forces, assuming that all we had to do was to add the effects of the former to those of the latter. It is not a foregone conclusion, however, that such an assumption can legitimately be made; in other words, it is not a matter of course that, in this case, the effect of the sum of the causes is the same as the sum of the effects of each of the causes individually. However, the possible error involved in treating the matter in this way appears to be a minor one.

In the south-west of the Netherlands the peaks of the rises during the storm surges of December 1954 were reached, not at high tide but at about low tide. But things were different in the Wadden Sea; moreover, at places along the Frisian and Groningen coast an extra upsurge of the waters from the Wadden Sea was added on to the elevation of the North Sea, with very high water levels along those coasts as the result. Indeed, on both occasions the highest water level ever previously recorded was exceeded in the vicinity of Harlingen. At Harlingen itself the level rose to 3·70 metres above Amsterdam water-mark (AOD) and at Kornwerderzand to 3·90 above this mark. At the latter place the rise induced by the wind at first high tide on 22nd December amounted to 3·05 metres and at the second high tide on 23rd December exactly 3 metres. There is no doubt, therefore, but that this twin storm flood was quite exceptional.

Chapter Six

OCEAN CURRENTS

' There is a river in the ocean.'
(Maury)

'THERE is a river in the ocean; in the severest droughts it never fails, and in the mightiest floods it never overflows; its banks and its bottom are of cold water, while its current is of warm; the Gulf of Mexico is its fountain, and its mouth is in the Arctic Seas. It is the Gulf Stream. There is in the world no other such majestic flow of waters. Its current is more rapid than the Mississippi or the Amazon, and its volume more than a thousand times greater. Its waters, as far out from the Gulf as the Carolina coasts, are of indigo blue.'

Thus M. F. Maury in his famous book *The Physical Geography of the Sea and its Meteorology* (1855). Maury was an American naval officer who made a close study of the wind and weather over various regions of the oceans, and of the prevailing ocean currents. The experiences aboard merchantmen and warships sailing in those parts were his sources of information. He became the pioneer in the scientific compilation and analysis of these marine observations and in codifying the resulting data for the benefit of shipping.

He was by no means the first, however, to draw attention to the Gulf Stream, nor yet to map it. The first scientific chart of this mighty ocean current (see Fig. 95), dating from about 1770, was the work of Benjamin Franklin; and it was Alaminos, pilot of an expedition led by Ponce de Leon, who, in 1513, some twenty years after Columbus sailed for America, discovered the Gulf Stream in the Strait of Florida.

This great warm ocean current is the most familiar of all the phenomena of the seven seas. As schoolchildren we learned that we owed to it our temperate climate in western Europe, especially our comparatively mild winters. We shall presently consider that influence of the Gulf Stream on climate more closely, but let us first look at the map to see how Maury's 'river in the ocean' runs.

Franklin's chart (Fig. 95) does in fact show the Gulf Stream as a kind of river flowing through the apparently stationary surrounding parts of the ocean. Whereas it may be assumed that Franklin deliberately exaggerated the contrast between the current and the surrounding water, and will have known or surmised that sea-water nowhere remains strictly confined within certain well-defined boundaries, it is, nevertheless, a fact that the scientific world of his day was not all too well informed on the general movements of water in the oceans of the world.

The way in which Franklin came to draw up his chart is a typical instance of the conditions underlying the discoveries of those times. He was then Postmaster-General of the English–American Colonies, and he had noticed that the mail-boats often took two weeks longer crossing to New England than did many merchantmen, and notably whalers. In 1769 he found out from the skippers of the latter why this was; namely, because they knew the path and strength of the Gulf Stream, and made allowance for it when

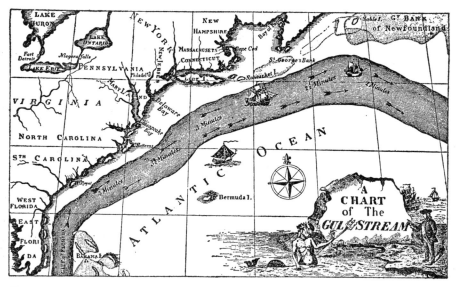

FIG. 95 Benjamin Franklin's chart of the Gulf Stream, 1770. In the bottom right-hand corner Franklin himself is seen talking to Neptune.

planning their course. He gained much detailed information from these seamen, and afterwards, building up his picture from the sailing experience of those days, he drew his chart. He gives four nautical miles per hour (two metres per second) as the speed of the first tract of the current and two nautical miles per hour (one metre per second) farther north, to the south of Newfoundland.

Later studies of the Gulf Stream were for a long time less concerned with measured displacements of water, such as follow from ships' observed positions, than with the effect of this current upon the temperature distribution over the surface of the Atlantic Ocean; for, as it carries warm water from the south, its course can be fairly well inferred from surface temperature recordings. In 1849, Von Humboldt stressed the great importance of the Gulf Stream to the climate of Europe, and in 1870, Petermann showed, from the temperature distribution of the North Atlantic (of which the ice boundaries are one manifestation!), that the waters of the Gulf Stream are

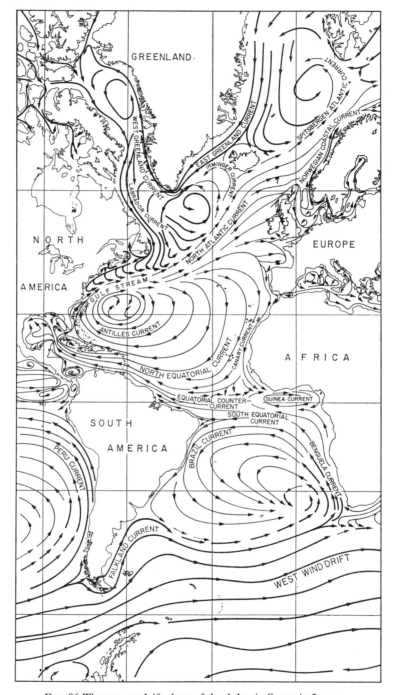

FIG. 96 The stream drift chart of the Atlantic Ocean in January.

noticeable in its last tentacles, right up to Spitsbergen, and in the Barents Sea. On the basis of these and similar considerations, somewhat over-simplified charts of the Gulf Stream continued to be drawn for quite a time.

In order to obtain an adequate picture of this ocean current as a movement of water, one should study the current charts constructed with reference to observations of ships' displacements. Such a chart is shown in Fig. 96. It will be seen that the Gulf Stream strikes one as anything but a 'river' in stagnant surroundings, though its course right up to Spitsbergen and beyond Cape North can easily be followed.

MEASURING THE FLOW OF OCEANIC WATER

It has been stated more than once that such charts of oceanic currents at the surface of the oceans are constructed mainly on the basis of data obtained from observations of the displacements of ships. Those who think these currents could be established with greater precision by direct measurement somewhere at sea, as air currents are on earth by taking local wind readings, are apt to forget that the observer in mid-ocean has not the benefit of fixed points like those along a river, where the rate of flow can be measured with reference to a bridge or points on the banks. At first sight a powerful movement of water like that of the Gulf Stream is unnoticeable from a ship on the spot, whether the vessel is sailing or merely drifting along with the current. It can only be discovered by taking accurate bearings at sea over and over again.

The only way to get a fixed point for direct flow measurement is to anchor a vessel (or buoy) to the bed. This has, in fact, been done right out at sea in water more than 500, 1000 or even 5000 metres; and the currents were then measured by the direct method with current-meters. A feat that has become classic was that performed in 1888 and 1889 by J. E. Pillsbury, an officer of the United States Coast and Geodetic Survey. From the survey ship *Blake* which lay at anchor for days on end, he took direct current measurements at various places with depths up to 4000 metres in the rapid Florida Current which is the powerful beginning of the Gulf Stream in the Florida Strait. In no other way can one really see how rapid the current is in places like that. The nautical technique required to maintain such an 'anchor station' is by no means easy, particularly in deep water. Later, led by Helland-Hansen the Norwegian ships *Michaël Sars* and *Armauer Hansen* lay at anchor in very deep water in the Atlantic Ocean; then there were the German vessels *Meteor* and *Altair*, the Dutch *Willebrord Snellius*, the American *Atlantis* and several other exploration vessels which lay anchored for varying periods (up to a couple of weeks) in waters more than 4500 metres deep. The anchors used weighed 180–225 kilograms and were attached to steel cables 1–1½ centimetres thick. The stronger the current is at the place where one anchors, the greater must be the slant of the anchor's cable to provide the necessary pull. In the strong Florida Current the length of the *Blake*'s

anchor cable was two to three times the local depth; but ratios of between
1·1 and 1·6 have been used for anchoring in the open sea.

All in all, the current readings taken from a vessel anchored in deep water
in the open ocean are still very few in number; too few ever to serve alone
for the construction of a chart of oceanic currents. Moreover, such figures
as we have cannot be taken at their face value, because a ship at anchor does
not lie absolutely still. She yaws; that is to say, at the free end of the anchor
cable she describes arcs of varying size through the water. As the current
meter suspended from the ship participates in these movements relative to
the water, the readings are imperfect and need correction.

As to the current meters themselves, most types consist essentially of a
sort of propeller or paddle wheel or the like, which rotates under the impact
of the water, the rate of revolution being recorded by a counting mechanism,
and, as the instrument has previously been calibrated, this constitutes a
measure of the velocity. If the driving mechanism is comparable to that of
a windmill, a kind of vane which is set in a certain direction by the current
has to keep the wheel or propeller directly facing the current. A vane of this
kind serves at the same time to show the direction of flow; it has a mechanism
by which its direction can be related to the compass North and either read
off when the instrument is pulled up, or recorded during the measurement.

We cannot here enter into the details of all the kinds of current meter,
that have been invented, some of which are very ingenious. Plate IX
illustrates an Ekman current meter, the classic instrument named after the
Swedish oceanographer who designed it. For a long time it was the standard
instrument used for measurements made at great depths. Many other types
exist nowadays, including those which are attached to a buoy where,
unattended, they record the current for a couple of weeks or transmit the
results immediately by radio. To avoid misunderstanding, we should add
that, although these current meters are not used much in the open ocean,
they have proved very convenient and useful for the study of currents in less
deep water, not far from the coast; this applies especially to the tidal currents
referred to in the preceding chapter. On various light-ships in the North Sea
(on all four of those of the Netherlands among others), continuous current
measurements are made by means of J. N. Carruthers' 'vertical log'.

Nowadays there is also an entirely different kind of current meter, which
records while suspended from a vessel under way. In America this instrument is known by the initials GEK, standing for Geomagnetic Electro-
Kinetograph, since it reacts to electric forces which are generated by the
geomagnetic field in moving sea water. We know that the latter is a conductor
of electricity, and it is a law of physics that, when such a conductor moves in
a magnetic field, it generates an electromotive force proportional to the
speed at which the conductor moves, and perpendicular to the direction of
movement and to the magnetic lines of force. A GEK has two electrodes,
acting as antennae, which are dragged through the water and, owing to the
phenomenon described above, acquire an electric potential difference; this

is a measure of the component of the oceanic current normal to the line connecting the two electrodes. Therefore, by sailing with the 'antennae' successively in two directions at right-angles to each other, one can measure the two components of the speed of flow which together determine the marine current. These readings need careful interpretation, however, because the electrical forces measured by the instrument are not determined only by the flow of sea-water at a single level. So, if the electrodes are dragged through the surface water, the velocities of flow at lower levels are also incorporated, to some extent, in the instrument's reading; that is to say, what one reads is a kind of average velocity of a certain layer.

The same electromagnetic principle upon which this instrument was designed has been utilized for measuring the current between two fixed points situated on either side of an arm of sea, such as the current running through the Straits of Dover. The electric voltage generated by the flow of sea-water between the two opposite coasts is measured by means of a telegraph cable. The tidal currents coming and going in the Straits of Dover were measured very neatly in this way.

An alternative method by which we can get to know something about ocean currents is that of keeping track of a drifting object, such as a bottle, an ice-floe or a drifting ship. Many tree trunks derived from Siberian rivers, which had drifted right across the Arctic Ocean, have been found in the Norwegian Sea. Glass balls, such as Japanese fishermen use, and flotsam from wrecked Chinese junks have been picked up along the west coast of North America, from which it can be inferred that a current runs from west to east right across the Pacific Ocean. Here is another example: In July 1884 documents and pieces of equipment were found on a drifting ice-floe near south-west Greenland; they came from the *Jeanette* which had been crushed in the ice on 12th June 1881 to the north of the New Siberian Islands at 77° 17′ N., 153° 42′ E. This discovery proved the existence of a marine surface stretching from Siberia to Greenland; and, as the objects were found on a drifting slab of ice, it was possible to estimate something like an average rate of drift.

When accidental discoveries like these are made, there are usually too many uncertain factors to permit any quantitative deductions. One may not know when the object started on its journey, or how long it had been lying on the beach before it was found; again, it may have followed a roundabout route, which one does not know; lastly, if the object projects quite appreciably above the water, its route may have been determined just as much by the wind as by the current. This is sometimes the case with icebergs, though when their base reaches far down in the water, as it often does, the movement of the water must be the dominant factor. Figures 43–45 show the drift-tracks of icebergs.

There is a very telling instance of the way in which wind and current may have contrary effects upon the direction of a drifting object. On 22nd June, 1892, there was a collision between the schooner *Fred Taylor* and S.S. *Trave*, when the *Fred Taylor* broke in two. This happened about 160 kilometres to the south-east of Nantucket Island, near Cape Cod (Massachusetts, U.S.A.). Both sections, carried along by the wind and the current, continued to drift for about six months, but strangely enough they went in contrary directions; the foreship drifted northward and eventually went aground on the Maine coast, whereas the stern drifted south-westward and finally sank in the mouth of Delaware Bay. Altogether, the two sections drifted some 700 kilometres apart. What had happened was that the forepart of the ship, which projected considerably above the surface of the ocean, was driven northward by the wind (which happened at that time to be predominantly a south-westerly). The stern, however, had settled down deeper into the water and was therefore more at the mercy of the current, which was running towards the south-west and carried the stern along with it.

More than a century ago attempts were made to gain better control of observations on drift by using 'drift bottles'. These are very carefully sealed and weighted (with sand, for instance) just enough to enable them to drift without projecting more than a very little above the surface, so that the wind can barely interfere with them. The bottle carries a card with a number—establishing the place and time of its 'launching'—and a request to the honest finder to complete the card with the place and time of its discovery and to send either the bottle with the card, or the card alone, to the appropriate institute. As a further precaution against any possible effect of the wind, a drift anchor, consisting perhaps of two crossed strips of metal, was sometimes suspended one metre beneath the bottle.

It is difficult to interpret the results of experiments with drift bottles, even if the exact times of the beginning and end of the voyage are known, because, as a rule, the route followed is unlikely to have been a straight one. The chances are, however, that many of the bottles will soon be picked up in an area like the North Sea, bounded as it is on the south, east and west by long stretches of coastline; and here a good deal of information can be obtained about the course of the current by collating the particulars of a large number. Figure 97 shows a pattern of lines of current in the North Sea which were derived from experiments carried out by Fulton (1897) with drift bottles.

Since the Second World War plastic envelopes, in addition to bottles, have been used on a large scale for the same purpose. Britain was among the countries that used them in the Atlantic to find out something about the spread of fuel oil with which ships contaminate the ocean and the beaches of Western Europe, and endanger the lives of sea-birds.

The success of all such observations depends upon the chance discovery of the drifting objects. The element of chance can be eliminated by following a floating object—for example, an almost completely submerged buoy—with a vessel (the vessel itself might be too much at the mercy of the wind), and keeping track of its exact position, which is quite feasible with modern electronic devices for location, such as Decca and Loran. If necessary, the position of a ship in relation to an anchored buoy can be determined very accurately by radar.

Even the course of the current in deeper layers of water can be measured in a similar manner. This is done with a 'Swallow buoy', so called after the English inventor of this ingenious method of current gauging. The Swallow buoy (also sometimes called a 'pinger') is so constructed that it can be made to drift at any depth desired. It sends out constant sound signals, which can be picked up by a ship several miles away; hence the ship can follow the 'buoy' and, by taking its own bearings, can measure the displacement of the buoy and thus the course of the current at depth. It was with this device

FIG. 97 Current tracts of drift bottles in the North Sea (after Fulton, 1897).

8*

that the countercurrent was discovered, which prevails deep down under the Gulf Stream.

Having shown what can be done today, let us remember the most 'classic' method of tracking ocean currents, namely by going adrift oneself, whether voluntarily or involuntarily, in a ship, in part of a ship or on floating ice. Instances were mentioned in Chapter 3 of those voluntary drifting voyages, especially in the Arctic Ocean.

After this brief digression into the observation of ocean currents by means of the drift of objects, ice or ships, we have, lastly, to consider the method adopted for computing currents from temperature and salinity readings taken at various depths and in different places.

The theoretical principles underlying this method will be discussed later. All we would say here is that deriving the course of currents from such data is comparable to deriving wind velocity on a weather chart from the distribution of the air pressure at a certain level, as the internal distribution of pressure to which the movements of water react can be calculated from the temperature and salinity readings. This provides a theoretical basis from which those movements of water can be computed if direct measurements are not available. Some degree of doubt may remain, but we shall deal with this presently.

It was stated in the preceding chapter that the International Ice Patrol employs this indirect method as a matter of routine (see Figs. 40 and 45). One of its advantages is that it is just as applicable to water movements at a certain level of depth as to surface currents.

This completes the review of the methods adopted to gain information about currents. All in all, it is still true to say that most of our knowledge of the great pattern of flow at the surface of the oceans rests on those good old observations made by commercial vessels; and indeed, they are still being made to this day. These observations are made by comparing the *position by dead reckoning* at stated intervals with the *true position*. 'Dead reckoning' is the nautical term for the position calculated for a given moment from a previous position, on the basis of the ship's speed and course with reference to the water; hence the position the ship would have reached after the lapse of a given time, if there were no current (or wind). The true position is that actually determined (by taking astronomical bearings or by using one of the modern radio aids to navigation). The distance from the position by dead reckoning to the true position is the distance of the vessel's displacement by the current. Leaving out of account for a moment the influence of the wind, the direction of this difference between one position and the other shows the direction in which the current is running, while its velocity is estimated by dividing the distance found by the elapsed time. If the wind is blowing hard enough also to push the vessel off course (this deviation due to the wind is called 'leeway'), this has to be allowed for in the dead reckoning. As to its direction, this can be gauged fairly easily in many cases by comparing the direction of the ship with that of the line of the wake behind her. That line indicates the actual direction in which the vessel is moving with reference to the water; if a strong side wind is blowing, that direction may be substantially different from her fore-and-aft line. Wind, of course, also affects the *speed* of progress; therefore, when a strong wind is blowing, it is as well, when making a dead reckoning, not only to rely on the theoretical speed of the ship, which is derived from the number of strokes of the engines, but also to measure its true speed through the water with a log. The simplest kind of log consists of a vertically floating block of wood, attached to a line marked at definite intervals; it is thrown overboard at the stern, and the line is paid out freely. With the aid of a watch or chronometer—formerly an hour-glass—the speed of the ship can then be gauged from the length of the section of line that had to be paid out within a certain time. In olden times the marks on the line consisted of knots, the distances between them being such that the number of knots paid out at the time when all the sand had passed through the hour-glass corresponded to the speed in nautical miles per hour. That is how the word 'knot' came to be a measure of speed, namely, one knot per 'glass' ($\frac{1}{2}$ min), that is, one nautical mile per hour. (A nautical mile is one minute of longitude measured along the Equator—1852 metres.) A knot amounts approximately to half a metre per second.

The practice is for ships' personnel to enter their calculations in their current log-books, and later to send these, together with the meteorological log-books, to the appropriate institute.

It will be evident that a single current observation may be subject to certain inaccuracies; but a reliable picture can be obtained by combining a great many observations and calculating the averages for each month of the year. The Oceanography and Maritime Meteorology Department of the Royal Netherlands Meteorological Institute at De Bilt, for instance, has records of ships' weather and current observations from 1870 up to this day—eighteen million in all—and has converted a large proportion of them into meteorological and current charts. The sea-chart having been divided into small areas, all observations are worked up statistically, by area and by month. Thanks to the work done here, and in institutes of other countries, we now have quite a good overall picture of the currents on the surface of the oceans, with the exception only of the Arctic and Antarctic Oceans, in which, of course, comparatively few observations have been made.

CURRENT CHARTS

Chart 4, opposite p. 317, gives a broad picture of the average currents in various oceans and seas in the early part of the year. Because it represents a general average distribution of current, we should not forget that the current actually changes from month to month. In the northern part of the Indian Ocean (see Figs. 99 and 101) the variations that take place in the course of a year with the changing seasons amount to a complete reversal of direction twice a year, namely, when the monsoon changes from east to west and vice versa. This is because the current here is predominantly driven by the

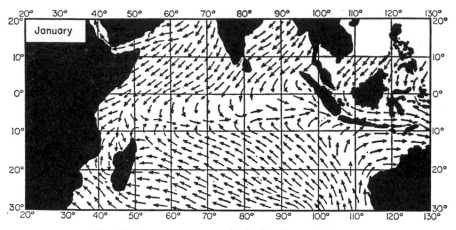

FIG. 98 Air movement over the Indian Ocean in January.

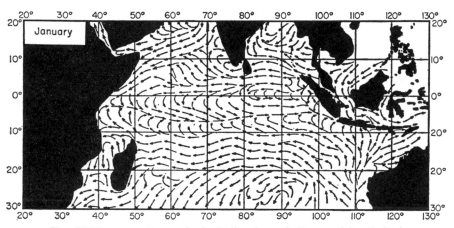

FIG. 99 Movement of water in the Indian Ocean in January (after Defant).

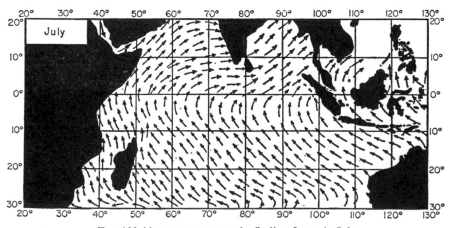

FIG. 100 Air movement over the Indian Ocean in July.

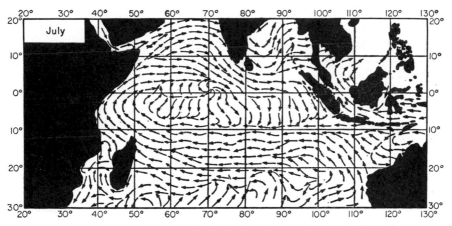

FIG. 101 Movement of water in the Indian Ocean in July (after Defant).

wind, and the change of the monsoons (actually the east monsoon is the N.E. trade-wind) is therefore followed by a reversal of the whole current pattern. Whereas the water flows from west to east in summer (Figs. 100 and 101), it runs from east to west in winter (Figs. 98 and 99).

Again, when we study a chart valid for a certain month of the year—like Fig. 96, representing the currents in the Atlantic for January—we must still remember that this, too, is an average, namely, an average drawn from the findings for the same month of many years. The flow of current in certain seas within the same month is liable to vary substantially from year to year, notably where two ocean currents meet, as in the region to the south of Newfoundland, where the cold Labrador Current coming from the north meets the warm Gulf Stream. An instance reflecting the differences which are apt to occur between like seasons of different years is furnished by the varying amounts of pack-ice (and icebergs) brought down here. We saw something of this in the section of Chapter 3 dealing with ice in the Atlantic Ocean. These irregular changes in marine currents must be due largely to erratic fluctuations in the wind systems. We shall see presently that these currents are kept going principally by the winds of the earth.

THE GENERAL PATTERNS OF THE GREAT OCEAN CURRENTS

A closer study of the world chart of marine currents soon shows that these follow a regular pattern. The most striking are the great currents running from east to west on either side of the Equator, in each of the three oceans, the *North Equatorial* and the *South Equatorial Currents*. On the western side of the Atlantic and Pacific Oceans the North Equatorial Current bends off northwards; the continuation of this current—called the *Gulf Stream* in the Atlantic and the *Kuru Shio* in the Pacific—turns eastward, runs on towards the eastern side of the ocean and part of it there loops back towards the south, thus closing the cycle. This mighty clockwise circulatory system is clearly developed in the North Atlantic and North Pacific, but there is not much room for it in the northern Indian Ocean, where, moreover, the situation changes with the seasons, as we have seen. A great circulatory system like this is sometimes called a circulation *cell.*

In the southern hemisphere we get a mirrored reflection of this cycle in each of the three oceans, including the Indian Ocean. Here there are clearly three cells, each with an anti-clockwise flow. A continuous flow from west to east—the great *West Wind Drift* connecting the three oceanic circulation cells and embracing the whole of the southern hemisphere—here runs along the southern margin of these vast current systems. This continuous flow cannot occur in the northern hemisphere, where the oceans are separated from each other by continents.

There is a different feature in the current pattern of each of the two big oceans of the northern hemisphere, the North Atlantic and North Pacific. An important branch of the east-west current running in moderate latitudes in both oceans goes off towards the north-east and north. In the Atlantic, part of this current, which, like that of which it is a continuation, is often also called the Gulf Stream, runs along the Irish, Scottish and Norwegian coasts, through to the Arctic Ocean; and part of it swerves along the coast of Iceland towards the west again, thus forming a kind of current circuit with a sense of rotation contrary to the great circulation cell to its south. In the Pacific, the corresponding branch flows northwards along Alaska (the Alaska Current) and farther on bends westwards; hence there too a kind of counter-cell is formed to the north of the main circulation cell.

Finally, there is a marine current, developed most clearly in the Pacific, but almost hidden on the chart, between the two broad equatorial currents; this is the *Equatorial Countercurrent.* It flows in the Pacific like a narrow river, yet clearly running from west to east, some five degrees to the north of the Equator, across the full width of the ocean, from the stretch between New Guinea and the Philippines to the head of South America. In the west it is fed by the great equatorial currents; in the east it swerves to the left and to the right to merge again with these two main streams. There is also an equatorial countercurrent in the Indian Ocean, notably in winter. In the Atlantic Ocean it is seen along the coast of Africa.

The mechanism behind all these currents will be dealt with later; our present purpose is to provide a descriptive overall picture. To complete this broad outline, reference must be made to the cold streams running southward along the north-western margins of both the Atlantic and Pacific Oceans, which can be regarded as compensatory for those penetrating far northward on the eastern side of these oceans, namely the East Greenland Current and Labrador Current in the Atlantic, compensating for the Norwegian branch of the Gulf Stream which penetrates even into the Arctic Ocean; and the Oya Shio in the Pacific, which compensates for the Alaska Current.

There are no such clear-cut north-south and south-north currents in high latitudes in the southern hemisphere, where the picture is dominated by the closed belt of the mighty West Wind Drift current. There is only the cold Falkland Current, which flows northward along the east coast from the southern tip of South America.

Lastly, there is the narrow stream from east to west (the opposite of the West Wind Drift) which laps the edges of Antarctica.

The principal ocean currents will be dealt with in greater detail later.

FORCES ACTING ON SEA WATER

Before taking a closer look at some of the outstanding currents in the oceans, it will be well to consider the forces responsible for these never-ceasing movements of water, and thereby, at the same time, to probe a little further into the nature of these currents. There are two kinds of forces that act, or may act, on sea water, namely, external and internal forces.

External Forces

The first of these is the dragging force of wind blowing over the surface of water, which we shall call the *wind drag* for short. It will be obvious that this force can initiate a horizontal flow.

There is also, of course, the ordinary air pressure which affects the sea's surface; a difference in air pressure between two places may produce a difference in sea level, and for that some displacement of water is necessary, but it is comparatively unimportant.

Then we have the forces of attraction emanating from the earth, moon and sun. It is more customary to speak of the first of these as *gravity*. This force is present in the sea, always and everywhere, but it is manifested chiefly by compression of the underlying layers of water by those above.

The attraction of the sun and moon, which is responsible for the tides, is likewise a typical external force; and, as was seen in the preceding chapter, it can induce tidal currents in certain areas. As powerful tidal currents, however, occur mainly in adjacent seas, bays and straits and, moreover, are alternating in type, they do not really fit into the picture of through-going ocean currents.

An external force of an entirely different nature is the *friction* set up when water flows along the sea bed. This friction exerted by the bed has little influence in deep oceans, but it may be a factor of importance in less deep water and in channels. As, however, it can only act as a brake, it can never induce or maintain marine currents.

Lastly there is the *Coriolis force*, to which all moving matter on the revolving earth is subject, on account of that rotation. It must not be confused with centrifugal force which, although likewise the result of the earth's rotation, is noticeable only by a very slight constant change in gravity which it brings about. The Coriolis force acts only on matter moving over the earth, and it is the rotation which generates it. Accordingly, the magnitude of this force is in proportion to the velocity of the physical object and to the velocity of the earth's rotation. The direction of the Coriolis force is normal to the direction in which that object is moving. Taking only the horizontal part of this force, which is enough for marine currents, we may put it this way: The Coriolis force tends to deflect every physical object moving horizontally on earth, towards the right in the northern hemisphere and towards the left in the southern hemisphere.

In addition to being proportional to the existing velocity, this horizontal Coriolis force is also proportional to the sine of the geographical latitude, from which it follows that the (horizontal) Coriolis force[1] is zero at the Equator.

From what has been said it will be clear that, while the Coriolis force may strongly affect existing movements of water, it can never initiate marine currents.

Internal Forces

First there is the *pressure* in sea-water, a stress which varies primarily with depth, but which also varies slightly in the same horizontal plane. That the internal pressure should be different at different depths is self-evident; the pressure at a given level down below is generally in equilibrium with the compression, i.e. the weight of the layer of water above it. Hence the deeper down one goes, the greater must be that pressure. But, as we have already said, this is where a vertical equilibrium prevails, and vertical movements do not arise as the result of that pressure, that is if we ignore the oscillating movements in the water waves.

Differences in pressure in a horizontal plane are another matter. The first question is how they arise. It should be recalled that roughly 10 metres of water represent a pressure of 1 atmosphere. Therefore, at a depth of, say, 200 metres there prevails a pressure of 20 atmospheres plus the air pressure, which is roughly 1 atmosphere, hence together 21 atmospheres. This applies to all points of a horizontal plane at a depth of 200 metres. If it be asked where, then, do the differences in pressure within such a plane come in, the answer is that those 21 atmospheres are not exact; 10 metres of water do not equal exactly 1 atmosphere, for the actual pressure depends on the exact weight of those 10 metres of water, and that again depends on the exact specific gravity, which in turn depends on the temperature and salt content. . . . Who can tell, moreover, whether an exactly horizontal plane is everywhere at precisely equal depth under the surface of the sea? Suppose that surface itself is not exactly horizontal, even if all the waves have been flattened out; then a horizontal plane inside the water will not be everywhere at equal depth beneath the surface and the prevailing pressure there will not be the same everywhere. See Fig. 102. Line *AB* represents the smoothed surface of the sea, *CD* an exactly horizontal plane, i.e. a plane exactly normal to the direction of gravity. If the depth *BD* is 50 centimetres greater than *AC*, then the surface of the sea will not be exactly horizontal; there will instead be a downward slope of 50 centimetres from *B* to *A*. That kind of

---

[1] For the sake of brevity we shall usually, henceforth, omit 'horizontal'.

thing does actually occur, though a considerable distance (maybe one hundred kilometres or more) between A and B is needed to produce a difference of half a metre. Then if the depth at AC is 5 metres, that at BD is 5·5 metres. If the water below B has the same temperature and salinity as the water under A, the difference in pressure between C and D will therefore equal the pressure of 50 centimetres of water. This is not much along such a distance, but it is enough to create within a horizontal plane CD a difference in pressure capable of setting the water in motion horizontally. As gravity does not operate along a horizontal plane like this, it cannot neutralize this difference in pressure, however small it may be. The pressure in D is greater than in C; the water in between will therefore tend to be pushed from right to left. This drop in pressure within a horizontal plane in the sea is called a horizontal pressure *gradient*.

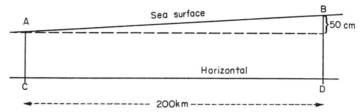

FIG. 102 Vertical cross-section to illustrate how a horizontal gradient of pressure is brought about.

Let us suppose that C and D are not 5·0 and 5·5 metres, but 500·0 and 500·5 metres under the surface of the sea. This by no means necessarily implies that the pressure in D is again 50 centimetres water pressure greater than in C, for the weights of the long columns of water above C and D depend on the temperatures and salinities above them. Indeed, the specific gravity of the sea-water above C *could* so much exceed that of the water above D that the pressure in the former (even though above it there is half a metre less water) would be even greater than in the latter.

However these pressure differences may be, it is a fact that they are generally liable to occur in a horizontal level both at minor and at major depths, also that they are mostly small compared with the absolute pressures prevailing at considerable depths.

The *decibar* is a unit of pressure often used in the physics of the sea; it is equal to 100 *millibars* (a familiar word in weather reports, in which it is used to express the air pressure (barometer reading)). As the millibar quite closely approximates $\frac{3}{4}$ mm mercury and 1 cm water-pressure, 1 decibar (1 db) is equal to 7·5 cm mercury and about equal to 1 m water-pressure. Thus the pressure difference of 0·5 m water, given above as an example, is 0·5 db; and the absolute pressures are approximately as much in *decibars* as is the depth in *metres*. It could be that the pressures in two points, C and D, of a horizontal plane situated at a certain place 500 metres under the surface of the sea were, for example, 512·34 db and 512·82 db respectively. The difference of 0·48 db is *relatively* small, but in itself it nevertheless generates sufficient force to set up a horizontal movement of the water at that depth. What happens to that movement is a matter we shall discuss later.

To sum up the foregoing, it can be said that there are active internal horizontal forces in the sea resulting from *horizontal pressure gradients* caused either by a slightly sloping surface of the sea across large distances, or by differences in the specific gravity of sea water, or by the two factors combined.

One more operative internal force to consider is internal *friction*. Wherever contiguous particles or layers of water are moving at different speeds, the faster-moving is braked in its speed by the slower, whereas the latter is dragged along by the faster-moving layer (or particles); the ultimate result of internal friction is a transfer of velocity from one layer of water to the other.

This completes our survey of the various forces that act upon or in the sea. These were:

External forces:

        (*a*) Wind drag
        (*b*) Air pressure
        (*c*) Gravity
        (*d*) Attraction of the sun and moon
        (*e*) Friction of the sea bed
        (*f*) Coriolis force

Internal forces:

        (*g*) Vertical pressure differences
        (*h*) Horizontal pressure differences, or pressure
              gradients
        (*i*) Internal friction.

We must now return to our ocean currents.

The main operative external forces in the mechanism of ocean currents are the *wind drag* (*a*) and the *Coriolis force* (*f*); and the internal ones are the horizontal *pressure gradients* (*h*) and *internal friction* (*i*). Although gravity (*c*) and vertical pressure differences (*g*) are very important in themselves, they always cancel each other out almost exactly, as we have seen; air pressure (*b*) is less important, as is also, at first, the friction of the sea bed (*e*) in sufficiently deep seas; while the sun and moon are responsible only for the to-and-fro movements of the tidal currents.

This leaves us, as the main active factors, the four forces mentioned, namely, *wind-drag*, horizontal *pressure gradients*, the *Coriolis force* and *internal friction*. We have deliberately mentioned these in a slightly different order because there is an important difference between the first and second pairs; the Coriolis force and internal friction become operative only in the presence of, and as a result of, movements. So they do affect (and very considerably) currents that exist, but they themselves can never set water in motion. This, on the contrary, is precisely what wind-drag and pressure gradients do; these two are as it were the motors, whereas the others stand only for steering and transmission.

Thus we recognize two distinct fundamental types of ocean current, wind-drift currents and pressure gradient currents, briefly designated as *drift-currents* and *gradient currents*. It does not often occur that either of these two driving forces acts alone; many ocean currents owe their existence to the interplay or counteraction of these two forces, but there are cases in which one or the other is clearly the dominating factor. Thus the North and South Equatorial Currents and also (in the southern hemisphere) the West-Wind Drift are clear examples of drift currents, though this does not necessarily imply that horizontal pressure gradients do not come into the picture at all. On the other side, the Gulf Stream, along the American coast, and the Kuru Shio (or Japan Current) furnish examples of gradient currents, though this does not mean that the wind does not affect these currents.

That the influence of the wind is so much greater in one case than in another can be explained by the fact that, in some regions, it is fairly constant and blows predominantly from one particular quarter; as, for instance, in the trade-wind belts and, to a certain extent, in the belt of west winds in the southern hemisphere. In other regions the winds are so variable, both in direction and force, that they play only a subsidiary part in the local impulsion of the principal currents there.

DRIFT-CURRENTS

It has long been known to seafarers that wind blowing over the water sets it in motion and may thus start marine currents on their way. A more elaborate theory was first suggested by the German physicist Zöppritz in 1878. According to his calculations, through friction with the water (dragging force) the wind would generate flow at the surface of the sea in the same direction as the wind. Owing to internal friction, the moving upper layer of the sea would set the layer underneath in motion and this in turn would do the same to a still deeper layer, and so on. In course of time—a very long time, because Zöppritz's calculations took into account only molecular friction, which is very weak—the whole mass of water from above downwards would thus be in motion, provided the wind was sufficiently constant, i.e. blowing predominantly in the same direction. All this water would be moving in the direction of the wind and, according to Zöppritz's mathematical equations, the velocity would diminish proportionally with increasing depth.

For about twenty years, the conclusions following from Zöppritz's theory were accepted fairly generally. It had, however, one important omission, namely that of the Coriolis force, the deflecting force of the earth's rotation. Zöppritz had ignored it because, compared with wind velocities, those involved in drifting currents are never very considerable; and because the Coriolis force is always proportional to the velocity.

In 1900 or thereabouts, Fridtjof Nansen was working out the results of his investigations into the movements of polar ice, with which he had drifted in the *Fram* through the Arctic Ocean in 1893–96. He was struck by the fact that, when the wind had blown in a certain direction for some time, the ice began to drift some 20–40 degrees to the right of that direction. After pondering over this strange phenomenon, he came to the conclusion that the deflecting action of the earth's rotation (the Coriolis force) must be responsible for it. He then reasoned further that deeper layers of water probably move in a direction deviating to the right even more than does the upper layer, his argument being that, just as the wind pushes the ice-fields and the topmost water, so does this upper layer drag along the layers beneath it; but, just as the upper layer (the ice) is deflected by the earth's rotation to the right with reference to the direction of the wind, so are the deeper layers of water deflected towards the right with reference to the upper layer, and therefore deviate from the wind at an even greater angle.

In 1902, at Nansen's instigation, Walfrid Ekman, then still a young physicist, studied the problem mathematically. The outcome was a theory of wind-drift currents taking account of the earth's rotation. In its simplest form, Ekman's theory is based on certain suppositions which, although simplifying reality, do not prevent the theory from presenting a good general picture of the nature of wind-drift currents. According to Ekman's theory, the current initiated by the wind deviates 45 degrees from the direction of the wind at its surface, notably to the right in the northern hemisphere and to the left in the southern. The theory furthermore bears out Nansen's conclusion that the movement of the water is deflected increasingly towards the right at lower and lower levels, until, indeed, there comes a depth at which the current runs in a contrary direction to that of the wind! The *velocity* of the current decreases considerably with increasing depth, in such a way that the figures form a geometrical progression (having equal ratios) when the depths form an arithmetical progression (equal differences). Here is an example:

Suppose the velocity at 30 metres' depth is $4/10 \times$ the velocity at the surface; then at 60 metres the velocity will be $4/10 \times 4/10 \, V$, or $0 \cdot 16 \, V$, and at 90 metres $4/10 \times 4/10 \times 4/10$, or $0 \cdot 064$ of the surface velocity.

In Fig. 103 a set of arrows shows the movements of water at various depths, according to direction and velocity. The topmost arrow points in the direction of the wind. If the tips of the current arrows are joined by an imaginary line in space, this line becomes a kind of spiral, called the 'Ekman spiral'. The depth at which the direction of the current arrow is contrary to the surface current is sometimes called the depth of friction, and at this depth the velocity of the current is only (roughly) 0·04 times that of the surface current. Below this depth the current is barely, if at all, perceptible. It could therefore be said that the depth of friction is the thickness of the water layer to which the movement is imparted by the internal friction, the value of this depth of friction depending on the degree of internal friction (or viscosity).

If the internal friction of sea water is known, Ekman's theory makes it possible to calculate the depth of friction. However, the use of viscosity values derived from laboratory measurements produces a rather astonishing result, namely that the depth of friction is extremely small, merely half a

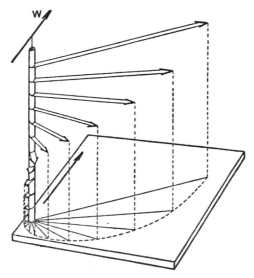

FIG. 103 The Ekman spiral. *W* shows the direction of the wind.

metre! The actual facts show, however, that wind-drift currents go far deeper; down to 100 metres or more when a strong wind is blowing. The facts would seem to be in serious conflict with the theory.

The only way to 'save' the theory is to take a far larger value for the internal friction than the viscosity, called the 'molecular viscosity', which is measured in the laboratory. One can put it this way: the depth of friction found in the sea *implies* a value of the internal friction in the sea, which is far larger than the molecular viscosity. It furthermore emerges that the value found in the sea increases with the wind. This far greater internal friction is called the 'turbulent viscosity' or 'eddy viscosity', and, as may be gathered from the term, it is accounted for by the turbulence of sea-water. By *turbulence* we mean a disorderly state of motion giving rise to a continuous commingling of small or large masses of fluid. Thus, stirring is attended by considerable turbulence; also, rapid flow along an uneven wall, or the passing of obstacles, sets up turbulence. In the ocean, the wind, together with the waves, causes turbulence, an intermingling of the uppermost layers of water, involving both their composition and thermal content; moreover, owing to this turbulence, the movement imparted to the 'face' of the waters is passed on downwards far more vigorously than would be the case through molecular internal friction.

On this basis, it is assumed that the layer of water above friction depth—to which the drift-current imparts itself—corresponds approximately to the layer which is mixed by turbulence caused by the wind. A mixed top layer like this is homogeneous in temperature, salinity and other properties; it is isothermal (of uniform temperature) and isohaline (of uniform salinity). Figure 28 provides an example of a temperature–depth diagram in which the isothermal top layer is easily discernible.

Although it would not be true to say that the depth of the homogeneous top layer and the depth of friction are quite the same, they certainly are very closely allied. Both increase with increasing wind strength.

The depth of friction depends on the geographical latitude as well as on the wind-strength. According to Ekman's theory it increases with decrease of latitude[1]; but the theory is no longer applicable to very low latitudes— places close to the Equator—because there the Coriolis force virtually ceases to operate (and Ekman's theory presupposes equilibrium between this force and internal friction). The following relation, based on experience, gives a good approximation for moderate latitudes and for not unduly light winds (more than $4\frac{1}{2}$ metres per second): Depth of friction (expressed in metres) = 9 times the velocity of the wind (expressed in metres per second). Hence, provided it blows long enough to bring about a stationary condition of flow (a provision which is basic to the whole theory), a wind of 8 metres per second will entail a depth of friction of 72 metres. Consequently, the drift-current will in this case be barely perceptible below those 72 metres. This example is valid for moderate latitudes, but the depth would be somewhat less at higher, and somewhat more at lower latitudes.

As to the strength of the generated drift-current, this appears to depend likewise on the latitude (similarly to the depth of friction) and to be approximately proportional to the velocity of the wind. At moderate latitudes the velocity of the drift-current at the surface will be about 1·5 per cent. of the average velocity of the wind. Thus a wind of 8 metres per second will be associated with a current running at 12 centimetres per second. It should be noted, by the way, that, like the dependence on latitude, the proportionality of current to wind follows from the theory, but the proportional factor (1·5 per cent. at latitudes around 45°) rests on experience.

Now, what of the observed deviation of the current relative to the wind? It is not surprising that Nansen should have found less than 45° in the Arctic Ocean, for Ekman's theory proceeds from the supposition that the wind has been blowing in one direction long enough to produce a stationary con-

[1] To be precise, according to the theory it is in inverse ratio to the root extracted from the sine of the latitude.

dition of flow and that current movements are unimpeded in all directions. The latter condition could certainly not have been met in the Arctic Ocean, as regards the movements of ice with which Nansen's observations were concerned, nor would the former (stationary) condition. Many current measurements were compared with the wind in the vast open oceans, long ago, by the Dutch marine scientist Gallé among others. Although sometimes smaller, and sometimes larger, values are found for the angle of deviation, on the *average* it was approximately 45°, except in the lowest latitudes. This deviation proves to be to the right in the northern hemisphere, and to the left in the southern hemisphere.

There is, besides those already mentioned, another condition of the simple theory of drift-currents. It was assumed in the foregoing paragraphs that the depth of the ocean was too great for the bottom to exert any influence. In waters of less than friction depth however, the current suffers friction from the bottom, and this affects both the strength and direction of such currents. In such cases, the current deviates less from the direction of the wind than it does in very deep water. The shallower the sea is, the smaller is the deviation of the current from the direction of the wind. This conclusion, which follows from mathematical calculations, has been found to be fully borne out by observation.

UPWELLING

A very different kind of complication occurs when a steady wind gives rise to a current running *near a coast*, for in that event the horizontal movements of the water are in large measure guided by that coast and the currents are therefore not unimpeded. A case in point is the north-west coast of Africa, where the wind very often blows parallel (more or less) to the shore with the land to the left, if one looks in the direction of the wind. This situation is represented by Fig. 104; to simplify matters, the coastline has been drawn from north to south, and the wind is approximately from the north, but slightly onshore.

The north wind will generate a drift-current which will deviate to the right (in the northern hemisphere) as the result of the earth's rotation. According to Ekman's theory the surface current would run out from the shore at an angle of 45°; a little below the surface, the water would run outward at a greater angle. (At one-fourth of the depth of friction the angle would be 90°.) Now the theory is valid only for a drift-current which is unimpeded on all sides, so we may not assume that the deviation angles mentioned will be found here near the coast. The fact remains, however, that the water set in motion by the wind is irrevocably driven sideways by the earth's rotation, unless there should be some counter-force to compensate for this effect. The result is that the topmost layers of water are gradually driven away from the coast. This, however, cannot continue without some compensation for the water driven away, and this compensation is effected by water carried up from below to replenish the surface flow

away from the coast. A slow circulation is set up as shown on the right of
Fig. 104.

Naturally, the water coming up from the depths is far colder than the
surface water which is carried away; that is why the inshore water in areas of
upwelling is far colder on the surface than elsewhere in the same geographical
latitude.

This rise of water from the depths is called upwelling, and it occurs along
the coasts of North-West Africa (Morocco), South-West Africa, California,
Peru and other places. In the northern hemisphere northerly winds, and in
the southern hemisphere southerly winds, cause upwelling along the west
coast of a continent. The cold surface water off the coast of Peru is particularly well known. The temperature of the sea along the coastline near

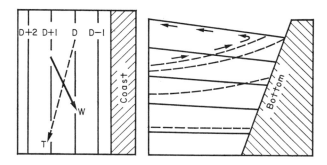

F$_{IG}$. 104 Diagrammatic representation of a situation when upwelling occurs as the result of a
steady wind blowing approximately parallel to a shore. W stands for wind and T for water
transport under the surface. Sea levels are denoted by $D + 2, D + 1, D, D - 1$.

Callao (latitude 10° S.) is often a mere 16°C, whereas temperatures as high
as 25°C are recorded at no great distance seaward in these tropical latitudes.
We shall have more to say about this cold water lapping Peru when, at the
end of this chapter, we come to discuss the effect of ocean currents upon
climates.

Another example is the region of Cape Guardafui, where, especially in
summer when the south-west monsoon is blowing along the coast (hence
this time a southerly wind on an east coast), upwelled cold water brings the
surface temperature of the sea down to 16°C, whereas 250 kilometres farther
north it is 28°C.

The water welling up does not come from any great depth, usually from
200–300 metres, but it is enough to make a considerable difference to the
surface temperature. It is, therefore, the upper 200–300 metres of water
which participate in the vertical circulation shown on the right of Fig. 104.
This replacement of warmer (lighter) by colder (heavier) water has its
impact upon the distribution of pressure in the mass of water involved, and
therefore upon the slope of the sea's surface; consequently the wind is here

indirectly responsible for pressure distribution changes which, in turn, cause other movements of water. This, however, is a subject to be considered when we come to discuss gradient currents.

Lastly, upwelling plays an important part in the foodstuff economy of the sea. The rising water brings to the surface nutrients (generated by the decomposition of organic remains which had sunk down) which there replenish the foodstuffs for vegetable plankton. Indeed, the sea teems with life in places where upwelling occurs.

DIVERGENCES AND CONVERGENCES

The situation associated with upwelling, as outlined above, can equally well be described as *divergence*. In cases like that represented by Fig. 104, the water at some distance from the shore has a component of movement away from the coast, while immediately inshore the movement cannot be other than parallel to the coast. In between, therefore, a divergence takes place, and it is this which would cause a deficit if there were no compensating supply of water from below. This vertical movement is extremely slow, and the surface transport away from the coast also proceeds slowly.

The opposite of divergence is *convergence*, i.e. the meeting at a given place or stretch, of waters which are thereby to some extent forced downward. This process is likely to occur where a longshore wind is driving the water towards the coast, hence where the situation is the reverse of that shown in Fig. 104; the situation exists in the northern hemisphere when a northerly wind is blowing along the east coast of a country, as it often does on the eastern shores of Labrador and Greenland.

Convergence also takes place under the central parts of atmospheric anticyclones (high-pressure cells around which the winds blow, clockwise in the northern hemisphere and counter-clockwise in the southern hemisphere). The best examples are the semi-permanent, sub-tropical, high-pressure areas, one of which is the so-called 'Azores high'. Were the drift-current generated by this kind of anticyclonic wind system to deflect considerably to the right everywhere, the water would swerve towards the innermost parts of the area involved, and would inevitably pile up. Such an accumulation, however, would soon set up counter-pressure and the inward deviation to the right would be only partly developed. But, as there will be *some* inward urge, convergence will take place within the circulation cell, with the result that water from the surface will push downward in the innermost parts—the converse, that is, of upwelling. One site for this play of the waters is the Sargasso Sea in the subtropical part of the North Atlantic Ocean, around which the wind and current run in an anticyclonic sense; see Fig. 96. In the southern hemisphere there is a subtropical strip of convergence passing through all three oceans between latitudes 30° and 40°.

An even better-known example is the *Antarctic convergence* which, in the southern hemisphere, winds as a closed line around the Antarctic Continent, between latitudes 50° and 60°. As cold waters from higher latitudes and warmer waters from mid-latitudes meet more or less along this line or strip, the temperature at the surface of the sea there is found to make a considerable jump. Moving from the north (from lower latitudes) to the south, one may find a quite abrupt drop of two or three degrees within a very short distance.

Mention was made of this Antarctic convergence to complete our picture, but its generation cannot be associated with the mechanism of drift currents in such simple terms as the convergences and divergences mentioned earlier. It plays a conspicuous part in deep-sea circulation, a subject to be dealt with in our final chapter, and we shall have more to say about it there.

GRADIENT CURRENTS

Apart from drift-currents, which owe their existence directly to the wind, there are those differently-constituted currents which are controlled mainly by internal differences of pressure in the ocean, namely, *gradient currents*. Whereas it is in the nature of drift-currents to be confined to an upper layer of 50–200 metres thickness, there is no reason why gradient currents should not just as well prevail at lower levels. At most, it could be said that strong gradient currents are not likely to occur at very great depths because there are only slight differences in specific gravity there, and, most probably as a consequence of that, only minor horizontal pressure differences. It is by no means our intention to suggest that the deep sea is completely at rest—far from it! What we mean is that the strongest gradient currents are found at depths of less than 1000 metres.

To understand the mechanism of these currents in the oceans, it is necessary to distinguish clearly between the currents controlled by a gradient in rivers, channels and other comparatively narrow passages, like straits, and gradient currents in open seas and oceans. The former currents flow mainly in the direction of the gradient, which is also approximately the direction of the current bed. In contrast, the gradient currents in the open sea are largely controlled by the Coriolis force, and therefore do not run directly from higher pressure to lower pressure, but in between, with the lower pressure on the left-hand side (on the right-hand side in the southern hemisphere). We know that the pressure differences in a horizontal plane, at some depth, are small in comparison with the prevailing pressures themselves, but this will not deter us from referring to 'higher pressures' and 'lower pressures' on the analogy of 'high pressure' and 'low pressure' on a weather chart. Indeed, the situation is entirely similar. Just as, on a weather chart, the wind does not blow straight from high pressure to low pressure, but approximately follows the isobars (lines of equal pressure in a horizontal plane)—in keeping with Buys Ballot's law—so, in the ocean, the gradient current approximately follows the horizontal isobars which portray the pressure distribution in the sea-water. Such a movement can be stable precisely because, only when the lower pressure is on the left (in the northern hemisphere) relative to the direction of the current, can the pressure gradient force—directed towards the left—be compensated by the Coriolis force, acting towards the right. (See Fig. 105.) It is the earth's rotation which tends to make the current run normal to the direction of the steepest horizontal gradient. This state of things is fairly well realized in the ocean, as it also is at some altitude in the free atmosphere. Considering once again the situation as shown in Fig. 102, we now know that, thanks to the earth's

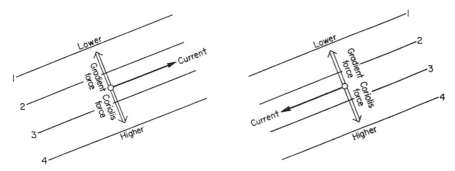

FIG. 105 Balance of forces occurring in association with a gradient current; *left*, in the northern hemisphere; *right*, in the southern hemisphere. 1, 2, 3, 4 indicate a progressive series of water pressures on a horizontal plane.

rotation (the Coriolis force), the current will run, not from *B* to *A* or from *D* to *C*, but right across the plane of the drawing, away from the observer (or, if the points lie to the south of the Equator, towards the observer).

Are we to assume that the earth's rotation is not involved in the former class of currents, which are guided more or less by their banks? No, but in their case the direction of the current is dictated by the bed and the velocity is determined by the friction along it. The Coriolis force operates in their case as everywhere else, but it merely produces a somewhat higher level of water on one bank than on the other. Thus, the waters of the Florida Current which, coming from the Gulf of Mexico, passes between Florida and the Bahamas, must stand a little higher on the right-hand side—that is, on the eastern side—than on the other. The extent of the difference in level can be calculated if the average velocity of the current is known, because the Coriolis force is proportional to it, and balances the slope of the water surface. The average velocity in the Florida Strait is approximately 1·2 metres per second, and at latitude 25° N. (on which roughly, the strait lies) this velocity entails a Coriolis force which is compensated by an average upslope of the surface (from left to right) of 7 in 1,000,000, i.e. of 7 millimetres in

1 kilometre. Applied to the width of the Florida Strait, this gives a difference in level of 60 centimetres between the average water levels on the eastern and western sides.

As the Coriolis force is proportional to the sine of the geographical latitude, for the same velocity, it is greater at higher than at lower latitude; hence it takes a steeper gradient to compensate for it at higher latitudes. Therefore, at latitude 50° N. or S., a cross-gradient of about 1 centimetre in 1 kilometre, or 1 millimetre in 100 metres, corresponds to a velocity of 1 metre per second.

To illustrate this, let us take an example a little nearer home. At Wageningen, in Holland, the Rhine is about 200 metres wide. Therefore, if its average velocity there is 1·5 metres a second, the transverse slope of the water as the result of the earth's rotation will be 1·5 millimetres in 100 metres, hence 3 millimetres in 200 metres. This means that the water on the right bank must stand about three millimetres higher than that on the left bank. So the effect of the Coriolis force on a river like this is ridiculously slight. Nor, in fact, is the 60 centimetres' difference in level between the left and right banks of the Florida current very impressive. But the matter can be put in another way. In the examples given, the current velocity was known and the transverse gradient was the calculable result of the flow. But, in the ocean, there may be instances when the gradient is known, and the velocity follows from that. Then those small gradients become important. Let us look at this a little more closely.

With reference again to Fig. 102, suppose the horizontal plane of which CD is a cross-section to be *isobaric*, that is, to have the same pressure everywhere, and to be in repose like the whole mass of water under it. One of the implications of equal pressure everywhere along CD is that, per square metre, the column of water AC is just as heavy as column BD, which does not necessarily mean that they are equally tall. Let AC be 500 metres and the average temperature between A and C be 12°C, then the result of a 1°C higher average temperature (hence 13°C) between B and D will be that BD is taller by 10 centimetres than AC; this is simply the result of the thermal expansion of column BD with respect to the (equally heavy) column AC. Thus in this case a difference in temperature of one degree makes the sea level at B 10 centimetres higher than at A.

Now suppose that there is a physical cause maintaining this difference in temperature; the associated slope will then likewise tend to persist; but it can be in equilibrium only if a current is running normal to it, because the Coriolis force involved can compensate for the pressure gradient accompanying the slope of the surface of the sea in the uppermost layers. Without such a current the water would tend to run from B to A; with it, however, the forces are in equilibrium.

As to where that current comes from, it may be supposed that at first the water really does begin to flow from B towards A; but the Coriolis force then imposes a transverse deflection, hence an impetus away from the onlooker, and that continues until the movement is almost entirely from front to back (in relation to the plane of our drawing), with a velocity, moreover, at which the Coriolis force, which is proportional to the velocity and operates from left to right, just cancels out the gradient force, which operates from right to left.

Hence the velocity can also be calculated if the slope is known. And we already know that a very slight slope is enough for a measurable, indeed for a considerable, current. If the one degree Celsius difference in temperature referred to were found along a distance of 20 kilometres, this would produce a gradient of the sea's surface of 10 centimetres in 20 kilometres, or 0·5 cm in 1 km. We know that, at moderate latitudes, this corresponds to a velocity of half a metre per second, or one nautical mile per hour, or 24 nautical miles per 24 hours; certainly not a negligible current.

Suppose we were able—we shall see later how—to establish the differences in height between various points of the sea's surface over a vast area. We should then be able to map these differences and draw lines of equal height, *level-lines* or contour lines, in the same way as the height differences of a landscape are indicated on a topographical map. The only difference would be that the gradients of the sea's surface are slight compared with those found even in as flat a country as the Netherlands. Moreover, the major inequalities in the topography of the 'seascape', namely the waves, are flattened out.

Figure 45 provides an example of a sea-surface topography like this; it was constructed on the basis of measurements made by the International Ice Patrol in the neighbourhood of Newfoundland. The numerals on the contour lines stand for metres and are referred to a certain (to some extent arbitrary) zero level, which is irrelevant at the moment, as we are only concerned with the differences. As the reader will see, those differences amount to only fractions of metres, but we know that this is enough to involve marine currents. The use of such topography for the calculation of marine currents is entirely analogous to that made of isobaric weather charts for the computation of wind velocities. In so far as it may be assumed that in certain regions the prevailing movements of water are determined predominantly by the pressure gradients in the water and, therefore, near the surface by the gradients of this surface, we may conclude that, at a given point, the current will follow the contour-line through that point, since it has to run normal to the direction of the gradient and the contour-line likewise runs normal to it. Further, the current's direction is such that the lower parts of the surface are situated on its left side (right in the southern hemisphere); and its velocity is in inverse ratio to the distance between two neighbouring contour-lines—in exactly the same way as the relation between the wind's velocity and the distance between isobars appears on weather charts. Thus the contour-lines of this sea-surface topography can be regarded as stream-lines of the water movement. The velocity of the current can be calculated with the aid of a formula which produces the following results for various latitudes with a slope of 1 in 1,000,000, i.e. 1 mm in 1 km or 0·1 m in 100 km.

Table 24

Velocity of a gradient current with a transverse slope of 10 centimetres per 100 kilometres.

Geogr. lat. °	10	20	30	40	50	60	70	90
Velocity (cm/sec)	40	20	14	11	9	8	7	7

The figure given at latitude 50° agrees with the rounded-off value of 1 metre per second, already stated to correspond to a gradient of 1 centimetre in 1 kilometre in moderate latitudes.

This is all very well, but the question naturally arises as to how we are to determine such slopes, other than by deduction from the current velocities. The above discussion of Fig. 102 points the way. As stated, the slope of the surface of the sea is associated with the differences in specific gravity between the various water masses. An example was given of a calculation of the gradient, based on the assumption that at a given level deep down the water is at rest and a *horizontal* plane is therefore *isobaric*, i.e. without pressure differences. This primary assumption is highly important; we shall see that to prove it is the outstanding problem with which this theory of gradient currents is confronted. Meanwhile, accepting the postulate provisionally, the procedure for finding the differences in level of the surface of the sea is to work out the difference in height of two columns of water above two points (C and D) of the deep isobaric horizontal plane. The weights of these columns are the same (given equal diameter), since the pressures at their bases (at C and D) are the same; their heights must then be in inverse ratio to their mean specific gravities. The difference in height gives the difference in level between their tops (A and B).

The example given earlier, in which the temperature of one mass of water was 12°C and that of the other 13°C was, of course, highly simplified. Actually, the temperature changes from level to level downwards; so the column of water cannot be said to have one temperature only. Moreover, differences in salinity at various places and levels are not without effect and, lastly, the pressure, which becomes quite formidable at some depth, affects the specific gravity to some extent. These three factors make the calculations somewhat cumbersome and laborious and we shall not go further into them. The main thing is that the differences in level of the surface of the sea can be computed if, in various places, the temperatures and the salinities at different depths above the deep plane (assumed to be in repose) are known. To obtain this information it is necessary to measure the temperatures and collect specimens of water with the instruments described in Chapter 2, and that in several places (stations). Bodies like the International Ice Patrol, for example, make such 'serial observations' for the express purpose of finding out more about the currents in the area explored. And the deep-sea samplings of all important expeditions and oceanographic surveys, besides being dealt with in other ways and put to other purposes, are usually also worked over in the above sense for the 'dynamic' current computation. (The method was worked out chiefly by V. Bjerkens, the Norwegian physicist, meteorologist and oceanographer.)

The procedure for calculating the topography of the surface of the sea and thus of currents at the surface, is equally applicable to currents at levels below the surface. Charts like those of Figs. 40 and 45 can also be made in this way for deeper layers of water; in this case the lines do not denote the contour-lines of the sea-surface, but still, in such a chart they do carry the significance of stream-lines of the water movement at the given depth. These lines may be compared to isobars, lines of equal pressure in a horizontal plane, at about the depth under consideration.

One considerable difficulty, already hinted at, is to find the places in the deep where there is no current. These were our theoretical starting point for calculations of sea-surface gradients. They are, for instance, points C and D in Fig. 102, and there are reasons for assuming in other cases (see discussion of Fig. 110) that currentless regions in different places are at different depths. But can a general rule be formulated whereby we can postulate the existence of a currentless region at a certain depth in the sea? Without this knowledge there is no basis for dynamic calculations. Reverting once more to Fig. 102, if we do not know that the waters are at rest at the depth of C and D, then, for all our calculations, we still know nothing more about the currents above them than the *difference* between the current below and the current above. For, if we first pretend that the current in level CD is zero, calculate on that assumption the current in a higher layer of water, say the surface, by the dynamic method, and then abandon the assumption that the current below is zero, the calculated result will still be a valid expression of the difference between the currents above and below. Thus, if the gradient current is known at one depth, it can be calculated for others; and it would be very useful to know where there is no current at all.

Without actual current measurements, however, no general rule can be stated which would provide a guide as to the depth where there is no flow. In many cases it may be assumed that at great depths, for example, 1000 metres, the velocity of flow, if any, is so trifling that, compared with that in the upper layers of water, it may be set at zero. Yet there are known cases in which, although the water is in repose at a given depth, it is no longer so at yet greater depths, where it then moves in an opposite direction. This has been verified by direct current measurements on the west side of the North Atlantic Ocean near the Gulf Stream, as we shall see presently when considering the latter. There are also currents which are by no means negligible 3000–5000 metres down on the western side of the South Atlantic. There is, notably, a southerly current running parallel to the coast of South America at a speed of up to 18 centimetres per second and a bottom current flowing northward at up to 12·5 centimetres per second. This follows from a comparative dynamic analysis of the serial observations (not direct current measurements) taken by the *Meteor* expedition.

If the point of enquiry is the flow through an entire vertical cross-section of a sea or oceanic area, rather than the current in one particular place, and if that area is enclosed, or virtually enclosed, at one end, it is useful to know that the total transport through a cross-section must, on an average, be zero. (Were it not zero, the sea would have to ascend or descend at one end—irrespective of evaporation and rainfall—and this it does not do in the mean.) Cases in point are cross-sections of the Baltic and the Mediterranean, also of the Atlantic Ocean, between South America and Africa, since, together with the Arctic Ocean, the northern end of the Atlantic is virtually closed off. (The trickle of water let through by the Bering Strait is negligible.) If, therefore, we can assume that the total transport through a cross-section is zero, this is a datum which, combined with our dynamic calculations, enables us to discover the depth in the cross-section at which the coast-to-coast average of the current is zero. The mean 'zero level' thus found by calculation for the South Atlantic at latitude 29° S. was at 1300 metres depth; the total transport above it is northward, while that under it is southward.

Other means have been sought of ascertaining the level at which the speed of flow is zero, one being to take note of the oxygen content and find the level at which this is lowest. The oxygen content of the water in the deep sea can only be maintained by a kind of slow ventilation, consisting in the horizontal supply of oxygenated water deriving from places to which it has sunk from the surface. Where there is no horizontal movement there will be little ventilation and the oxygen content will therefore be very low. This reasoning is not entirely faultless, as it disregards differences in oxygen consumption (by animal organisms) at different depths.

A different approach to the problem, adopted by some, is that of studying the distribution of the salt content and drawing their conclusions as to the movement of the water from this quantity.

The slow currents at very great depths of the oceans of the world will be discussed in greater detail in the last chapter.

HOW SURFACE SLOPES AND PRESSURE DIFFERENCES ARE MAINTAINED

This question has not yet been dealt with at all, except where the current is given as the primary factor and the slope is therefore necessarily brought into being by sideways urge of the water as the result of the Coriolis force. In such cases, surface slopes and pressure differences are maintained by a current produced by other causes. Rivers and the Florida Current are examples. The cause, the driving force of such a current, is then either a pressure drop in the longitudinal direction of the current, or a wind. The origin of such a pressure drop (a difference in level of the water's surface—also called 'grade') is, of course, another matter. In rivers it is caused by the supply of

PLATE XXIV

In the long swell of equatorial waters. (Photograph Larisch.)

PLATE XXV

The ridge of a swell hides the Coast Guard cutter which is towing the ship in the foreground. (Photograph by Jan Hahn.)

water (melt-water, rain-water) from the hinterland, in conjunction with the slope of the bedding. The Florida Current will be dealt with presently. If the current is not the primary factor, and the transverse slopes are controlled by other causes, the latter may be either differences in specific gravity, or a driving-up connected with wind-action. An example of the effect of differences in specific gravity was discussed with reference to Fig. 102. Sea-level usually rises in the direction of heavier to lighter water and the current will therefore have the lighter water on its right (on its left, south of the Equator).

Differences in specific gravity are due mostly to differences in temperature. Of this, too, we have seen an example. To the extent that temperature differences are responsible for the grades, then, the course of the current will generally be so directed that it has the warmer water on its right, or the colder on its left (in the northern hemisphere). A striking example of this is furnished by that branch of the Gulf Stream which flows from Cape Hatteras north-eastwards along the coast of Newfoundland, with the warmer water on its right and the cold coastal waters on its left and, farther northward, the cold water of the Labrador Current.

It may now well be asked how such temperature differences are maintained. Differences in warmth caused by differences of climate, notably through the position of the sun in the heavens, cannot be the answer, seeing that they stretch across such vast distances that, even if they do cause a sea-surface slope, this will be too small to start off currents of any significance. Only considerable differences in temperature within comparatively small distances can cause significant gradients, and those differences can only be maintained if water masses of different origin, flowing from different directions, run alongside, as, for instance, in the above case of the Gulf Stream near the east coast of North America, where the cold coastal waters and the Labrador Current meet it.

Our next topic must be the effect of wind-drift on sea-level. If a drift-current is not free on all sides, there must necessarily be boundary effects which impart gradients to the sea-level. The associated phenomena have already been noted in the paragraphs dealing with upwelling, divergence (Fig. 104) and convergence. More precisely, a wind blowing parallel to a coast will set the water in motion in such a way that the earth's rotation will drive it towards the coast or away from it, depending on the position of the coast. The result is a slope, which sets up a secondary *gradient current* and this combines with the *drift-current*. Situations of this kind occur along the western shores of Africa and America, where, at subtropical latitudes, winds and currents are frequently observed to tend towards the Equator, when water is pushed sideways away from the coast.

The one-sided drive of the water is limited in these cases mainly to the warmer upper layer of the ocean. Consequently, only that warmer layer is thicker on one side (on the right of the current in the northern hemisphere) than on the other side; and, not only is it higher at the top (causing the slope),

9

but also deeper on the under-side. Hence in the regions referred to, the thickness of the lighter upper layer increases at increasing distance from the shore. See Fig. 104, right-hand side.

A similar situation prevails with the circular anticyclonic currents in the subtropical parts of the oceans where, as we saw before, in the innermost parts there is a certain amount of piling-up of the water which has everywhere drifted somewhat towards the right. Here again it is chiefly the lighter, warmer, upper water which is thicker in the inner parts than on the outside.

CLASSIFICATION OF OCEAN CURRENTS

Ocean currents can be classified according to different points of view. One, for instance, is the distinction made between warm and cold currents, which are of particular interest to the climatologist. From the point of view of *dynamics*, however, the forces involved are more important; but, as these too can be considered from two points of view, we have two dynamic classifications. There is classification *A*, based on the question as to what force compensates the Coriolis force with which the motion of the water is automatically coupled. The operative question for classification *B* is: What is the motive force of the current?

So far as *A* is concerned, the compensating force can be supplied by (1) the horizontal pressure gradient in the water, when we speak of a *gradient* current; or (2) the internal friction in and on the water, in which case we speak of a *frictional* current, or more commonly, of a drift current; better still, of a free drift current or pure drift current; this is apt, because compensation for the Coriolis force by internal friction *alone* is found only when the wind is exerting a frictional force at the surface, so that the current really can be called a (wind) drift-current and, indeed, a *free* drift-current if there are no acting horizontal pressure gradients. In actuality, gradient and drift currents are usually mingled in the sea.

Classification *B* is causal, and differentiates between the currents according to their energy supplier, namely, (1) wind-driven, or briefly, *wind*-currents; and (2) *gravity* currents. In the latter case, gravity makes the water flow from one place to another, either (*a*) as a *grade current*, because (in a river, for instance) the water runs down a slope which is not the result of wind action; or (*b*) as a *density current* owing to the juxtaposition of waters of different specific gravity, (e.g. in the Straits of Gibraltar).

A further differentiation is also possible for wind-currents. In case (*a*) the current may be the result of, and run coincidently with, the wind locally; we then call it a *direct* wind-current or wind-drift current. Then again (*b*) the current may be dominated by the wind *elsewhere*, a clear example of which is the Equatorial Countercurrent. In that case we speak of an *indirect* wind-current, or sometimes of a compensation current. Thus, in the latter case the current drains away water that has been piled up by wind elsewhere, or compensates for water drained away by that wind.

All this can be summarized as follows:

Classification A

Coriolis force compensated by	Current
I Pressure gradient forces	Gradient current
II Frictional forces	Friction current or free drift current
III Both	Mixed

Classification B

Motive force	Current
I Wind field	Wind-current
(a) Wind at site	Direct wind-current or wind-drift
(b) Wind elsewhere	Indirect wind-current, compensation current
II Gravity	Gravity current
(a) Slope of the surface not caused by wind	Slope current
(b) Horizontal differences in specific gravity	Density current

Let us now explore more closely some of the most striking currents of the oceans, again beginning, it need hardly be said, with the Gulf Stream.

HOW DOES THERE COME TO BE A GULF STREAM?

Why is it that such a conspicuously strong current runs on the western side of the North Atlantic Ocean and not on the eastern side? And why is this also the case in the North Pacific (the Kuru Shio) and, in the southern hemisphere, at the western boundary of the Indian Ocean (the Agulhas Current) and, to somewhat lesser extent, in the South Atlantic (the Brazil Current)?

The general pattern of the oceanic currents in moderate and lower latitudes is fairly clear. It is governed by the trade-winds which drive the waters westward; they then have to swerve towards higher latitudes, where they are driven eastward by west winds, and ultimately drain back towards the Equator. But why is the current flowing towards the Pole on the western side of the ocean so much more concentrated, and therefore so much faster, than the current flowing in the opposite direction on the eastern side?

The main credit for finding the way to answer this question goes to the American oceanographers Munk and Stommel. The crux of the matter is that, even if the wind is the same on both sides, the play of forces on the western side is different from that on the eastern, owing to the earth's rotation. As we know, the Coriolis force augments with increasing distance from the Equator. The front, i.e. the northern face, of a body of water on the western side travelling northward, therefore experiences a somewhat greater Coriolis force, directed to the right, than does its rear, i.e. its southern end;

(see Fig. 106). It is therefore subjected to a force couple, or torque, tending to rotate it clockwise (as seen from above).

By contrast, the forces acting on a body of water travelling southward on the eastern side of the ocean tend to rotate it counterclockwise; see Fig. 106, right. It is due to this difference between the eastern and western sides of an ocean that a current pattern is not symmetrical, even if the windfield, which causes it, *is* symmetrical. It can be demonstrated mathematically that this asymmetry culminates in compression of the current on the western side. Hence that concentrated flow there; hence the Gulf Stream and those other powerful currents mentioned above.

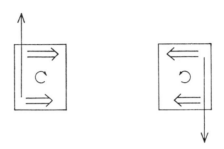

FIG. 106 Torque generated by the difference in the Coriolis force acting upon different parts of a body of water travelling northward (left) or southward (right).

THE GULF STREAM

Some historical facts pertaining to this ocean current were related at the beginning of this chapter.

If we look again at the chart of the Atlantic ocean currents (Fig. 96), we shall see that both the North Equatorial and a considerable portion of the South Equatorial Current are driven by the trade-winds along the northern coast of South America and Central America towards the Gulf of Mexico. Through the channels between the Antilles the current, which is here called the Caribbean Current, passes on to the Yucatan Strait, where it fans out into the Gulf of Mexico. Owing to this steady supply of water, an excess of pressure, so to speak, builds up here, the only vent for which is the Florida Strait. Accurate levelling has shown that the level of the sea in the Gulf of Mexico on the western shore of the Florida peninsula actually is 19 centimetres higher than on the Atlantic shore on the opposite side of the tip of the peninsula. This difference in level is enough to keep in motion the gigantic masses of water constantly flowing through the Florida Strait. At the narrowest part of this Strait, the Narrows of Bimini, which are 80 kilometres wide, concentration of the stream-lines increases the velocity to 1·7 metres per second in the middle. It should be noted that this is an average covered by some considerable time. Sometimes, in the middle, the velocity increases to as much as 2–2·5 metres per second; the great terrestrial rivers reach this only at high water. The fact that a ship, without any propulsion of her own, would be swept about 200 kilometres northward in the space of 24 hours by the current in the narrows of Bimini, may impress the reader more vividly with the significance of such velocities.

This mighty flow becomes even more impressive when it is realized that these tremendous velocities prevail, not only at the surface, but down to great depths as well. Figure 109 shows the distribution of velocity in the cross-section of the narrowest part of the strait. With velocities of more than 1·6 metres per second at the surface, water masses are being displaced at the rate of more than one metre per second in a cross-section 200 metres deep and about 70 kilometres wide. Six hundred metres down, the speed is still 40 centimetres per second on the right flank. These are exceptionally high speeds at such great depths. These data derive mainly from the admirable current readings taken between 1885 and 1889 aboard the *Blake* of the American Coast and Geodetic Survey under the leadership of J. E. Pillsbury, to which we referred earlier.

Only if the Florida Current is compared with the rivers of the continents can the significance of these figures be properly appreciated. Whereas the former is at least 80 kilometres wide, the depth of its current bed is 600–700 metres, as against the depths of rivers which amount to at most 5–10 metres.

Indeed, the masses of water gushing every second out of the Gulf of Mexico into the Atlantic Ocean are almost unimaginably huge: on an average the water transport here is 26 million cubic metres per second. Compared with this, the Amazon, the mightiest of all the rivers, is a mere streamlet, discharging 'only' one-tenth of a million cubic metres a second into the sea. The total transport of all rivers and glaciers is estimated at 1·0 million cubic metres per second. This means that, on an average, the Florida Strait conveys 26 times as much water as all the currents of the land together.

Figures 107 and 108 show the temperature and salinity distribution in the same cross-section as for the velocity distribution. A striking resemblance is at once apparent between the course of the isotherms and isohalines (lines of equal salt content) and that of the lines of equal velocity (Fig. 109). This is not surprising, seeing how much the velocity depends on the distribution of the specific gravity. The steep down-slope to the right of the water layers having temperatures between 20° and 10°C is most conspicuous. Whereas the temperature drops rapidly from the top downwards on the left flank of the current, the temperatures on its right are, on the whole, still something between 10° and 15°C, even 600 metres down. The water layers of 20–10°C represent the transition from the warm, swift-flowing, upper layer to the cold, more or less stationary, under layer. Hence the slope of these inter-mediate layers is just an expression of the fact that, on the right, the warm upper layer reaches much farther down than it does on the left. And this is a result of the strong Coriolis force to the right, to which the swift, warm upper current is subject, unlike the cold water underneath. As a consequence, these warm masses of water have been shifted to the right and have forced to the left the cold water below.

This means that the underside of the warm upper layer slopes down towards the right. As we have seen, the upper side, i.e. the surface of the sea, rises slightly to the right (there is 60 centimetres' difference in level between right and left); it is this downslope to the left that keeps the Coriolis force of the surface current in balance.

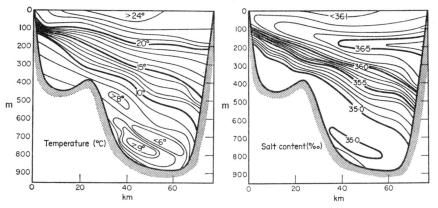

FIG. 107 Temperature readings in the narrowest part of the Strait of Florida, between Miami and Bimini.

FIG. 108 Measured salt contents in the same cross-section.

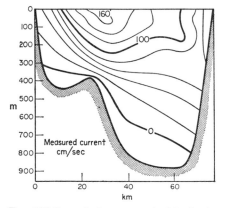
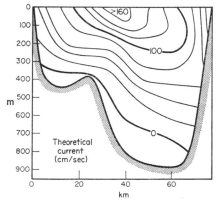

FIG. 109 Recorded current velocities in the Strait of Florida.

FIG. 110 Distribution of current in the same cross-section according to Wüst's computation from the distribution of the specific gravity.

In 1924, Wüst, the German oceanographer, applied to all the available records of temperature and salinity in the Florida Strait the dynamic method of current computation which was discussed above. Arguing from the distribution of salinity and temperature, he assumed that there was a stationary zone, slanting downwards to the right, at great depths. Thus he was able to *calculate* the velocity at a great many points of varying depths in the Strait—see Fig. 110—and to compare his result with the known *measured* velocities. The agreement between the two sets of figures is really astonishing; and this test of the validity of the 'dynamic method' has in fact contributed, in no small measure, to the confidence that has since been placed in it.

FROM FLORIDA TO THE NEWFOUNDLAND BANK

Let us now follow the Gulf Stream on its way to the north.

When it leaves the Florida Strait, its waters have temperatures of about 27°C and their salinity is 36·5‰; both high figures.

That part of the Stream which travels between the Florida Strait and Cape Hatteras, latitude 35° N., is also sometimes called the Florida Current. Here the Gulf Stream hugs the coast—brushing the continental slope down below—and flows on, at great speed, in the same direction it had when leaving the Straits of Florida. It is reinforced on the right by the *Antilles Current*, a branch of the North Equatorial Current which has skirted the Antilles. This reinforcement increases the transport of water from 26 million cubic metres per second to roughly 38 million. The Sargasso Sea now lies on the right; a sea famed since the days of Columbus for its great transparency and for the *sargassum*, a weed, masses of which float in some places on these waters.

A second portion of the Gulf Stream begins at Cape Hatteras. To the north of this cape, it is gradually pushed further away from the American coast by off-shore winds, the action of the earth's rotation (Coriolis force) and colder coastal currents. At first its average velocity is still considerable, having been established as 1·2 metres per second at latitude 36° N. and 1·4 metres per second at 38° N. As it is also reinforced on its right-hand side, in this neighbourhood, by water of high salt content from the Sargasso Sea, the total transport of water across the full width increases further to 55 million cubic metres per second. Farther on, however, some part of the mass of current again turns southward towards a zone of convergence in the Sargasso Sea, so that, by the time the current reaches the Great Bank to the south-east of Newfoundland, its volume has diminished to something less than 40 million cubic metres per second. Quite a respectable amount none the less!

These figures become all the more impressive when we consider that it is not so much the breadth of the current at the surface which is the exceptional feature of the Gulf Stream. It is apparent from a mere glance at a chart of the average ocean currents in the Atlantic (Fig. 96 for instance) that, at the surface, the Gulf Stream looks far less awe-inspiring than, say, the wide equatorial currents. But look at them about 200 metres down and the impression is very different. Our knowledge of what happens in the depths has been gained from the interpretation of a great many sub-surface observations made by various expeditions to the North Atlantic, notably of temperatures

and salinities at various depths in several places. As we have learnt, observations of this kind provide the basis for calculations of currents from the
premise of a prevailing balance everywhere between the Coriolis force and
the pressure gradient forces. Research work in these vast and deep oceanic
areas, however, is by no means complete yet. More specifically, little is
known, so far, about possible changes or fluctuations in conditions and flow
from year to year, though the average stream-lines are known approximately.
The closer these are together in some particular place, the stronger will the
movement of water be. (As we have already said, the lines can also be considered as isobars in a horizontal plane.) Already at 200 metres' depth,
and even more so at depths from 400 to 1000 metres, the Gulf Stream, by

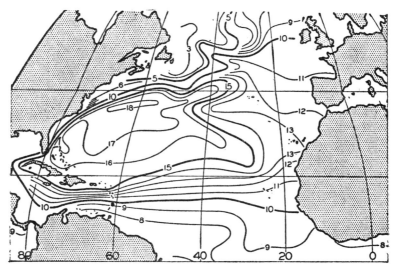

FIG. 111 Temperatures at 400 metres' depth in the western part of the North Atlantic Ocean.

the strong crowding of the stream-lines, strikes the eye as the *dominating*
current of the Atlantic Ocean, whereas drift-currents like the Equatorial
Currents, which are so mighty at the surface, are only just perceptible at
these depths, between latitudes 10° and 20° N.

Between Cape Hatteras and the Newfoundland Bank, the pressure gradients are being constantly strengthened by contact between the warm, highly
saline Gulf Stream water and the cold, less saline water masses of the coastal
waters, the Cabot Current and the Labrador Current. Thus, to the south of
the Newfoundland Bank, the Gulf Stream, now a *gradient current*, has, so to
speak, been injected with fresh potential energy.

Here, as in the Straits of Florida, the current pattern is closely associated
with the physical properties of the ocean water, particularly its temperature.
At exactly the place where the current chart shows marked crowding of the
stream-lines, a chart of temperature distribution in a horizontal plane in the
ocean reveals an exceedingly strong crowding of the isotherms, greater than

is to be found anywhere else. The depth to which the Gulf Stream extends can be seen on a chart of temperatures at 400 metres down (Fig. 111). Whereas temperatures around 6°C prevail at this depth on the American side, they rise to more than 16°C towards the ocean side. Here the right flank of the Gulf Stream is accompanied by a tongue of exceptionally warm water, ranging from 16 to 18°C, which is very unusual at this depth, as will be evident from comparison with the 8°C which prevails at the same depth under the Equator. The presence of this warm water here is due to the velocity of the Gulf Stream which, as a result of the earth's rotation, causes a deflection of the swiftly-moving warm water to the right and a downward accumulation, with simultaneous displacement of the cold, sluggish, deep water to the left; see Fig. 112.

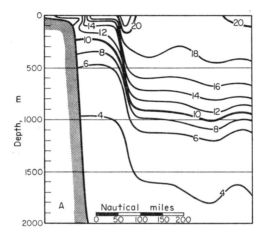

FIG. 112 Cross-section with temperature distribution in the Gulf Stream to the east of Cape Hatteras, according to readings taken aboard the *Atlantis*. The Gulf Stream is here concentrated within the narrow strip where the isotherms dip steeply. This shows that it is strongly developed down to 900 metres.

A COUNTERCURRENT UNDER THE GULF STREAM

It was discovered, in 1957, that a countercurrent runs from north to south, 2000–3000 metres down, under the Gulf Stream where it skirts the American seaboard. The discovery did not come as a surprise, for Stommel (U.S.A.) had already inferred the existence of such a countercurrent from theoretical considerations regarding the general circulation in the oceans. Wüst, too, (following Defant) had concluded, on the basis of dynamic calculations which started from the observed distribution of temperature and salinity in that region, that there must be a southward displacement of water at great depths there. These were, however, unconfirmed assumptions until soundings taken with a number of Swallow buoys in 1957 provided proof of that current's existence. Soundings taken aboard the English *Discovery II* revealed a current 2800 metres below the surface, running southward at

9*

velocities of between 10 and 20 centimetres per second. That is anything but slow at so great a depth. Somewhere between 1500 and 2000 metres down lies a level of virtually stationary water sandwiched in between the discovered deep current and the northward-flowing Gulf Stream.

Let us now return to the surface.

THERE IS A RIVER IN THE OCEAN

We have found that, in a surface-current chart like that in Fig. 96, the shallow wind-drift currents strongly influence the total picture, thereby relatively dwarfing a mighty, deep-seated current like the Gulf Stream. There is, however, another reason why the latter does not stand out in these charts as boldly as it should. The current velocities are not shown in our average charts, but if those calculated by averaging the many navigational observations collected over the years *were* shown, they would not convey an adequate impression of the velocities actually existing. Extensive research carried out since 1945, by oceanographers of the Woods Hole Oceanographic Institution, aboard the *Atlantis* and other vessels, has produced definite evidence of velocities in the Gulf Stream which far exceed those inferred from ships' displacements. These great velocities of 2–2·5 metres per second are confined to a comparatively narrow belt 20–30 kilometres wide, demarcated very sharply on the left-hand side (see Fig. 113). This belt does indeed run like a 'river in the ocean' (Maury), but like a meandering river, one that twists and winds and has a course that is far from being fixed. It has been found that, in a week, its course is liable to deviate in a certain region, by as much as 70 kilometres to the north or south. Flanking the main current, moreover, a marginal vortex, a stream circuit, often forms, in which the water close to the main current may sweep at a good speed in the contrary direction; counter-current velocities of more than 1·5 metres per second have been noted.

During a combined oceanographic campaign by six vessels in June 1950, one of these bordering eddies was seen to evolve from a double 'loop' in the Gulf Stream. The ships participating in this seventeen-day campaign (five of which were owned by the United States and one by Canada) reconnoitred and charted the Gulf Stream day by day from Cape Hatteras (longitude 76° W.) to south of the Newfoundland Bank (longitude 50° W.). A special watch was kept on one particular stretch during the last twelve days, because something unusual was seen to be happening. Two large waves were seen on the ribbon of current there, divided by a narrow hairpin bend (Fig. 114). At the end of the period of observation the current was seen to cut off this bend, leaving detached an elongated closed circuit of current at the southern end. This development can be seen clearly in Fig. 115, in which, as in Fig. 114, the pattern of the current is represented by a temperature pattern, notably the distribution of the average temperature of the upper 200 metres of water. It has been found that the isotherms of this

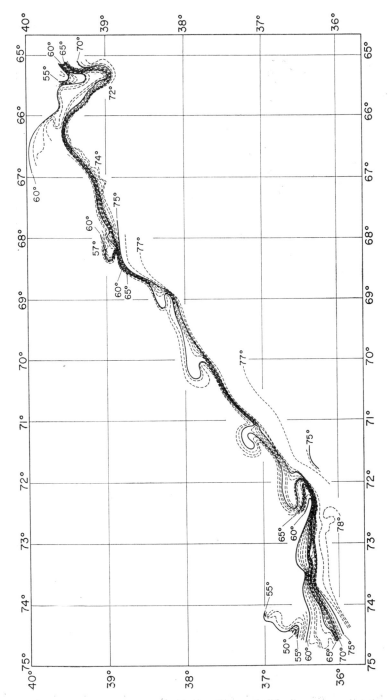

Fig. 113 The Gulf Stream in the second half of May 1946 (after Fuglister). Its course is shown by the strongly crowding isotherms of the sea's surface.

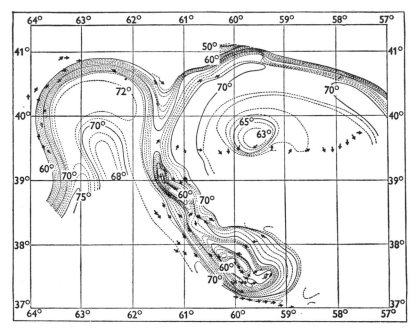

FIG. 114 Detailed pattern of a section of the Gulf Stream on 17th June 1950. The lines are lines of equal average temperature (in °F) of the uppermost 200 metres of water. Current readings are indicated by arrows.

temperature distribution actually do coincide approximately with the flow lines of the moving water; this also follows from current measurements made, in the course of this campaign, with the GEK described earlier in this book. The dividing line between water of below 65°F and the warmer water

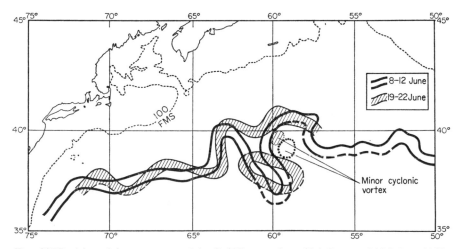

FIG. 115 Position of the warm core of the Gulf Stream about 10th June and 20th June 1950. The large bulge was cut off, leaving a circular current behind.

indicates the axis of the current, where the velocity is at its greatest; the current flows from left to right, and revolves anti-clockwise (cyclonically) in the cut-off circuit.

Another fact which came to light in these and other studies was that, farther on (for example at latitude 50° W.), the Gulf Stream throws out a couple of more or less parallel veins, in between which there is a strip with little flow, and even some countercurrent. The fundamentals of this are not yet properly understood.

It will be evident from the foregoing that the usual calculations made aboard merchantmen from the difference between the true position and that by dead reckoning are likely to produce only a nett effect comprising contributions by currents in various directions through which the ship has passed within the specified time. This nett effect, divided by the time, gives a much lower (because average) current velocity, of course, than the current actually encountered successively and in various directions. Considering, moreover, that the current has shifted backward and forward in a given area, so that some particular spot may now have been in, and later outside the main stream, and that the customary current charts merely indicate the average velocities in the various places, it will be obvious that the pattern shown by these charts must be so much 'evened out' as not to show the actual state of affairs at any given moment.

THE COLD WALL

The same applies to the temperature differences found on the left-hand margin of the Gulf Stream. It has already been noted that the part of the current running from north of Cape Hatteras to the Newfoundland Bank is bounded on its left by far colder waters. The temperature of the coastal waters above the continental shelf rises and falls with the seasons, but these waters are permanently colder than the warm southern water of the Gulf Stream. See Fig. 116.

The water between the inshore waters and the Gulf Stream moves from north to south above the continental slope; it is water of a more northerly origin, with an admixture of Gulf Stream water, which has turned off to the left farther up, and returns with this colder water. The boundary between this cold water and the Gulf Stream is very sharply defined, and it is referred to as the 'cold wall'. It is not unusual for the temperature here to drop by 10°C within a distance of 20 kilometres; and the difference in temperature fore and aft of a sizeable vessel crossing the borderline is sometimes quite marked. The colours are also markedly different, the Gulf Stream water being a deep blue, whereas the colder waters to landward are greenish and far less transparent.

From about longitude 56° W., the Gulf Stream meets the very cold Labrador Current on its left flank, which carries polar waters often burdened with ice, especially in spring. The meeting takes place to the south of the Great Newfoundland Bank, and is responsible for disparities in temperature, within short distances, which verge on the improbable. For instance, when the Coast Guard frigate *Tampa* passed the cold wall while on Ice Patrol in March, 1922, the temperature reading of the sea-water at her bows was 1°C, whereas that at her stern was 13°C, a difference of no less than 12°C! The

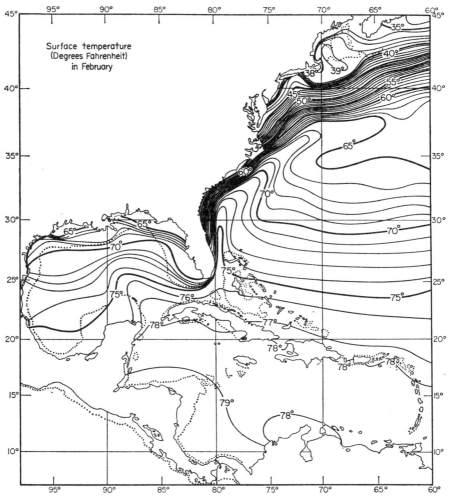

FIG. 116 Average temperature distribution along part of the East Coast of North America in winter (after Fuglister).

figures already given on page 111 are not as fantastic as these, but they too, are amazing enough.

The Labrador Current was described in some detail in Chapter 3. Some of its icy, eddying waters (see Fig. 39), mingling with the warm waters of the Gulf Stream, are carried eastward with the latter; some dive under them at the sharply-defined front formed between the two kinds of water. The confluence of the warm southern and the cold polar water in this region is responsible for the notorious fog above the Newfoundland Bank, to which we have likewise already referred. Some surface effects of this very dynamic oceanic region are depicted in Figs. 38–41.

THE NORTH ATLANTIC CURRENT

The continuation of the Gulf Stream, from Newfoundland to Norway, is often called the North Atlantic Current, though in common parlance the name Gulf Stream is often given to the whole current system running from Florida to North Cape. To the east of the Great Bank the Stream begins to widen gradually, at the same time flowing at a much slower rate than it did along its earlier course. Its speed drops below one nautical mile per hour (half a metre per second), the average becoming 5 nautical miles per 24 hours.

As it approaches the shores of Europe, a part of the Stream branches off to the south and becomes the *Portugal Current*. This proceeds on a southward course and, to the west of North Africa, merges into the *Canaries Current*, which, as it passes into the North Equatorial Currents, closes the great current circuit around the subtropical convergence area.

The northern branch of the North Atlantic Current turns northward along the coast of Ireland (where it is called the *Irish Current*). Another branch, the *Irminger Current*, bends to the left under Iceland, up to the southern tip of Greenland. The main stream proceeds further northward past Scotland and Norway, where it is called the *Atlantic Current* or sometimes the *Norwegian Current*. A small portion of the Gulf Stream waters also penetrates into the North Sea, mainly southward around Scotland.

The last offshoots of the Atlantic Current find their way to the west of Novaya Zemlya, into the Barents Sea, and along the West Coast of Spitsbergen. As we have already said, these farthest offshoots of the Gulf Stream are plainly shown by the boundaries of the pack-ice.

Thus, right up to latitude 77° N., these waters betray their partly tropical origin. Admittedly, first flowing along the northern coast of South America, then through the Caribbean Sea and Gulf of Mexico, and lastly beginning, at the tip of Florida, their long journey to the north, these waters are constantly mixed with colder water of more northerly and polar origin. Nevertheless, they retain the characteristics of their origin right up to high latitudes, namely higher temperatures than appropriate to waters at those latitudes, and greater salinity, likewise due to their origin in subtropical regions where there is little rainfall and much evaporation.

Finally, some of the waters of the Atlantic Current dive under the Arctic water which, containing less salt, is lighter in spite of its lower temperature. Atlantic water has even been detected deep down under the Pole itself. And this deep stream, distinguishable by its higher temperature and salinity, also extends far to the east; at depths of 275–950 metres it is found at longitude 178° E. and latitude 81° N.

THE GULF STREAM AND THE CLIMATE OF WESTERN EUROPE

One needs only to glance at a chart of the average sea-surface temperatures (Chart 2 at the end of this book) to realize how strongly the Gulf Stream affects the climate of the North Atlantic Ocean. Wherever the Gulf Stream system is well developed, the lines of equal temperature (isotherms) bulge markedly northward, with the result that the average temperature for the year is still 5°C at North Cape, the most northerly tip of Norway, situated at latitude 71° N.

This effect is also clearly manifest, as we noted before, in the ice boundaries of the northern part of the Atlantic Ocean (see Figs. 34 and 36), where the sea is generally still open, even in winter, to the north of Norway up to latitude 74° N. Readers will remember the difference in habitability between the coast of Norway, right up to the extreme tip, and the east coast of Greenland, which is blocked by pack-ice even in summer.

How does all this influence the climates ashore? Perhaps the answer is most apparent by reference to the so-called temperature surplus, especially for winter months like January. The temperature surplus for January at some particular place is the difference between the average January temperature there and the January temperature characteristic of that geographical latitude—in other words, the average for all places along that particular parallel. The mildness of the winter climate of North-West Europe is strikingly apparent from temperature deviations calculated in this way.

The greatest temperature surplus occurs along the Norwegian coast, notably to the west of the Lofoten Islands, where it amounts to 27°C. In Scandinavia and Iceland, this warming oceanic influence, for which not only the Gulf Stream water, but also, to some extent, the very presence of the sea, which tends to temper the climate, is responsible, amounts to roughly 15–20°C; in the British Isles, it amounts to about 15°C; in western France, Belgium, the Netherlands and North Germany to 10°C; in Russia and Austria still to 5°C, and it is only when we get down to the Black Sea that there is nothing left of any oceanic influence at all. Think, too, of the difference between the fjords of northern Norway, which are always open even up to latitude 71° N., and the port of Riga, 1500 kilometres to the south, at latitude 57° N., which is blocked by ice in winter, owing chiefly to its distance from the Gulf Stream system, but also, in part, to the meagre salinity of the Baltic.

The Swedish meteorologist Sandström said that, but for the Gulf Stream, Scandinavia would probably be just as much a desert of ice as Greenland, only the littoral of which can sustain Eskimos and arctic animals. It should be added that this description of the population of Greenland is no longer altogether valid, especially so far as West Greenland is concerned.

Oddly enough, the immense influence exerted by the Gulf Stream upon the climate of north-west Europe contrasts conspicuously with the slight effect it has upon that of the eastern parts of North America, even the coastal regions which it skirts. The winters in the north-eastern parts of the United States, for instance, are much more severe than those of the South of France and northern Spain, which regions are situated in the same geographical latitudes. Think of the notorious blizzards there!

At one time, there were some people who seriously considered plans for making the Gulf Stream flow closer to the Northern States of the U.S.A., hoping thereby to make milder the winters there. It is a positive fact, however, that, even supposing it were within the bounds of possibility to alter the course of the Gulf Stream (which it certainly is not!) the attempt would not only inevitably fail, but would probably have precisely the opposite effect. For meteorology teaches us that the action of warm sea-water involves more than meets the eye. North-west winds, i.e. winds blowing offshore, predominate in the north-eastern parts of the United States and eastern Canada, especially in winter; so it is scarcely surprising that the effect of the warm Gulf Stream waters should not extend to these regions. In fact, the warm sea-water to the south and east of Newfoundland is, in part, responsible for the predominance of the north-west wind here. Places on the surface of our earth which are warmer than their surroundings have a tendency to produce (thermal) low-pressure areas, and a low-pressure area of this kind has north-west winds on its western side; hence the prevalence of this wind on the western side of the Gulf Stream region.

The foregoing will have made it clear that the influence of the Gulf Stream upon the climate of north-west Europe is not as simple as might seem at first sight. It is not just a matter of the proximity of the warmer water; it is also the tendency of this warmer water to create a low-pressure area to the west of Norway, establishing the necessary conditions for the prevalence of south-west winds in western Europe. Hence it is thanks to the intervention of the air circulation influenced by the Gulf Stream that this part of the world benefits from the comparatively high temperature of the sea, above all in winter.

In conclusion, let us dwell for a moment, however superficially, upon the possibility of making long-term weather forecasts for Europe, on the basis of the Gulf Stream's influence. We know that this current is by no means invariable. Since Pillsbury's famous studies it has been known that the strength of the current in the Florida Strait is subject to considerable periodic and non-periodic fluctuations. Obviously, variations in the strength of the Gulf Stream will be reflected in changes in the weather, such as colder or milder winters, in the regions where its influence is felt. It is also a fact, however, that it takes quite a time for such changes in the Gulf Stream to cross from the western side of the Ocean to the European side, and to make their impact felt there.

Sandström demonstrated this on the basis of the occurrences between 1928 and 1930. There was a temporary strengthening of the Gulf Stream, and so long as this prevailed to the south of Iceland, east winds blew, chiefly across Scandinavia, bringing cold weather (the winter of 1928–29!); but the farther north it travelled, the more southerly did the wind become, finally blowing predominantly from the south-west. There followed the very mild west-European winter of 1929–30. In the summer of 1930 this mass of water reached the Arctic Ocean, where it caused rapid melting of the ice on the southern margin.

The interplay is, therefore, a complex one, involving a reciprocal relationship, in which marine currents influence the circulation of the air, while, conversely, the latter affects the currents. It is a complicated interaction, of which we are just aware, but which we have not yet fathomed sufficiently to be able to say with confidence: 'Study the Gulf Stream and you will know what next winter or summer will be like'. The whole subject still requires a great deal of study.

A BIRD'S-EYE VIEW OF OTHER OCEAN CURRENTS

THE ATLANTIC OCEAN

The foregoing discussion of the Gulf Stream and the currents associated with it comprised the main feature in the circulation pattern of the North Atlantic Ocean. In the north, there are furthermore, the compensating *East Greenland Current* and the *Baffin-Labrador Current*, which carry southward polar waters and large amounts of ice. Both, however, were dealt with in our chapter on ice in the sea, as was also the *West Greenland Current*, which runs from south to north, and is partly a continuation of the East Greenland Current mixed with the less cold water of the Irminger Current. The other part of the East Greenland Current turns off eastward, strikes the left flank of the Atlantic Current and returns northward with it. Figure 117 gives an idea of the currents in the Norwegian Sea and the adjacent marine areas of the North Atlantic Ocean.

The *North Sea* is one of these adjacent areas. The prevailing currents here, namely the *residual currents* which remain if we eliminate the tidal currents, are not strong. The pattern of flow in the North Sea is shown in broad outline by Figure 97. Atlantic water enters the North Sea mainly from the north, otherwise coming only into the most southerly part of it, via the English Channel.

Mainly an outgoing current of low salinity, the *Baltic Current* passes out through the opening of the Baltic Sea, between southern Sweden and Denmark, while under it enters the compensating stream of Atlantic water.

Something similar occurs in the *Bosphorus*, the mouth of the *Black Sea*. As the Black Sea receives far more fresh water from the great rivers emptying into it than it evaporates, more flows out in the upper current of low salinity into the Mediterranean than enters with the highly saline undercurrent. These currents are comparable to two rivers, one flowing above the other in a bed 4 kilometres wide and 40–90 metres deep. The outward and inward transport of water are estimated to be respectively 12,600 and 6,100 cubic metres per second.

In Chapter 2 we touched on the important currents in the *Straits of Gibraltar*, and we shall revert to these in our final chapter.

The wide trade-wind drift currents, the *North* and the *South Equatorial Current*, predominate in the equatorial part of the Atlantic Ocean. It has

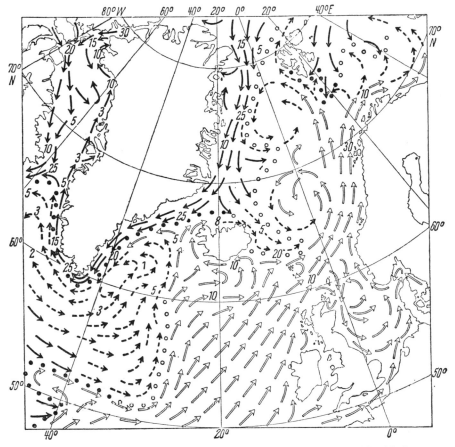

FIG. 117 Currents in the North of the Atlantic Ocean (after Dietrich). The black arrows indicate polar water, the white arrows Atlantic water, and the broken arrows mixed water. The points and circles stand for the so-called polar front, the points being placed where this front varies little. The numbers represent average velocities in centimetres per second.

already been said that a considerable portion of the South Equatorial Current swerves away along the north coast of South America towards the north-west, joining the North Equatorial Current and flowing with it (as the *Caribbean Current*) through the Caribbean Sea to the Gulf of Mexico.

Between the North and the South Equatorial Currents, in the eastern half of the middle part of the Atlantic Ocean, runs the *Equatorial Countercurrent*, which carries back a small quantity of the waters of the equatorial drift currents, notably the South Equatorial Current.

The mechanism of the Equatorial Countercurrent will be considered in greater detail under the heading of the Pacific Ocean, in which another such countercurrent occurs. Meanwhile, the reader is referred to the cross-section given in Fig. 118. Where the Countercurrent continues along the Ivory Coast and Gold Coast of Africa—as the *Guinea Current*—it is reinforced by the continuation of the *Canaries Current*. The latter flows from north to south along the west coast of North Africa, where it carries comparatively cold water, the effect of which is intensified by upwelling of subsurface water.

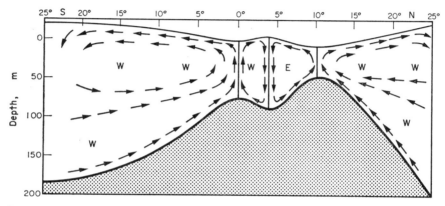

FIG. 118 Diagrammatic representation of the water circulation in a vertical plane, running from south to north through the region of the equatorial currents in the Atlantic Ocean in summer (after Defant and Sverdrup). The letter *W* marks the areas where the current flows westward, in between which it runs eastward. The shaded part represents the water under the thermocline which is presumed to be approximately at rest. The so-called 'equatorial undercurrent' (*see* p. 266) is not represented in this picture.

The pattern of circulation in the South Atlantic resembles that in the North Atlantic (around the subtropical area), but the sense of rotation is opposite. The *South Equatorial Current* forms the northern side of a kind of current circuit, the opposite side being formed by the broad *West-Wind Drift*. That part of the former current which does not flow towards the sources of the Gulf Stream turns off to the south and forms the *Brazil Current*, on the western side of the circulation cell. The *Benguela Current* constitutes the eastern side, a very strong oceanic current which carries cold water northward along the west coast of South Africa, and ultimately discharges into the beginning of the South Equatorial Current. In the same way as the comparatively low temperatures along the north-west coast are due not only to the Canaries Current itself, but also largely to upwelling, so the coldness of the waters brought to the south-west coast by the Benguela Current is accentuated by upwelling, with the result that here too, the temperatures are lower than they normally would be in these latitudes

(35°–20° S.). At latitude 30° S. the water transport of the Benguela Current is estimated to be 16 million cubic metres per second.

Whereas the warm current on the western side is the most important feature of the North Atlantic Ocean, to the south of the Equator it is the cold current on the eastern side, the Benguela Current, which predominates.

Lastly, a brief word about the *Falkland Current*. It runs northwards from the southern tip of South America along the coast of the Argentine, a cold current carrying northward waters, often iceberg-laden, from fairly high latitudes.

THE INDIAN OCEAN

Although part of the Indian Ocean is situated to the north of the Equator, it is difficult to draw a parallel between the currents in this part and those in comparable areas of the Atlantic Ocean, since the former, being more or less seasonal, and subject to the alternation of trade-winds and monsoon winds, are far more variable. (See Figs. 98–101.)

In February and March, when the north-east monsoon prevails, the North Equatorial Current is well developed, and an Equatorial Counter-current is also running, with its axis at approximately latitude 7° S. In summer on the other hand, when the south-west monsoon reigns, the North Equatorial Current is replaced by the *Monsoon Current* heading in the opposite direction. On the western side, where the current flows along the coast of Somaliland, the effect of the monsoon drift at this season is to initiate a strong upwelling which causes (relatively speaking) very low surface temperatures of the coastal waters.

The *South Equatorial Current* is dominant throughout the year, although its velocity changes a little with the season, running fastest during the southern winter. Part of this current turns southward on the African coast—chiefly west of Madagascar—and feeds the immensely powerful *Agulhas Current* (so named after Cape Agulhas), which transports more than 20 million cubic metres of water per second. The speed of this current, well known to seafarers in these parts, is barely less than that of the Gulf Stream. There have been reports of displacements of more than 100 nautical miles per 24 hours, corresponding to velocities of more than 2 metres per second or 4 knots (4 nautical miles per hour). To the south of latitude 30° S. the current is fairly sharply-defined and narrow; its outer boundary is less than 100 kilometres from the coast. As a gradient current, it must be associated with a transverse slope of the water surface which (being in the southern hemisphere) goes up from right to left, hence, in this case, rises from the coast outwards. At the latitude of Port Elizabeth this slope is estimated to be 30 centimetres for a distance of 100 kilometres, which corresponds to an average speed, within that distance, of 0·4 metre per second. As in the case of the Gulf Stream, the boundary layer, between the warm upper and the cold

lower water, slopes in the contrary sense, i.e. downward from the coast out
to sea. Therefore the warm upper water reaches least deep inshore and
deepest far out at sea.

To the south of South Africa, most of the waters of the Agulhas Current
swerve southward and then eastward, thus returning to the Indian Ocean;
they join the great west-to-east stream at the northern margin of the West
Wind Drift, which flows from South Africa to Australia. But a small portion
of the Agulhas Current continues westward, past the Cape of Good Hope,
into the Atlantic.

On the eastern side, near Australia and in the waters of the East Indian
Archipelago, the general pattern of the current is variable, following the
alternation of trade and monsoon winds.

THE PACIFIC OCEAN

The trade-wind drift currents predominate, of course, in the equatorial
part of the Pacific Ocean. Whereas the North Equatorial Current is always
within the northern hemisphere, the South Equatorial Current usually
ranges beyond the Equator, on an average to about latitude 4° N.

The Equatorial Countercurrent is very conspicuous and strong in this
ocean. It spans practically the whole breadth of the ocean throughout the
year, notably to the north of the Equator along the strip where there is little
wind—the 'Doldrums' in between the two trade-wind belts—which is
likewise situated just north of the Equator. It is this belt of calms which,
despite a slight movement of air, predominantly from east to west, allows the
countercurrent to flow from west to east between the trade-wind streams
moving in the opposite direction. Because the 'calm belt' lies in a somewhat
more northerly position in (our) summer than in winter, the Equatorial
Countercurrent also lies in its most northerly position in summer; but these
are no great displacements.

The velocities attained by the Countercurrent are liable to become quite
considerable, sometimes reaching two nautical miles per hour (1 metre per
second). The motive force of this strong current, which goes its own way
regardless of the local wind, is the propulsion of the surface water by the
two trade-winds towards the western side of the ocean basin, owing to
which it builds up to a higher level near Asia than along the opposite coast of
Central America. Within the two trade belts, this difference in level is
balanced by the pull of the wind on the surface of the water, but in the strip
in between, where there is little wind, this eastward downslope results in the
flow of a compensating current, like a river, from west to east.

Let us not, however, overrate the difference in level between the western
and eastern sides. Here we have another impressive illustration of the
ability of comparatively small differences between forces to keep the powerful mechanism of the ocean currents going. The estimated difference
between sea level on the western side and that on the eastern side is . . . 63
centimetres! This difference was calculated by the method briefly described

when we discussed gradient currents, that is, from the differences in temperatures and salinities (especially the former) found at the same depths in the west and the east. Calculations also show that the trade-winds are themselves sufficient to maintain this difference in level.

It will be evident, moreover, that the Countercurrent will likewise induce a drop in level across the direction of flow, just as the Florida Current is associated with a transverse slope. The Countercurrent is almost a pure gradient current between two drift currents. A cross-section can be seen in Fig. 118, but it should be noted that this figure applies to the Atlantic Ocean and that there is another feature of the Pacific Ocean, which does not appear in it, to which we shall revert presently. Furthermore, the Countercurrent goes far deeper in the Pacific, down to as much as 800 metres in some places. Between latitudes 4° and 10° N., in which the Countercurrent flows, the surface of the sea slopes down towards the north; as we look at this figure, the current is coming towards us, i.e. it is flowing eastward. To the left and right of this region, where the two trade-wind currents, the North Equatorial and the South Equatorial Current, prevail, the current is flowing away from us, towards the west.

The reader will have noticed that there is also a drop in sea level within these currents, despite the fact that they are drift-currents. This is because they are not pure drift-currents in the strict sense; that is to say, although the wind is their only motive force, there is nevertheless a certain amount of shifting of the water masses causing surface slopes. The situation is similar to that of drift-currents running along a coast. The Coriolis force pushes the surface water of the North Equatorial Current to the right; hence the formation of a kind of 'valley' on the northern margin of the Countercurrent, to the north of which the water level slopes upward. The surface water between the Equator and the southern margin of the Countercurrent is likewise pushed slightly to the right. (Here the current is again flowing from east to west, i.e. away from us.) That is why the sea level slopes slightly upwards from south to north here, too. But to the south of the Equator, the Coriolis force operates in the reverse direction, so the water within the same current (the South Equatorial) is pushed to the left. A 'valley' is again formed on the surface of the sea on the Equator.

The total water transport of the Equatorial Countercurrent is estimated at fifty million cubic metres per second, about the same as that of the Gulf Stream.

Just as there is a transverse slope of the interface between the warm, fast-flowing upper water and cold, slow-moving lower water in the Florida Current, a slope which is a strongly magnified mirror-image of the surface slope, so also do such internal slopes occur in this case; see Fig. 118. Whereas the isotherm of 12·5°C is found on the northern margin of the Counter-current, at latitude 11° N., at a depth of 60 metres, on the southern margin at latitude 3° N., it is situated 240 metres down, while at a depth of 60 metres water of 27°C is found.

In Fig. 118, the lateral movements of the surface water, to which reference has been made, are indicated by arrows. Since, as can be seen, convergence takes place on the southern margin of the Countercurrent, the water there has to sink, whereas divergence, and hence upwelling, occurs both on the northern margin and at the Equator. Along with all this, there is a slow circulation in the topmost waters. Were one able to follow the movements of just one particle of water, it would be seen moving mainly from west to east, but also to be included in a slower, transverse circuit. The combination of movements creates a kind of flat spiral path; flat because, in cross-section, the vertical dimensions—a few hundred metres—are far smaller than the horizontal ones, which span hundreds of kilometres.

There is one important current in the equatorial area of the Pacific Ocean not shown in Fig. 118, which was constructed with reference to the Atlantic. It is the *Equatorial Undercurrent*, discovered in 1952 and sometimes called the *Cromwell Current* after its discoverer. (In later years its counterpart in the Atlantic, though less developed, has also been found.) This fast current flows at some depth under the surface, exactly under the Equator, from west to east, hence in an opposite direction to that of the surface water, which at this point still belongs to the South Equatorial Current. It is 400 kilometres wide (between 2° N. and 2° S.), is roughly 250 metres thick (from, say, 30 metres to about 300 metres depth) and its axis is found in the middle of the ocean, at a depth of 100 metres where velocities of no less than 1·5 metres per second have been measured. Lengthwise it extends from at least longitude 150° W., to near the Galapagos Islands, longitude 90° W. Its water transport in the middle of the ocean amounts to 30 million cubic metres per second, so not much less than that of the Equatorial Countercurrent which flows at the surface, somewhat to the north.

Rather variable conditions, including great eddies, prevail both on the western and eastern sides of the equatorial area of the Pacific Ocean, where coasts force all east-west or west-east currents to bend. Near America, the Countercurrent despatches most of its waters northward and a smaller amount southward. Sometimes the southern branch is more than normally developed, and continues for a considerable distance to the south of the Equator. We shall revert to this later.

The most conspicuous current in the northern Pacific is that called the *Kuru Shio* (which means 'dark current') or the Japan Current. It shows a remarkable resemblance to the Gulf Stream in the Atlantic.

The source of the Kuru Shio is where the major part of the North Equatorial Current turns off northward along Luzon (Philippines) and Formosa. (A smaller part of it turns southward along Mindanao, and then feeds the Countercurrent.)

Up to latitude 35° N. the Kuru Shio hugs the coast of Japan, just as the Gulf Stream hugs that of the United States up to about the same latitude (Cape Hatteras). Between Formosa and the Riu Kiu Islands the current runs at speeds of up to 1 metre per second; it reaches a depth of 700 metres, and the water transport is estimated to be 20 million cubic metres per second. Farther along, the velocity increases considerably, 1·5–2 metres per second having been found at latitude 33° N., to the south of Shiono-misaki. Here the current is confined mainly to within 140 kilometres of the coast; farther out to sea there is a countercurrent running at approximately 20 centimetres per second.

At about latitude 35° N., the Kuru Shio sheers off from the shores of Japan, widening fanwise as it flows eastward and later merging into what is called the North Pacific Current. Meanwhile, the *Oya Shio*, a cold stream running southward along the coast of Japan, strikes the left flank of the Kuru Shio between latitudes 37° and 35° N. Here much the same thing happens as when the Labrador Current meets the Gulf Stream, although the Oya Shio is not as cold as the Labrador Current and does not carry icebergs. Numerous large eddies are formed between the two currents, the waters of different origin mingle to some extent, and some of the cold water flows eastward with the Kuru Shio whilst some of it submerges.

The *North Pacific Current* is comparable with the North Atlantic Current. Usually the northernmost and colder branch of the broad west-to-east stream is called by another name, viz. the *Aleutian Current*. Where it impinges on the American Continent, it turns partly northward along the coast as the *Alaska Current*, the climatic effect of which upon the western coast of Alaska is similar to that of the Atlantic, or Norwegian, Current upon the west coast of Norway.

The other important branch of the Aleutian Current runs southward, and ultimately along California as the *California Current*. Its origin being quite northerly, it is a rather cold current on that account, but also because northwest winds very often blow parallel to the Californian coast in spring and early summer, so that cold water wells up, with all the consequences which we have had occasion to note in various places. Although this upwelled water does not rise from any great depth—no more than 200 metres—it brings with it many nutrients ('fertilizers' derived from the decomposition of organic remains which have sunk downward). This creates an abundance of plankton which, in its turn, sustains plentiful animal life. The upwelling is a slow process with a vertical movement not exceeding 20 metres per month, and it ceases, together with the prevalence of the north-west winds, at the end of summer. The California Current then gradually withdraws from the coast, and for a time a south-to-north flow develops between this north-south current and the coast.

There now remains the South Pacific. In the eastern half of the ocean there is a clearly distinguishable current circuit between the broad *West-Wind Drift* (or Antarctic Current) spanning the entire southern hemisphere in the south, and the South Equatorial Current at the Equator. It is more difficult to present an overall picture of the western half, because the pattern of flow there undergoes considerable variation in the course of the year; but, for all that, a kind of current circuit is often quite evident.

The most interesting and best-known current of the Southern Pacific
is the *Peru* or *Humboldt Current* (see Fig. 119), which carries northward,
along the coasts of Chile and Peru, the comparatively cool waters of the
West Wind Drift. It can be followed to near the Equator, where it turns
westward to merge into the South Equatorial Current. Although it does not
flow very fast, its effect upon the temperature of the sea seems to be very
great, even near the Equator. We know, however, that upwelling is again
involved, owing to the predominant direction of the wind, which, because of
the earth's rotation, causes the warmer, upper water to be driven off to the

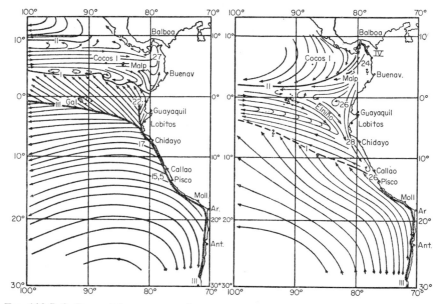

FIG. 119 *Left*. State of the current, and sea-water temperatures along the western shores of
South America in August and September. *Right*. El Niño, in March of the abnormal year
1891 (after Schott). Lines I and II mark the boundaries of the equatorial water; III is the
line along which divergence and upwelling occur.

left, i.e. away from the coast. Consequently, sea temperature off the coast
of Peru is only 16½°C at latitude 10° S. in August, too low a temperature for
the liking of most swimmers. This is in the tropics, be it noted, where,
elsewhere, the temperature of the sea exceeds 25°C. (The surface temperature 900 kilometres to the west is again 20°.) Passengers in a ship sailing
southward from Panama, after enjoying the tropical sun above the tepid
water become sharply aware of the change-over to the cold water of the
Peru Current, shortly after crossing the Equator. The air temperature
drops, and there is often an overcast sky, because the cold water is apt to
bring low clouds and mist with it. There is usually a rush to cabins for warmer
clothing!

Even though the Peru Current is limited to a width of some 800 kilometres, reckoned from the coast, and even though upwelling does not occur always and everywhere along the coast, this cold water dominates the climate of the littoral. It is a dry climate, because there is little precipitation from the stratus clouds.

THE OCEAN CURRENT CALLED 'THE CHILD'

During northern winter, a branch of the Equatorial Countercurrent passes southward over the Equator, along the Ecuador coast to latitude 2° or 3° S. (see Fig. 119). Because this current puts in an appearance there after Christmas, it is called El Niño (Spanish for 'The Child'). However, there are years, like 1891 and 1925, when El Niño penetrates much farther south and its warm waters mingle with the cold coastal waters off Peru. In 1925 this warm current reached almost to latitude 14° S. Over the whole area of its sphere of influence, temperatures were abnormally high. It would be wrong to imagine that this was a piece of good luck for the Peruvians, for it would not be an exaggeration to say that the consequences were disastrous.

When the warm equatorial waters mingle with the cool coastal waters, this spells death to the majority of the organisms with which this cool water is so richly populated, from plankton to fish. The beach is later strewn with dead fish, decomposing and polluting air and water. Sometimes there is so much hydrogen sulphide in the water as a result of this putrefaction that the paint on ships is blackened. The nickname for this phenomenon is 'Callao painter'[1] (Callao being a coastal town at latitude 12° S., close to Lima, the capital).

A more serious consequence of all this is the shortage of food for the economically important birds that live there, owing to which they die of starvation or disease or else desert their breeding grounds and so their young die; all of which means an enormous loss to the guano industry.[2] Added to all this are the meteorological effects of the water. Whereas, normally, the Peruvian seaboard has very little rainfall, the warm equatorial waters bring their load of tropical precipitation. In March 1925 this amounted to 395 mm at Trujillo (latitude 8° S.) against an average rainfall of 4·4 mm in the eight preceding years. It was again superabundant in 1941. These terrific showers cause flooding and serious erosion; the vegetation of the landscape not being inured to tropical rainfall, soil is everywhere washed away on sloping ground.

Abnormal atmospheric circulation, whereby there is a temporary complete absence of the south wind, which otherwise prevails almost up to the

---

[1] In comparatively normal years the cold, upwelled water seldom forms a continuous strip along the coast. There is often a possibility, therefore, for the less cold waters to mix with the colder, with local death of plankton and fish as the result. That is also why the 'Callao painter' is not wholly limited to the very abnormal years.

[2] *Guano* is the name for the excrement of these birds.

Equator, is responsible for the wide penetration of El Niño in some years. Of the one hundred and forty years between 1791 and 1931, twelve brought an excessive amount of rain, and twenty-one had moderate rainfall. In all other years there was little precipitation upon the northern part of the Peruvian coast.

El Niño and the Peru Current are certainly most eloquent examples of the effect oceanic currents can have on the weather.

Chapter Seven

CIRCULATION OF MATTER AND HEAT IN THE OCEANS

All the rivers run into the sea; yet
the sea is not full (Ecclesiastes)

WHAT an extraordinary thing water is! That may seem a strange thing to say about the most common substance in nature, and the one most used by man and beast alike. And in that sense it *is*, of course, the most ordinary thing in the world. In its physical attributes, however, it is unique, holding several records among fluids for such properties as thermal conductivity, solvent power, latent heat of vaporization and surface tension. It is also remarkable in other respects; for instance, in that it expands on solidifying (freezing), which is why ice floats on water. Again, it is the only substance occurring in nature in all three states of aggregation, solid, liquid and gaseous.

It is the special properties of water—far more than have been mentioned here—which make it the one substance without which life on earth would be inconceivable. All the processes in living organisms are intimately bound up with the unique properties of water. Seen in this light, the superabundant ubiquity of precisely this substance, H_2O, which is physically and chemically so strikingly exceptional, is a highly significant fact.

THE GREAT ECONOMICS OF WATER

The oceans form the vast reservoir of this substance. Those organisms which live in the sea—and they are by no means few—are surrounded on all sides by it; but those living ashore far from the coast benefit no less from this vast reservoir, for it is the sea which furnishes most of the water vapour to our atmosphere; that water vapour which is distributed all over the earth by air currents, and from which clouds and rain are formed and which, therefore, keeps rivers flowing.

According to reliable estimates, the water budget of the oceans looks something like this: The evaporation per year from all seas amounts to 360,000 cubic kilometres, which is approximately seven times the entire water content of the North Sea. To put it differently, this quantity corresponds to a one-metre layer of water over the total surface of all seas. All this quantity of water evaporates, and becomes water vapour. But rain (and snow and hail) also drop into the sea; thus 329,000 cubic kilometres return to the sea as precipitation. This income clearly does not cover the above expenditure; so the sea would be consistently losing water, were it not for rivers and icebergs which supply the deficit of 31,000 cubic kilometres, and thus balance the budget. Naturally, these 31,000 cubic kilometres of water flowing back into the sea from the land also appear in the latter's water budget as representing the difference between the quantity of precipitation on land (101,000 km³) and the amount of water evaporating from the land itself (70,000 km³).

In order to set at rest the mind of any reader who is inclined to regard this apparently specious balancing feat with some suspicion, let us suppose that the account did not balance, and that, for instance, the oceans' receipts exceeded their expenditure. If that were so, we should find the sea level rising, which would mean an increase in the total oceanic surface at the expense of land surface, the result of which, in turn, would be increased total evaporation from the oceans. Moreover, if the ocean's receipts exceed its expenditure, then either the land or the atmosphere must suffer deprivation, since the water entering the sea must come from somewhere. In the former case less water will flow from land to the sea every year; in the latter case there will inevitably be less precipitation. In either case, therefore, the oceans' income declines, and their expenditure increases. The obvious conclusion is that receipts and expenditure move towards each other, and that, eventually, a balance is struck. Similar reasoning can be applied to the opposite postulate, whereby more water evaporates from the sea than comes into it. In that case the above picture would be reversed; but, again, profit and loss would move towards each other eventually, and equilibrium would be established in the end.

EVAPORATION, PRECIPITATION AND THE SALINITY OF THE OCEAN

The foregoing figures have referred to the overall budget for the oceans of the world. They show that the total evaporation is somewhat in excess of total precipitation. If we study certain areas of the oceans individually, however, we find that this ratio of evaporation to precipitation is liable to vary from place to place. There are zones where precipitation exceeds evaporation, as in rainy areas at moderate and higher latitudes on the one hand, where depressions travel from west to east, and the equatorial zone of tropical rains on the other. As against this there are the subtropical high-pressure belts where evaporation far exceeds precipitation, thanks to the prevalence of clear and sunny weather.

These differences in water economy are, of course, reflected in differences in salinity. Wherever evaporation predominates, the upper layers of the ocean will become more saline through loss of water than in areas of preponderant precipitation, where the addition of fresh water lowers the salinity. That this is so is borne out by Fig. 120, one of whose two graphs shows the average differences between evaporation and precipitation at various geographical latitudes, and the other the average salinity, likewise for various geographical latitudes. The similarity of these two curves is striking, the salinity proving to be relatively high wherever there is much evaporation, and relatively low where there is much rainfall.

We are now faced with a new question. Does the excess of evaporation in subtropical regions steadily increase the salinity of the water; and does the surplus of precipitation elsewhere make the water become progressively less saline? Let it be said at once that we know from observation that this is not so. It must be inferred, therefore, that there is some compensation for these effects. This compensatory action must be attributed to the sea itself; notably to the ocean currents which ensure horizontal circulation of the water masses, thus preventing the build-up of large differences in salinity;

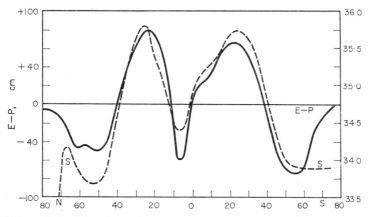

FIG. 120 The salinity (S) and the difference between evaporation and precipitation ($E-P$), on an average along each parallel of latitude, over the oceans without adjacent seas (after Wüst).

also to the slow, vertical circulation movements and turbulence in the oceans, which are constantly bringing new water, and sweeping away the old. The Gulf Stream, for instance, continually carries very saline water to higher latitudes; on the other hand, there are certain places, like the Sargasso Sea, where water which evaporation has made very saline, and which has therefore increased in specific gravity, sinks precisely on account of its weight. At greater depths, this water is then subjected to slow but steady water displacements which are in operation almost everywhere in the deep, and which form part of that great deep-sea circulation which we shall consider in more detail at the end of this chapter.

The foregoing furnishes an answer to the question of how the profit and loss accounts of the individual zones of the oceans can be made to balance if, unlike the oceans as a whole, they lose more, or less, water through evaporation than they receive through precipitation and supplies from rivers. (See Fig. 121.) Apparently, water is transported right through the atmosphere from the subtropical belts, to the areas in higher latitudes on the one hand, and to the equatorial zone of tropical rains on the other. How, then, are these losses and gains of water equalized, since, as we know, there is neither a fall nor a rise worth mentioning in sea level at the places concerned? Obviously by the movement of water in the ocean itself. There must be slow nett transportations of water in the ocean between the various latitudes, as indicated by the arrows in the water in the figure below. By 'nett transportations' we mean the difference, at a given latitude, between the transportations of the northward and southward currents, which may be flowing either at the surface or at great depths.

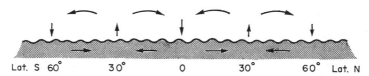

Lat. S 60°   30°   0   30°   60° Lat. N

FIG. 121 Diagram of meridional water transport through the atmosphere and the ocean.

RAINFALL ON LAND AND BRACKISH COASTAL WATERS

Above, we have given only the estimated total amount of water that drains off the land into the sea—the 'run-off', as we call it—namely 37,000 cubic kilometres. But there is much more to be said about it when we come to look at the individual marine areas. Seas like the Black Sea and the Baltic have low salinity because many rivers flow into them; consequently, a considerable portion of the precipitation falling on the hinterland ends up in these seas. Another instance is the St. Lawrence Bay, in which much of the run-off from the eastern parts of Canada and north-eastern parts of the United States is discharged via the St. Lawrence River.

Another fact about the Baltic Sea is that the influence of its waters extends far beyond its own confines. The brackish waters at its mouth form an upper current, the Baltic Current, which flows through the Kattegat and Skagerrak and proceeds along the coast of Norway, first westgoing and later northward, floating on the briny Atlantic water (which is driven northward by the Gulf Stream). Thus the rainfall of the whole of Scandinavia, and of a large part of Central Europe (which discharges surplus water through several rivers into the Baltic) manifests itself in the coastal waters of Norway.

The *differences* in run-off which mark different seasons are likewise reflected in varying salinity in marine areas of this kind, generally speaking, therefore, in the coastal waters. Lastly, differences in terrestrial precipitation in different years have their local effect on the sea water. An interesting example of this was worked out, a long time ago, by Helland Hansen.

Figure 122 shows a cross-section running approximately from east to west, from the Sogne Fjord to just north of the Faroes. A few isolines have been drawn to indicate the distribution of the salinity and the temperature. The Gulf Stream water of comparatively high salinity (more than 35‰), which flows northward, is the shaded part. Note, once again (see Chapter 6), that this water is pushed to the right by the Coriolis force and therefore reaches much farther down on the eastern side (off the Norwegian coast)

Above: Close-up of a plunging breaker. (Photograph Scripps Institution.)

Below: Aerial photograph taken above the Californian coast at Oceanside. In addition to small wind-driven waves one sees long crests of a swell gradually swerving, and a strip of surf. The scale is in feet. (Photograph U.S. Navy.)

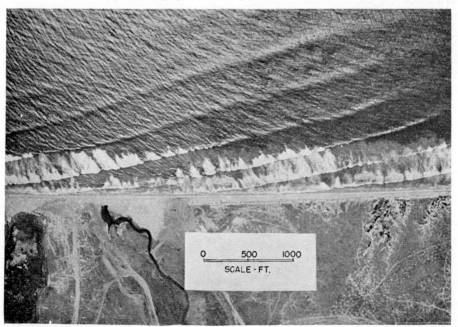

PLATE XXVIII

Refraction of waves near Bolinas, California. The waves are here breaking on a reef. (Photograph U.S. Navy.)

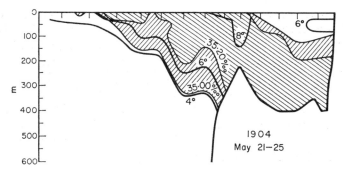

FIG. 122 Distribution of salinity (and temperature) in a cross-section of the marine area off Sogne Fjord, in May 1904 (after Helland Hansen). Note the unshaded part (above, right), with less than 35‰.

than on the western side. What concerns us most at the moment, however, is the belt of less saline water fringing the Norwegian coast, namely the coastal waters, formed partly of run-off from the western slopes of the Norwegian mountains and partly of the Baltic Current which derives from the Baltic Sea; these coastal waters, therefore, contain the run-off from the whole of the Scandinavian peninsula and from part of Central Europe. The surface area occupied in this cross-section by the coastal waters (i.e. the white panel, above, right) is a measure of the quantity of coastal waters present.

This cross-section has now been studied for several successive years, always for the month of May, and in each case the area (in square kilometres) of the section occupied by the coastal waters has been determined.

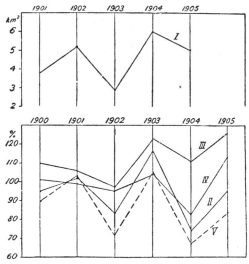

FIG. 123 Line I: Variation from year to year in the vertical section of the brackish coastal waters near the Sogne Fjord, in the month of May.
Lines II, III, IV: Proportion of preceding annual totals of precipitation at Oslo, Bergen and in Germany to normal annual totals.
Line V: How precipitation in Norway, from October to December inclusive, differed from normal in successive years (after Helland Hansen).

10

The top curve in Fig. 123 shows how this section of coastal waters has changed in area, from year to year, in May. It now transpires that (as was to be expected) these changes correspond, more or less, to variations in rainfall as may be seen from the other curves which show the ratio (in per cent.) of precipitation, in various places (Oslo, Bergen, Germany) in the preceding year, to the normal annual total precipitation. Curve V shows, additionally, variations from the normal precipitation in Norway during October, November and December. It will be seen that on the whole there is agreement between the amount of rainfall and the cross-section of coastal waters some time afterwards. For example, there was comparatively little

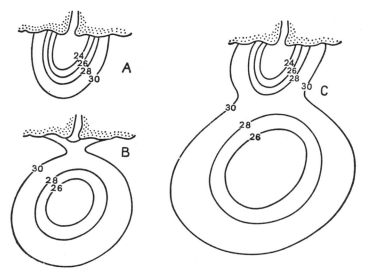

FIG. 124 Pulsating outflow of water at the mouth of a river. The numbers stand for (reduced) salinity.

rainfall in 1902, and in May 1903 the coastal waters occupied a relatively small cross-section; there was much rainfall in 1903, and much coastal water in May 1904, and so on. The effect of precipitation (rain and snow) on land is not *immediately* noticeable in the coastal waters of Norway; some time has to elapse before it is, and this makes it possible to predict, some time ahead, whether the coastal waters will bulk above normal or otherwise.

An interesting phenomenon is to be observed when river water enters the sea at places where there are strong tidal movements. The fresh water at the river's mouth fans out somewhat over the salty sea, and mingles with it. This is especially marked when the water is falling and the outgoing current off the coast is strengthened by the ebbing tide. If the salinity figures are plotted at a moment like this, and lines of equal salinity are drawn in the graph, the resultant pattern will be as in Fig. 124. But when the tide later turns, the 'pool' of fresh or brackish water at the mouth of the river is not, of course, drawn in again, because even if the current at the mouth were to flow upstream for a time, it would never attain the strength of the outgoing current at ebb tide. What often happens at the mouth of the river is that saltier water runs inwards from both sides, and cuts off the area of brackish water formed at low tide; see Fig. 124(*B*). It then becomes an isolated patch, as it were. When the tide again turns, later, and more river-water empties into the sea, brackish water again fans out at the mouth while the still remaining patch produced by the previous ebb-tide drifts away; see Fig. 124(*C*). It dissolves gradually by mixing into the surrounding sea-water.

THE HEAT BUDGET OF THE OCEANS

A balance sheet of the heat budget of the oceans can be drawn up in much the same way as was attempted for incoming and outgoing water.

In this case the main source of income is sunlight. True, a little heat flows from the interior of the earth through the sea-bottom, but the amount of warmth received in this way is small compared with solar heat. The supply of terrestrial heat through the bed has been determined in several places and has been found to vary from 10 to 100 gram-calories per year per square centimetre of sea-bottom. These amounts are more graphic if converted to kilowatt-hours, when we find that the earth's heat compares with the energy supplied by an electric heater which converts something of the order of 0·1 watt *per square metre*. So we see that it is a source of only a very small amount of heat.

The supply of heat from above by direct and scattered solar radiation, over all seas and the whole year round, is approximately equal to an average supply of energy of 147 watts per square metre. So this means 147 watt-hours per hour per square metre, or 0·147 kilowatt hours per hour per square metre, or 3·5 kilowatt hours per 24 hours[1] per square metre. This, it must be emphasized, holds only as an average over all the seas; so that at a given moment there are places receiving less warmth, and others receiving more. The same applies to other figures yet to be given.

The figure of 147 watts per square metre represents the stream of light-energy actually penetrating into the sea, which is slightly less than that impinging on the surface, as some of the latter radiation is reflected back. In our estimates of the thermal economy of the oceans we are concerned only with nett receipts.

Now we have to set the outgoing against the incoming items. There are three ways in which the seas lose heat: firstly by evaporation, which consumes heat; secondly by direct transmission of heat to the atmosphere with which the sea is in contact, and, thirdly by radiation. The first item incurs an average net loss of energy corresponding to 75 watts per square metre of the whole of the sea's surface. We say *net* loss, because in some places the oppo-

---

[1] Here we have to multiply the previous figure by the whole 24 hours, even if the sun does not shine the full 24 hours in a given spot, as our first figure is an average over all seas for all 24-hour days of the year.

site of evaporation, i.e. condensation of water vapour on the surface, takes place, and this gives warmth. But evaporation far exceeds condensation.

The second item, i.e. loss of heat to the atmosphere through contact conduction, is far smaller than the first, namely only about 10 watts per square metre. This too is a nett item, for the sea is by no means everywhere and always warmer than the air just above it.

The third item is again considerable. Here, the word radiation is used in the sense of effective radiation, meaning that the sea loses more by radiation upward than it gets back by irradiation from the atmosphere. This is genuine radiation, not reflection. It depends only on the surface temperature of the sea, and takes place night and day. By the way, it is even possible to determine sea-surface temperatures by measuring from an aeroplane the infrared radiation emitted by the sea. In recent years this rapid temperature measuring technique, by means of what is called an airborne radiation thermometer, has come more and more into use, especially in areas where strong temperature gradients are found.

It is this radiation which causes the earth's surface (both sea and land) to lose heat at night; but the loss would be far greater were it not for the day and night downward, as well as upward, radiation of the atmosphere, whereby part of the loss is made good. The difference, the *nett* loss, is called effective radiation. The back radiation from the atmosphere upon some particular place is not a constant, but depends upon air temperatures at various altitudes, on the water vapour content, and, particularly, on the cloud cover. The more overcast the sky, and the lower the clouds, the greater is the down-radiation, and therefore the less the effective radiation. Consequently, this latter (which also depends on sea temperature), like the other items of the thermal balance sheet, is a quantity which varies from place to place and from time to time. But it is responsible for a loss of energy, averaged over all the seas throughout the year, corresponding to 62 watts per square metre of the sea's surface.

If we now add up the heat-loss items, we get $75 + 10 + 62 = 147$ watts per square metre, which is the same as the heat gains mentioned earlier. And this is as it should be, because on the average the sea becomes, in fact, neither warmer nor colder.

It is clear from the foregoing that the heat of evaporation is the heaviest of the three losses. It may be added that, strange as it may seem at first sight, the greatest evaporation takes place in winter, or at any rate in those areas where definitely wintry conditions prevail. It is commonly believed that the hotter it is, the greater is the evaporation, but in actual fact evaporation is determined less by the actual temperature of water or air than by the difference in temperature between them. The sea, being far slower to cool down than the land and the atmosphere, as we shall see later, is, in winter, warmer than the air, in most places; and this provides ample opportunity for evaporation with its concomitant loss of heat. When, on the other hand, the air is warmer than the water, the opposite may happen under certain circumstances; that is to say, water vapour drops from the air on to the colder surface of the sea. And this is more likely to happen in summer than in winter.

Just as the water economy was found to be in equilibrium, so also can it be said that the thermal gains and losses of the oceans of the world, taken as a whole, balance; though this need not necessarily be so in the case of some particular marine area at a given moment. It may not even hold for the annual average of a given area. For example, in the north-eastern part of the Atlantic Ocean (say to the west of Norway), expenditure in the form of heat transfer to the atmosphere and upward radiation exceeds the incoming radiation. It is only thanks to the Gulf Stream, which carries warmth through the ocean, that this area does not cool down permanently. We have the exact reverse in the north-western part of the same ocean. Here, the cold brought down by the Labrador Current with its burden of ice-fields, balances out the surplus of heat created by the excess of receipts, from above, over expenditure, in the form of radiation and heat exchange with the atmosphere. Whereas little evaporation takes place here, there is much condensation, to which the Newfoundland fog bears eloquent witness!

SEASONAL CHANGES IN TEMPERATURE

If, lastly, we consider the matter not in its time-average aspects, but at a particular time of the year, we shall see that, in general, there will be no equilibrium in the thermal economy even if we allow for heat transport by marine currents. As a rule, the sea gradually warms up in spring and summer, at all events in those regions which can be said to have a spring and summer. The gain in heat then exceeds its loss. In autumn and winter the sea gets colder by degrees, and the loss of heat exceeds its gain. Though the same happens on land, there is this difference, that, owing to the properties of sea-water, the changes in temperature are not large, much smaller than on land, despite any predominant gain or loss of heat. The differences between summer and winter temperatures are far smaller at sea than on land in the same latitude. That is why the proximity of the sea tempers the climate of nearby land areas, where summers are cooler, and winters less cold than elsewhere in the same latitude. This is called a maritime climate, of which that of the British Isles and the Low Countries is a very good example. Its opposite is a continental climate, so-called because it is subject solely to terrestrial temperature effects, and at moderate latitudes therefore, has hot summers and severe winters. Siberia offers the classic example of a continental climate. To realize this, one has only to compare the average January temperature of 2°C in the Netherlands with the −26°C in parts of Eastern Siberia in the same latitude; while the average July temperatures in these two areas are 17°C and 21°C respectively.

Let us now return to the sea itself. Its change of temperature in the course of the year is even smaller than the change in air temperature in a definitely maritime climate. This fact, as has been pointed out, is due to the peculiar properties of sea-water. First of all, the incident rays of the sun are not only absorbed at the surface as they are on land, but, thanks to the transparency of sea-water, they penetrate well into its interior layers; thus heat is at once distributed over a whole layer of the sea. Consequently, any rise in temperature is comparatively limited. On the other hand, when the surface cools down, increased specific gravity causes the upper layer to sink into, and to mix with, the water beneath it. This, again, moderates the cooling of the surface. Moreover, the action of the wind on the sea also results in a mixing of water layers, which additionally distributes any heat gain or loss over a rather large mass of water. Lastly, water has great specific heat, which means that a great deal of heat or cold is required to raise or lower the temperature of a quantity of water through one degree. All in all, the sea is comparatively slow to take on temperature changes; it acts as a moderator of temperature variations on earth.

As to the extent of the temperature changes which the sea undergoes in the course of a year, this is least of course in the tropics and polar regions. There the annual range, i.e. the difference between the highest and lowest average monthly temperature, is only 1–2°C. The largest is the annual range in the North Atlantic Ocean, where, between latitudes 40° and 45° N., it amounts roughly to 8–9°C, and in the North Pacific, where, at the same latitudes, it is approximately 9–10°C. In these regions, especially on the western side, the annual range is increased by cold, offshore, winds in winter which bring down the winter temperatures of the sea-water. There is scarcely any sign of this kind of thing in the southern hemisphere, where the largest annual range, of roughly 5–6°C is found between latitudes 30° and 40° S.

It will be evident that, as a rule, the annual range is greater in shallow, adjacent seas than in mid-ocean, to which the above ranges apply. For example, the temperature of the North Sea off the Dutch coast ranges approximately from 4°C in February to 17°C in August; see Figs. 139 and 140.

Since even the annual range of sea temperature is, as a rule, comparatively small, the daily range is, not surprisingly, very small indeed (on an average a couple of tenths of a degree, i.e. usually negligible).

Let us now see what temperature changes sea-water undergoes at certain depths under the surface in the course of a year, that is to say the annual range at depth. The deeper one goes, the smaller are the changes. Temperature readings in various places have shown that, generally, the yearly temperature changes are perceptible down to 300 metres at most; and they often reach no farther down than about 100 metres.

It is a notable fact that the temperature maxima and minima in the deeper layers of water occur later than those at the surface. This is because the rises and falls of temperature have to be propagated downward, which is why the deeper layers always lag behind. Readings taken repeatedly to the west of the Sogne Fjord, at the beginning of the century, provide a well-known example of this shift of the 'seasons' at depth. The following temperatures were found in 1903:

	February	May	August	November
	°C	°C	°C	°C
Surface	4·8	7·3	13·8	8·7
100 metres	6·8	6·4	6·9	9·3
200 metres	7·9	7·0	6·7	7·9

We see that at 100 metres it was coldest in May and warmest in November; at 200 metres it was coldest in August and warmest in winter! So there was a reversal of the seasons. Nevertheless, at that depth the differences are very trifling.

Another feature of the temperature changes during the year is the *isothermal upper layer* which is often present. This was mentioned in Chapter 2; see Fig. 28. As a rule this isothermal layer results from mixing caused by the wind, or by cooling from above which induces vertical circulation (convection), or by both simultaneously. These factors tend to make the isothermal layer reach down to its greatest depth, in many places as far down as 100 metres, in winter and in spring. A fairly abrupt drop in temperature is often found immediately below it (Fig. 28), in a thin layer called the 'thermocline'. These thermoclines play an important part in the propagation of sound under water, because they form a 'shadow zone' at a certain distance from the source of sound, into which it barely penetrates at all. (This is a factor to be reckoned with in echo-sounding for submarines.)

COMPARATIVE CONSTANCY OF THE PROPERTIES OF THE DEEP SEA

A thermocline may often be the seat of internal waves (Figs. 78 and 79). We may think of these waves as a kind of restlessness of deep layers of water. One of the effects they have upon the distribution of the properties in these layers is to cause the temperature at a given depth to fluctuate; for the layers of water at that depth under the surface are changing from moment to moment. If, in a state of rest, the temperature is found to be 10°C at, say, 150 metres' depth, and 11°C at 140 metres, some high internal waves may lift the 10°C layer some 10 metres, so that, for an instant, the temperature reading, 140 metres down, will be 10°C, but a moment later it will again be 11°, and after a further minute or two perhaps 12° when a 'trough' is passing, and water deriving from a depth of 130 metres has temporarily sunk some 10 metres.

Fluctuations of this kind are naturally most conspicuous where the most salient vertical drop in temperature takes place; it is there that vertical movements of the water layers will produce the greatest temperature shifts. But internal waves also occur lower down, and those with long periods are, in particular, apt to produce considerable vertical displacements. We shall not enter into further details here; our sole purpose in touching on this internal restlessness of the sea was to make it clear that even the short-term values of the properties of sea-water measured at certain depths are not absolutely *constant*. This fact, it will be understood, leaves a certain margin of uncertainty when we combine readings at different places at various times.

Apart from short-term, chance fluctuations of this kind, there are very slow changes, at great depths as well, attributable to minor changes in the properties of the large masses of water circulating slowly through the deep; changes which themselves may be the result of certain climatic variations in sea areas whence these water masses derive. We shall have occasion to describe this circulation, and the formation of 'water types' and water masses in greater detail presently. To mention one example: in June, 1910, the *Michael Sars* found, at a locality in the North Atlantic below 2000 metres, virtually the same temperatures as those measured thirty-seven years earlier, in the same neighbourhood, by the *Challenger*. This proved that the thermometers agreed; but between depths of 200 and 2000 metres the temperatures were quite appreciably lower in 1910 than in 1873. In the 1957–58 International Geophysical Year the same places in the South Atlantic Ocean, along two lines running from east to west between Africa and South America, where the *Meteor* expedition had taken soundings thirty years previously, were visited systematically. It was found that the temperatures between 2000 and 4000 metres down were a little lower than on the earlier occasions, but the difference amounted to less than 0·04°C. A slight increase, amounting to 0·02°C, was found in the temperature of the bottom water on the western side of the Mid-Atlantic Ridge. So these are minor differences. The Russians, however, report that, in 1957, their *Vityaz* expedition registered temperatures at depths of 7000–9000 metres which were 0·11–0·16°C lower than those recorded by the Danish *Galathea* in 1952.

Nevertheless, such differences in the deeper layers of the ocean, below 500–1000 metres, are the exception rather than the rule. Pairs of serial readings, taken in different years at approximately the same places, have shown that, on the whole, conditions in the deeps are remarkably stable.

It is fortunate for research that there should be this comparative constancy of conditions in the deep sea. It enables us to combine observations made at various times, and to build up from them a fairly reliable picture, notwithstanding the lapse of time, from which we can gain some insight into the general circulation of the deep sea. When we were considering the Gulf Stream, we saw that considerable changes *are* liable to take place in the uppermost layers, not only with the changing seasons as studied earlier in the present chapter, but also in the short term.

INDICATIONS OF ORIGIN

This combining of various soundings or serial readings to which we have referred usually consists in drawing through a marine area either vertical cross-sections, i.e. sections along certain lines of observation stations, in which lines of like temperature, salinity, oxygen content or other properties are drawn, or horizontal cross-sections, hence plans for certain depths, in which the distribution of properties can likewise be indicated by 'isolines'. Figures 112, 128, 134 and 137 are specimens of these vertical cross-sections, while Figs. 111 and 125 furnish examples of the charts-in-depth. Depicting, as they do, the properties of the sea spatially, these charts provide us with information in themselves; in addition, however, they have yet more to reveal, as we have already seen in the chapter on oceanic currents when we considered the association between the distribution of temperature and salinity, on the one hand, and the dynamics of water movements on the other. But that is not all. The properties of sea-water at a given place and depth can serve as *indicators* of origin when compared with the like properties elsewhere and at other depths. The reader may, perhaps, find it easier to understand why this is so if we furnish an example.

MEDITERRANEAN SEA WATER IN THE ATLANTIC

If we compare Fig. 125, a chart representing the salinity distribution 1000 metres down in the Atlantic, to the west of southern Europe and North Africa, with Chart 3 at the end of this book, which shows the salinity at the surface of the sea, we shall see that a fan-shaped patch of high salinity on the former does not appear in the latter chart. We shall remember the high salinity of the Mediterranean waters which, comparatively heavy as they

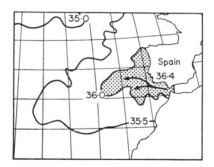

FIG. 125 Salinity distribution at 1000 metres' depth to the west of Gibraltar.

are, flow over the sill of the Straits of Gibraltar into the ocean; also that there is a double current in the Straits, an upper one bringing ocean water in, and an undercurrent carrying Mediterranean water out. Although the latter has a salt content of 38‰ near Gibraltar, it already mingles to some extent, in the Straits, with the incoming ocean waters of about 36‰ salinity. Owing to their greater salinity, the former, flowing from the sill (which is about 320 metres deep) along the sloping sea bottom, sink further down, under oceanic water layers which, despite their lower temperature, are less dense because they are less saline. This Mediterranean water, gradually becoming

10*

somewhat 'diluted' by mixing with the Atlantic water layers, has to sink to a depth of about 1000 metres before it is in equilibrium with its surroundings. At that depth it spreads horizontally, more or less fanwise. This is seen on a chart like Fig. 125; and in a cross-section, too, the course of this water derived from the Mediterranean Sea is visible by the tongue of salt-rich water extending downward and westward from the sill. (Actually, of course, the slope is a very gentle one.) See Fig. 126.

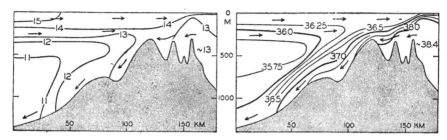

FIG. 126 Vertical cross-sections through the Straits of Gibraltar. *Left:* Temperature distribution. *Right:* Salinity distribution.

It was known, long before charts or cross-sections like those in Fig. 126 were constructed, that water flowed out of the Straits of Gibraltar into the ocean. Indeed, we referred to the charts only as an eloquent example of how, even if nothing were known about the passage of water from the Straits of Gibraltar, conclusions could be drawn, from a pointer like salinity, as to the origin of water masses, and as to some particular movement of water—in this case the movement of highly saline water from the Straits of Gibraltar into the vastness of the Atlantic Ocean. There have been cases, as we shall presently show, in which little or nothing was known about movements of water, when a similar, indirect method of approach enabled oceanographers to realize what was going on.

TRANSPORT THROUGH THE STRAITS OF GIBRALTAR AND OTHER STRAITS

Here are a few more details about those movements of water through the 'Pillars of Hercules'.

The average velocity of the upper current over its width and depth is 1 metre per second; at the surface it reaches approximately 2 metres per second in places. Such a current could not escape notice, even in ancient times; and there were some, as far back as the seventeenth century, who were wondering what became of all that water, coming in continuously. A certain Dr. Smith seems to have been the first to think of a westward-running undercurrent as the answer; this was in 1673. Let no one suppose, however, that this suggestion was accepted out of hand; there were some learned gentlemen as little as a hundred years ago who refused to believe in the undercurrent. Yet, at about that time, Maury cited a tale told in 1712 which, to his mind, proved the existence of the undercurrent. In that year—so the tale goes—a French raider sank a Dutch ship in the middle of the strait, and rescued the whole crew. As to the Dutch ship, a few days later she surfaced with her cargo of liquor and oil, at a spot 12 miles at least to the *west* of the place where she had sunk. So she had progressed quite a distance in a direction contrary to that of the known surface current!

The thickness of the upper current in the strait is about 125 metres, but its base is lower on the African than on the European side, a slope resulting from the earth's rotation. Hence the maximum ingoing transport takes place on the southern side.

On the basis of flow measurements it is now estimated that the total water transport of the upper current is roughly 1,750,000 cubic metres per second. This is not enough to give us the magnitude of the outflowing current, because much water is known to evaporate from the Mediterranean. As, however, the salt does not evaporate, it is possible, by drawing up a salt balance based on the known difference between the mean salt content of the upper current (36·25‰) and that of the undercurrent (37·75‰), to make a rough computation of the amount of water carried away. The result is approximately 1,680,000 cubic metres per second. The difference, 70,000 cubic metres per second, apparently represents the excess of loss, by evaporation per second from the Mediterranean, over its receipts of rain and river water. (The Black Sea must be included here; the contribution of the Suez Canal is negligible.) As the Mediterranean's receipts are estimated to be 45,000 cubic metres per second, evaporation appears to amount to 115,000 cubic metres per second. This corresponds to a water layer of 145 centimetres a year, which is considerably more than the average annual evaporation throughout the oceans of the world, estimated at slightly less than one metre.

An entirely analogous case is to be found in the Bab-el-Mandeb Strait, the entrance to the Red Sea. There, too, though on a smaller scale, there is a briny undercurrent flowing outwards, and an upper current of lower salinity coming in from the Indian Ocean. As both here and near Gibraltar the tides and wind exert their varying influence, whatever has been said about a continuous inflow above and outflow below has to be taken in an average sense.

Examples of the reverse—where the upper current of lower salinity flows outward and the saltier undercurrent flows inward—are provided by the entrances to the Baltic and Black Seas, both of which contain comparatively little salt.

SALINITY AND TEMPERATURE AS INDICATORS

Taking up the thread of our story about indications of origin, let us look at *salinity* first. We have seen how the addition of Mediterranean water to Atlantic water is betrayed by the distribution of salinity in the depths of the Atlantic Ocean, far from Gibraltar. When we look at a lengthwise, vertical section of the Atlantic (Fig. 134, centre) showing the distribution of salinity in broad outline, a region of somewhat higher salinity, beginning at about latitude 35° N. (that of Gibraltar), is seen to reach downward and extend southward from near the surface. From that water body, the great masses of the Atlantic's deep water, at between 500 and 3500 metres, receive an injection, so to speak, of salt; and it is partly on this account that this deep water, which flows slowly from north to south, is richer in salt in the Middle and South Atlantic than both the overlying water and the very cold bottom

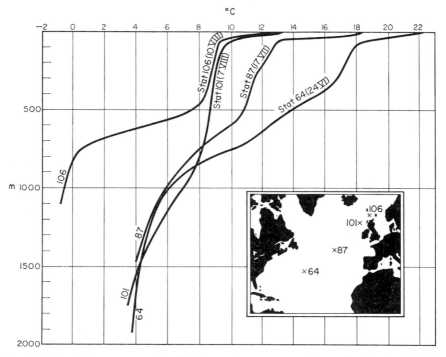

FIG. 127 Vertical temperature distribution on four oceanographic stations in the Atlantic in summer (after Helland Hansen). Station 64 is situated in subtropical, 87 in moderate latitudes, the Wyville-Thompson Ridge lying between 101 and 106.

water beneath. Thus, the Mediterranean waters make their imprint on the deep water of the Atlantic, to beyond the Cape of Good Hope.

It should be added that there is another source of comparatively salt water in the middle of the Atlantic, which is also traceable in the depths. This is the Sargasso Sea, from which there is much evaporation. The descent of water of high salinity there is due both to its weight and to the convergence of water movements.

In some cases temperature can be another indicator (cf. Fig. 127), a known example of which fact is provided by the Wyville-Thompson Ridge. The great submarine ridge of which it is a part, extends from the northernmost tip of Scotland to the Faroes, and continues from there to Iceland. It divides the deep basin of the Norwegian Sea in the north-east from that of the Atlantic Ocean to the south. Figure 128 reproduces a vertical section, running across this ridge from south-west to north-east, and cutting it at about latitude 60° N. Below the threshold depth of about 500 metres we see a very strong contrast in temperatures. On the right-hand side the temperature drops very rapidly below this depth, to less than 0°C at the bottom; but immediately on the other side it is no less than 7 degrees warmer at the same

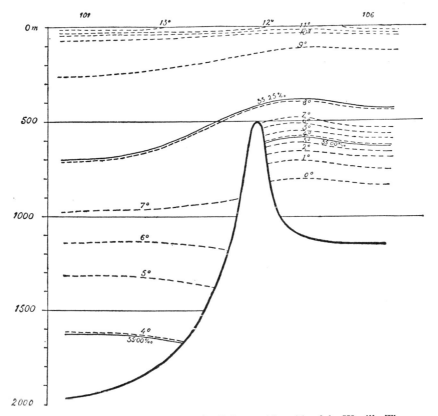

FIG. 128 Distribution of temperature and salinity on either side of the Wyville-Thompson Ridge in a SW–NE section, according to observations made by the *Michael Sars* (after Helland Hansen). Stations 101 and 106 are the same as in Fig. 127.

depth. Obviously these are entirely different kinds of water which are neither in direct contact here nor, apparently, elsewhere. On one side there is the icy cold water of the Norwegian Sea; on the other the far less cold Atlantic water. Between them, the Wyville-Thompson Ridge stands as an insurmountable barrier. Nor can there be any deeper passages through this barrier elsewhere; otherwise the disparity in temperatures below the depth of 500 metres could not be what our cross-section shows it to be.

Above the threshold of this ridge Atlantic waters flow towards the Norwegian Sea and the Arctic Ocean. Indeed, we know that the North

Atlantic Current, the continuation of the Gulf Stream, runs here. The situation differs from that near Gibraltar in that, in this case, the compensating return current from the Arctic does not pass under this Atlantic Current, but between Iceland and Greenland.

An interesting fact, associated with the disparity in temperature between the deep waters to the north and south of the Wyville-Thompson Ridge, is that there is also a difference in fauna on either side. Above the southern slope of the Ridge, all kinds of animals native to the Atlantic deep sea are found below 500 metres; but these are entirely absent from the icy cold, deep waters immediately to the north of the Ridge. We have here a typical discontinuity in the deep-sea fauna, which is caused by a temperature discontinuity between the two 'kinds' of deep-sea water involved.

THE BOTTOM WATERS OF THE EAST-INDIES DEEP-SEA BASINS

For the most part, the deep basins of the Moluccan seas are filled with very cold waters whose temperatures range from 3° to 1°C. It will be evident that only 'ventilation' could maintain such temperatures in these tropical regions; which means that these waters are continually being renewed from a reservoir of cold water. As to that reservoir, we shall have to turn our thoughts to the cold, deep water layers in the Pacific or Indian Ocean. We know that all oceans, at all latitudes, store very cold water in their depths. Where this comes from is another matter, which we shall consider presently. Now, as the various Indonesian deep-sea basins are surrounded on all sides by 'rises' or ridges of the sea bottom, the coldest water able to enter one of these basins from the ocean is the water lying in the ocean at the depth of the sill of the basin. By sill we mean the deepest place of the rim of the basin— the lowest pass, as it were.

So, across this sill, water of a certain temperature flows down the sloping bottom into the basin, filling the major part of it below the threshold level. Most of this space therefore acquires approximately the same temperature, notably that of the water flowing over the sill. See Fig. 129 for an example. Thus the temperature of the bottom water of a basin reveals the ocean level from which this water derives, and with it, therefore, the depth of the sill over which it enters, i.e. the deepest place in the rim of the basin. As soundings do not always find this deepest place exactly, temperature measurements can help to establish the depths of some submarine passes. Before citing examples, we wish to point out that there are two reasons why the temperature prevailing in a basin is not precisely the same over the whole space.

Firstly, through mingling with some of the water coming from higher levels, the water we are speaking of is gradually warmed up a little from above as it proceeds. Precisely because the water in the depths of basins becomes less cold, it does not stagnate, being displaced over and over again by 'new' water, heavier because it is colder, trying to creep under it. The effect of this gradual warming up is discernible in the depths by slightly increased temperatures at increasing distance from the 'source'.

Adiabatic compression, however, shares in the responsibility for the fact that the temperature is not everywhere the same beneath the sill level in a basin. When sea-water sinks from the threshold to lower levels, it becomes subject to higher pressure, and is slightly compressed, and this compression involves a small rise in temperature. It is this 'dynamic heating' which causes the temperature at great depths to increase again, towards the bottom of

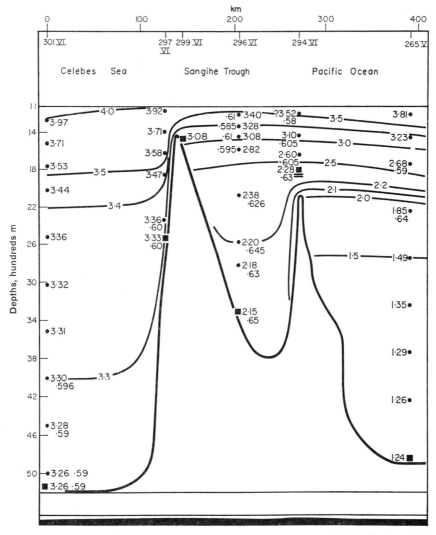

FIG. 129 Vertical section between the Pacific and the Celebes Sea with distribution of the potential temperature below 1100 metres (after Van Riel). The vertical series of points are points of observation of the stations of the *Snellius*, which are given under the upper edge, with the number of the month in which these observations were made. *Below*: Profile of the bottom with the slopes to actual scale.

many deep basins and troughs. We touched on this matter in Chapter 2 and there (Table 6) cited as an example the celebrated station of the *Snellius* in the Mindanao Trench.

Seeing that temperature is not an infallible indicator of the original level of a water mass, since it is not absolutely unchanging even if there is no transfer of heat, it was considered convenient to introduce the idea of *potential temperature*. This is the calculated temperature which a quantity of water would assume if it were brought to a certain standard pressure adiabatically, that is to say without heat transfer. If this standard pressure is assumed to be the pressure of the sea's surface, then the potential temperature of water at depth will be lower than the actual temperature, for reduced pressure would cause expansion and, consequently, cooling. Now if water (without heat transfer) really does come under another pressure, the temperature does change, but the potential temperature does not. There are no really great differences between the potential and the actual temperatures, because the compressibility of water is minute. But comparatively small temperature differences are essential in the depths of the oceans. At the greatest depths, for example 10,000 metres in the Mindanao Trench, the dynamic rise in temperature through the 1000 atmospheres pressure amounts to 1·3°C. There, the actual temperature is 2·5°C, so the potential temperature is 1·2°C. At 3500 metres, where the temperature is 1·6°C, the potential temperature is only 0·3°C lower, so 1·3°C. We see that this potential temperature is almost the same as that 6500 metres lower, near the bottom.

Hence, whereas strictly speaking the temperature is not invariable even if there is no heat exchange, the potential temperature *is*, if the water proceeds to other depths and is therefore subjected to a different pressure; so it can prove to be an excellent indicator. In actual fact, the numerals in Fig.129 stand for the potential temperature, not the actual temperature itself! As is evident from Table 6 which represents the temperature distribution in the deepest part of the Mindanao Trench, and from the next table, the temperatures themselves increase slightly, towards the bottom.

Thanks to the work of Van Riel, the leader of the *Snellius* expedition which sailed all the basins of the Moluccan seas in 1929 and 1930, making extensive observations everywhere, we are now fully informed of the conditions prevailing in these basins at the present time. Table 25 gives some of these observations made at five stations, one in the Sulu Basin (to the north of the Celebes Sea), one in the Morotai Basin (north of Halmahera), one in the Buru Basin, one in the Halmahera Basin and one in the Timor Trench.

The disparity in the temperatures down below in these basins is striking, and we now know the cause of it. It is the differences in depth of the thresholds over which the bottom water slides into them. The high minimum temperatures in the Sulu Sea and Halmahera Basin are particularly striking; they can be accounted for by the comparatively shallow sills of these two basins, the depth of the Sulu Sea sill being 400 metres and that of the

Table 25

Serial observations made by the *Snellius* expedition in several East Indies ocean basins. Minimum temperatures underlined. Depths in metres, temperatures in °C, salinity in ‰.

Depth	Sulu Basin Temp.	Sulu Basin Salinʸ	Morotai B. Temp.	Morotai B. Salinʸ	Buru Basin Temp.	Buru Basin Salinʸ	Halmahera B. Temp.	Halmahera B. Salinʸ	Timor Trench Temp.	Timor Trench Salinʸ
0	27·85	33·60	29·2	33·96	29·8	33·79	27·6	34·70	28·55	34·60
50	27·15	34·25	27·52	34·00	27·66	34·18	27·14	34·68	26·24	34·46
150	18·74	34·36	18·00	34·76	20·08	34·56	18·20	35·00	19·60	34·50
500	11·04	34·51	8·48	34·56	8·40	34·66	8·49	34·67	7·76	34·60
1000	10·09	34·49	4·68	34·59	4·96	34·60	7·90	34·62	4·80	34·60
1250	10·08	34·49	3·62	34·60	3·92	34·61	7·82	34·62	4·11	34·61
1750	10·11	34·47	2·54	34·63	3·41	34·62	7·77	34·60	2·93	34·69
2000	10·14	34·48	2·20	34·63	3·25	34·60	–	–	2·80	34·69
2375							–	–	2·77	
2500	10·21	34·47	1·81	34·65	3·08	34·60	–	–	2·78	34·68
3250					3·02		–	–	–	–
3500	10·35	34·48	1·84	34·65	3·03	34·62	–	–	–	–
4000	10·43	34·48	–	–	3·06	34·63	–	–	–	–
5000	–	–	–	–	3·18	34·63	–	–	–	–

Halmahera Basin 700 metres. Both basins receive their waters from the Pacific Ocean, as do almost all other East Indies basins, except the deep Sunda Trench (to the south of Java and the Lesser Sunda Islands) and the Timor Trench, which receive their bottom waters from the Indian Ocean.

The path of the waters of Pacific origin often twists and turns as, going from basin to basin, these waters seek out the lowest thresholds. The Halmahera and Morotai basins communicate direct with the Pacific via their sills, but the path to, say, the Buru Basin runs through the Morotai Basin, the Ternate Trench and the Batjan Basin. And from the Buru Basin the meandering route of the bottom waters takes them through the Banda Basin, the Weber Deep and the Wetar Basin all the way to the Savu Basin to the west of Timor (close to the Indian Ocean, but separated from it by a higher sill than that over which the Pacific waters come).

The circuitous paths of the bottom waters can be seen in Fig. 130. Van Riel tracked these paths from a careful comparison of the potential temperatures at the bottom of the basins and in the passages between them. He also took account of the salinity and oxygen content figures, which are likewise useful indicators in this type of research work. It is its salinity, for instance, which shows that the bottom water of the Timor and Sunda Trenches cannot be of Pacific origin, since it is 34·71‰ in the former localities, as in the adjacent deep waters of the Indian Ocean, whereas it is about 34·6‰ in all the other deep basins of the archipelago. The oxygen content, too, is higher in these two basins than in the neighbouring Savu Basin, for instance, and tallies with the oxygen content of the Indian Ocean.

The two cross-sections in Fig. 131 show that the Savu basin obtains its deep water from the Wetar basin, and not from the nearby Indian Ocean.

To any readers curious to know how quickly, or slowly, these ventilation currents move, it must be confessed that this is a very difficult question to answer. If one attempts to find out by current measurement, the passages through which the water has to pass to enter the basins would seem to offer the best chances of success, because the water flows fastest there, where widths and depths are restricted. Unfortunately, however, few successful deep-sea current measurements have been made up to the present, the only

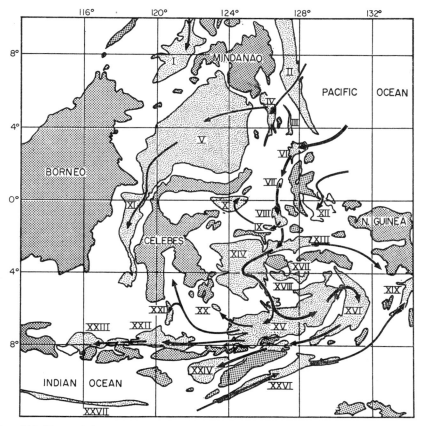

FIG. 130 Chart of the Indonesian ocean basins, with the circulation of the bottom water arrowed. Roman figures symbolize as follows: I = Sulu basin; II = Mindanao Trench; IV = Sangihe Trench; V = Celebes Sea; VI = Morotai basin; XII = Halmahera basin; XIII = Buru basin; XIV and XV = Banda basins; XVI = Weber Deep; XIX = Aru basin; XXII = Flores basin; XXIV = Savu basin; XXV = Wetar basin; XXVI = Timor Trench; XXVII = Sunda Trench.

straits in the Moluccas in which such measurements have been taken being those between Obi and the Sula Islands, the entrance to the Banda basins. A south-eastern current of about 5 centimetres per second has been measured there, between a depth of 1500 metres and the bottom, which lies at 1880 metres. Not a particularly fast flow! It becomes slower still some distance further on, where this current in the basin fans out in width and depth. The amount of the water transport can be calculated by multiplying the velocity in the strait by the area of the cross-section of the passage, in so far as it participates in this ventilation current. This gives us a transport of 17 cubic kilometres of water per 24 hours, or 6300 cubic kilometres per year. This is the quantity of water passing through the passage below the level where the potential temperature is 3°C. In the Banda Sea the same potential tempera- is found at a depth of about 2200 metres. Apparently, therefore, all the water below this level in the Banda Sea is renewed by this water transport.

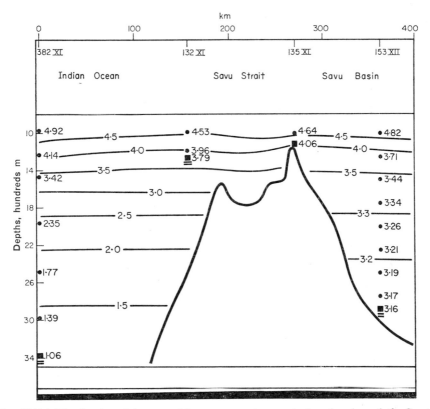

FIG. 131(a) Distribution of the potential temperature in a vertical section through the Savu Strait (after Van Riel). See also legend to Fig. 129.

If we divide the volume of that water of the Banda Sea (below 2200 metres) by the amount of transport given above, we find that three hundred years are needed to replace it all by new water. That which *is* replaced escapes very slowly upward and flows at a higher level, sideways, towards an adjacent basin. The 'speed' of the upward movement from 2200 metres is estimated to be seven metres a year. This upward movement from the depths does not entail a gradual drop of temperature at some particular level, because trans- fer of heat from above (the warmer layers of water) downward by turbulent exchange of heat cancels out the cooling which would otherwise be brought about by the rising of colder water.

OTHER INDICATORS: OXYGEN

There are several other substances or properties which can serve as indicators, or tracers, of a water mass, even if there are only traces of them in sea-water. To mention only a few, there is the dissolved oxygen, the phosphate content, the 'alkalinity', so-called, which comes to about the same thing as the calcium content, and, last but by no means least, the percentage of *radioactive carbon*, ^{14}C, about which we shall have more to say at the end of this chapter. At the moment we shall consider only the significance of the *oxygen content*.

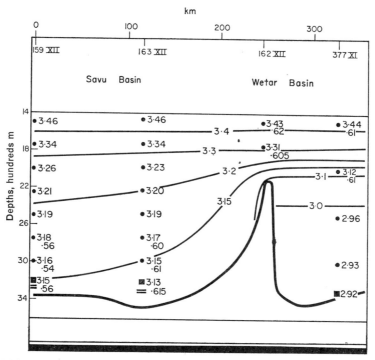

FIG. 131(*b*) Distribution of the potential temperature in a vertical section from the Savu Basin to the Wetar Basin (after Van Riel).

Sea-water can take up oxygen only at or near, the surface; so, as a certain amount of oxygen is consumed by animals, even at great depths, wherever a sizeable oxygen content is found in deep water it is safe to infer that that water derives from elsewhere, originally from some place at the surface. Thus the oxygen content of the bottom layers of the Atlantic is between 5 and 6 cubic centimetres per litre almost everywhere, and in tropical regions this is even more than is found there near the surface. (We know that, the warmer water is, the less oxygen it is able to contain.) This bears out the conclusion already drawn from the low temperatures of these deep and bottom waters, that they derive from cold regions of the ocean surface. We shall study this question in greater detail at the end of this chapter.

Oxygen is, however, consumed by deep-sea animals and by the decomposition of organic waste (which sinks from higher levels); so, if ventilation is slow, the farther the water is from its 'source', the lower will its oxygen content be. Again, the East Indian deep-sea basins exemplify this. In the Pacific, the oxygen content at sill depth is upwards of 3 c.c. per litre; a value of 3 c.c. was found in the Moluccan Passage; in the depths of the Banda Sea the content has fallen to 2·5 c.c. and, in the Savu Sea to the west of Timor, at the end of the 3000 kilometre course, the deepest water contains a mere 1·7 c.c. per litre. The content is higher, however, namely 2·9 c.c. per litre, in the Timor Trench at the other side of Timor. But this trough receives its deep water straight from the Indian Ocean, over a sill 2000 metres deep, where the oxygen content is 3·2 c.c. per litre.

There are basins whose deep waters are so much heavier than any water coming in at higher levels, or whose sill is so shallow, that the nether parts of those basins are virtually not ventilated at all. The best-known example, as we pointed out in Chapter 2, is the Black Sea. Therein, the stagnant water layers below 200 metres contain no oxygen at all and so normal life cannot be sustained there. The only living organisms that can subsist are sulphobacteria, so-called, which break down proteins derived from organic waste, and produce hydrogen sulphide, that malodorous substance, with which these deep-sea waters are wholly saturated. The bottom is covered with soft, black or green mud, in which the sunken corpses of vertebrates are buried. The bacteria living in this mud then go to work upon the digestible parts, leaving the skeleton behind. Many complete fossil skeletons have been preserved from the geological past by such processes, in basins of the kind we have been discussing.

The Kau Bay near Halmahera (see Fig. 29), which the *Snellius* expedition examined, is another virtually unventilated basin.

Lastly, several Norwegian fjords have a shallow sill (the terminal moraine of the glacier which formerly scoured the fjord!) which screens the fjord basin from the sea. But here the water behind the sill is occasionally replenished, by an invasion of heavier water from outside or above. This is because the upper layer in these fjords is rather brackish, and is therefore lighter than the more saline water down below. At some depth, the water is liable to become fairly warm through solar radiation, because the covering layer acts like the glass of a hothouse. When, in autumn, the upper layer becomes considerably colder, it may, despite its lower salinity, become heavier than the tepid water underneath. The latter then rises, and convection ensues. Alternatively, the level of the saline water, rich in oxygen, lying outside the sill under the brackish upper layer, may rise above the threshold level, in which case new water cascades over the sill into the basin.

DEEP-SEA CIRCULATION

After this excursion into details, let us now turn to the grand circulation of water masses in the depths of the oceans. Actually, there are two circulations, comparable in a way to the lesser and greater circulation of human blood. Like these, the two circulations in the oceans are associated, water from one passing into the other; but for all that they are distinguishable. In this context, the circulation we have in mind is not so much the horizontal circulation of surface currents on which we dwelt in Chapter 6, as the general displacements of water to all depths; our principal concern is with the components of movement in a vertical plane.

The two circulation systems are associated with the two parts of which the oceanic body could be said to consist, namely, (1) the warm, and moderately warm, upper waters of equatorial and subtropical regions, a layer several hundred metres thick, below the surface, situated roughly between latitudes 45° S. and 45–55° N.; the boundary is not sharply defined, certainly not in the eastern part of the Atlantic into which the Gulf Stream runs; (2) all the remaining cold waters, found at the surface at the higher latitudes and in the depths at all latitudes. The former layer, in which there are considerable temperature differences and variations, is sometimes called the (oceanic) *troposphere*, and the other layer, underneath and outside the former, with comparatively uniform low temperatures everywhere, the *stratosphere*, on the analogy of the atmosphere. As this analogy is rather a poor one, the terminology is somewhat infelicitous. Nor is the boundary well defined; the modern trend is to place it round about the isothermal level of 10°C. The important point is that each of the two portions of the world's oceans has roughly its own circulation (Figs. 118 and 135). Within this context we shall call them the lesser and greater circulation. Let us see how this idea of bipartition developed.

It has been pointed out repeatedly in this and the second chapter that the icy cold waters constituting the deepest layers of all oceans reveal their polar origin by their low temperature. That great naturalist Von Humboldt was the first to draw this conclusion, or at any rate to publish it. He maintained that the very low temperatures prevailing in the depths of the ocean, right down to below the Equator, bore witness to a constant supply of water deriving from high latitudes. This can only be provided by *circulation*, one branch of which is the bottom current coming from polar regions.

As little as fifty years ago, there were still some scholars, including the French oceanographer Thoulet, who rejected the idea of a vertical circulation of oceanic waters. Thoulet believed that these deep waters were completely still, and regarded them as the remains of a bygone ice age ('fossil' waters as it were). Since then, investigations, including those of the celebrated *Meteor* expedition, have convincingly proved the existence of a vertical circulation in the oceans.

It has now transpired, however, that this circulation is not quite as simple as was formerly believed. Lenz's view (1848) was long held, that the circulation of oceanic water took place in a more or less symmetrical, two-cell system; see Fig. 132. The underlying idea was that of a thermal circulation, such as may arise in a tub of water if there is a source of heat operating at one end and a source of cold, (e.g. a lump of ice) at the other. Sandström tested this with some very instructive experiments, amplified to embrace also circulations initiated by other causes. The cold sources of the oceans are situated in the polar regions; the source of heat is in tropical parts where the sun heats the water considerably. It appears, however, that circulation of this kind becomes extensive enough to embrace the whole mass of water only if the cold source is near surface and the warm source deep. Heat from above, for instance, is not a very effective inducer of an all-embracing thermal circulation. But it is to precisely that kind of heating that the oceans are exposed in tropical regions. Consequently, such simple thermal circulation by itself, far from occupying the whole volume of the oceans, as in Fig. 132, is restricted to a layer a few hundred metres thick at

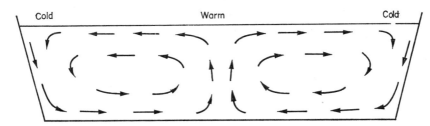

Fig. 132 A simple diagram of circulation as formerly thought to prevail in the oceans.

most—the 'troposphere', which stretches, on either side of the Equator, halfway to the Poles. Within this, the water flows at the surface from lower to higher latitudes, and returns at deeper levels.

This circulation is controlled not only by the differences in temperature between tropical and subtropical regions, but also by differences in salinity. Owing to excessive evaporation in subtropical high-pressure areas, the salinity increases; the surface water therefore becomes heavier and tends to sink. Because of these combined thermal and salinity effects, this is called *thermohaline* circulation.

We must not forget that the mighty drift-currents pass through this same oceanic upper layer and, on account of their far greater velocity, mask the pattern of flow of this thermohaline circulation. Nonetheless, the lesser circulation is, and remains, an important factor in the vertical movement of the water masses in the warm oceanic upper layer.

The interface beneath this upper storey is double-vaulted (see Fig. 135). It has a depth minimum in the vicinity of the Equator; the maximum depths of the boundary surface (which is, of course, by no means sharp) are found around latitudes 30° N. and 30° S.; thence, northward and southward respectively, it inclines towards the surface of the sea. At higher latitudes there is no upper storey; as we have said, the 'stratosphere' there extends to the surface. The warm upper waters are deepest in the area of the Sargasso Sea, where they reach down to 900 metres. We mentioned in the previous chapter that the high temperatures on the right flank of the Gulf Stream persist to great depths.

Near the Equator, where an equatorial countercurrent is flowing, the lesser circulation is further complicated by a small gyral of the uppermost layer of water in a contrary direction; see Fig. 118. This is associated with a convergence at the southern margin of the Equatorial Countercurrent which is usually situated north of the Equator. We have referred to this before. Surface water sinks a short distance into this convergence only to rise again, near the Equator on the one side, and at the northern margin of the countercurrent on the other. This refers mainly, however, to the more or less isothermal, warm, top layer, which is demarcated from the underlying, less warm waters (which nevertheless still belong to the 'upper storey', i.e. the troposphere) by a fairly abrupt jump in temperature. This interface lies highest in the neighbourhood of the Equator, at 50–150 metres below the surface, and highest of all on the eastern side of the oceans. The interface in both hemispheres slopes down from the equatorial zone towards higher latitudes. These slopes are due to the influence of the earth's rotation upon moving masses of warm water within the North and the South Equatorial Currents. (See Chapter 6.)

THE GREATER CIRCULATION

Now let us turn, once again, to the waters in the abyssal, dark depths of the oceans, about which there is a good deal more to tell than is at first suspected. It was formerly believed that this domain—by far the largest portion of the entire volume of the oceans throughout the world—was not only unilluminated and uniformly cold, but also lifeless and motionless.

By degrees, however, this picture has been taking on colour. After the work done by the deep-sea explorers during many oceanographic expeditions, first and foremost of which is that of the famous *Challenger*, we now know that the deep-sea is populated, even though sparsely, by multitudes of living organisms; also that, thanks to these creatures, the depths are not entirely bereft of light, because forty per cent. of all these inhabitants have light organs. So the night in these depths is not a starless night!

Nor, indeed, are the waters down there motionless. We know that a gigantic circulation is steadily at work, following a mighty pattern which encompasses all the oceans. Because it stirs as well as flows, this is the circulation which, everywhere, keeps the dissolved components of sea water in virtually fixed ratios.

This circulation of deep waters is no less impressive for being so slow that it could more aptly be said to creep than to flow. 'Quick' and 'slow' are merely relative concepts. The circulation of the oceans may be slow compared with that of our blood, but it is fast compared to the rate at which geological processes take place. If the pace of our consciousness were itself slower, we should no longer think of deep-sea circulation as slow.

Lastly, cold as the waters of the deep oceans are everywhere, they are not uniformly so. There is a certain design to be discerned in the temperature distribution down there, a pattern intimately associated with the great pattern of water circulation. The temperature differences registered, with amazing accuracy, by our reversing thermometers are but small, yet they testify just as much to what is going on as do the minor differences in salinity of the water samples which have been brought to the surface in various places.

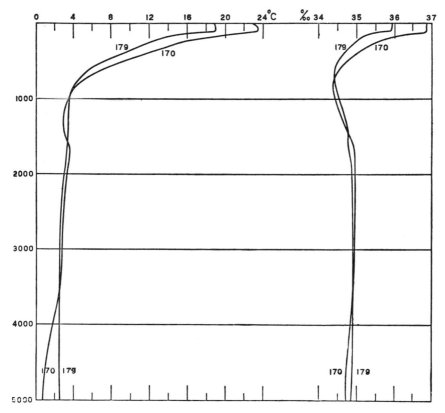

FIG. 133 Two observation stations of the *Meteor* in the Atlantic. 170 is situated at 22°39′ S. and 27°55′ W. to the west of the Mid-Atlantic Ridge; 179 at 21°30′ S. and 0°0′ W. to the east of that Ridge. Temperatures are on the left, salinities on the right.

Let us consider a couple of graphs of temperature and salinity of two stations in the Atlantic, both from the *Meteor* expedition, and both just within the Tropic of Capricorn; one to the west of the Mid-Atlantic Ridge (station 170) and the other to the east of it (station 179); see Fig. 133.

First of all, the low temperatures below 1000 metres again strike the eye. We have seen that Von Humboldt rightly concluded from these that the water deep down in the ocean is of polar origin, and as this is the southern hemisphere, the obvious place to look for this source is the edge of the Antarctic Continent where the ocean surface is coldest. The water descending thence along the continental slope, and flowing northward over the bottom of the ocean takes its low temperature with it, and gets only very slightly warmer under way. Slow as the advance may be, it must continue steadily; otherwise, the temperature of the deeps at low latitudes would necessarily rise in the long run, owing to warmth received from higher layers and, possibly, from the earth's heat below. This is to say once more that the supply of bottom water is a branch of some circulation. It follows, however, from a closer study of the observations represented graphically in Fig. 133, as well as from general principles of physics, that the circulatory pattern is not as simple as Fig. 132 would suggest.

Taking first the difference between the western and eastern stations situated at approximately the same latitude, namely 23° and 22° S. respectively, we see that the ocean is decidedly less cold on the eastern side than it is on the western side at the same depths. To account for this difference, we shall have to do some reconnoitring between these places and the basin of the Antarctic Ocean whence this water comes. We must therefore study two vertical longitudinal sections through the Atlantic Ocean, one on the eastern and the other on the western side. The former reveals the cause of the difference, namely the Walvis Ridge, which bars the northward passage of the bottom water, and constitutes, between the Angola basin in which Meteor station 179 lies and the Cape basin, a divide similar to that formed by the Wyville-Thompson Ridge and Faroes–Iceland Ridge between the basin of the Norwegian Sea and the Atlantic depths. There can be no mistaking the contrast in temperature between the waters at the bottom on the northern side of the Walvis Ridge and those on its southern side, which are just as cold as the waters to the west of the Mid-Atlantic Ridge.

Where, then, it may be asked, does the bottom water to the north of the Walvis Ridge come from? The answer is that it does come from the Antarctic, but along a very circuitous route. Just about on the Equator, the water on the western side finds a narrow passage in the deep Romanche Trench through the Mid-Atlantic Ridge and thus enters the basins on the eastern side. Flowing southward, it reaches the northern side of the Walvis Ridge and, having received some warmth from above on its long, difficult journey, it is ultimately less cold than either the water on the other side of the Mid-Atlantic Ridge or that on the other side of the Walvis Ridge.

This water deriving from the Antarctic Ocean is called *Antarctic Bottom Water*. The heaviest kind of water in all the oceans, it is formed at the margin of the Antarctic Continent by the process of freezing out. Sea-water which has cooled down to its freezing point ($-1.9°C$) gains a little in salinity through the freezing out of saltless ice crystals, and so sinks to the bottom. This process operates most efficiently in the Weddell Sea, the marginal sea of the polar continent to the south of the Atlantic Ocean; indeed, this sea is the principal region of origin of the Antarctic bottom water, which flows slowly downward along the submarine continental slope, spreads on the bottom of the Antarctic Ocean, and then northward over the beds of the three oceans.

If we look again at a longitudinal section through the Atlantic Ocean (Figs. 134 and 135), we shall see that the distribution of temperatures shows very

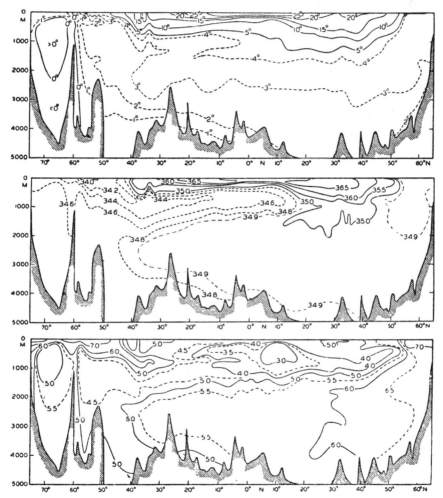

FIG. 134 Vertical longitudinal section of the Atlantic Ocean to the west of the Mid-Atlantic Ridge (after Wüst). *Above:* Temperature; *Middle:* Salinity; *Below:* Oxygen content.

clearly how the Antarctic bottom waters, down below, extend northward. The tongue of the coldest water projects far into the northern hemisphere. This is still more apparent from a section showing the potential temperatures, than from our picture.

If one asks whether an analogous type of water comes southward from the Arctic Ocean, the answer is that, indeed, very cold bottom water is formed in the north (with potential temperatures down to $-1\cdot4°C$), but only in a very limited area between Greenland and Spitsbergen; and as the Scotland–Iceland–Greenland Ridge largely blocks the northern entrance to the Atlantic deep sea, only a little of this water finds its way to the south. Very occasionally, it cascades over the sill for a short time, either between Greenland and Iceland or between Iceland and the Faroes. But this Arctic bottom water is not of much significance to the Atlantic Ocean as a whole; it is mainly Antarctic bottom water that is found in the northern hemisphere, as elsewhere in the ocean.

It is the same in the Indian and Pacific Oceans. The northern part of the latter—the largest of all the oceans—is almost entirely cut off from the Arctic Ocean by the shallow Bering Strait. The Weddell Sea, to the south of the Atlantic Ocean, is the main source of the Antarctic bottom water of the Pacific as well as of the Indian and Atlantic Oceans. In oceanography the *source region* of a water mass is comparable to what, in meteorology, is called the source region of an air mass. It is the region where the type of water in question has acquired its specific properties.

Now it is a curious fact that the source regions of the types of water of which the great masses of the oceans consist are quite small. The Weddell Sea is one of them, and it is mainly there that the bottom waters are formed.

The course of the bottom waters, however, constitutes only one branch of the greater circulation. To get a clearer picture of all this, let us turn again to the temperature and salinity distribution in our two tropical stations; see Fig. 133. They show a couple of facts which do not tie up with the simple circulation plan of Fig. 132. The temperature curve of the western station shows that, from 1300 metres' depth downwards, the temperature rises briefly instead of steadily dropping. The salinity curves of both stations first show a decline, from above downwards, but, as from a depth of 800 to 900 metres, there is an increase which continues down to almost 3000 metres, after which salinity decreases again, right down to the bottom. There is a layer of higher salinity, therefore, between the bottom waters and the waters at roughly 1000 metres. Moreover, they are slightly warmer, notably on the western side, than they would be if the temperature continued to drop steadily from 1000 metres down to the bottom. A spatial picture, like the longitudinal section of Fig. 134, is needed to demonstrate the significance of all this. A tongue-shaped protrusion from the right (north), between 1000 and 3500 metres, appears very distinctly in both the salinity and oxygen sections. This is what is known as the *Atlantic deep water*, which flows from north to south.

Thus, whereas the heaviest water, the Antarctic bottom water, is formed in the south and makes its presence felt well within the northern hemisphere, the next heaviest mass of water, the Atlantic deep water, is formed in the north and penetrates far into the southern hemisphere, right down to the Antarctic Ocean. Where is the source region of this deep water?

The high oxygen content provides a clue; it must be at the surface of the sea. It is where saline Gulf Stream water has mingled with cold polar water, and where there is severe cooling in winter, to near freezing point. This happens in two places, namely in the Irminger Sea between Iceland and southern Greenland (where the Irminger Current, an offshoot of the Gulf Stream, keeps salinity moderately high), and in the oceanic area between South Greenland and Labrador. In both places offshore winds make the surface of the sea very cold in winter, with the result that the top waters become heavier than the layers underneath, and sink. Owing to this convection, in such places the whole volume ultimately becomes filled with

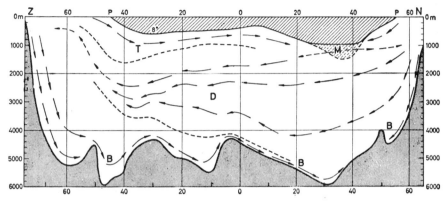

FIG. 135 Diagram of circulation in the depths of the Atlantic, in a vertical plane (after Wüst). B = bottom water; D = deep water; T = intermediate water; M = Mediterranean water; P represents the 'polar front' where, at the surface, the polar waters meet the waters of subtropical origin (shaded part). Here the 8° isotherm has been taken as the boundary between the colder and warmer waters; nowadays the somewhat higher 10° isotherm is preferred.

heavy sea-water, right down to the bottom; this water then presses on southwards and becomes the Atlantic deep water.

Somewhat farther along, however, there is a contributory source for this deep water; not a source of cold, but of salt; it is the Mediterranean. We dwelt on this before. The water flowing over the bed of the Straits of Gibraltar into the Atlantic Ocean is so salty that, higher though its temperature be, it nevertheless mingles with the Atlantic deep water. Something similar probably happens in the Sargasso Sea, farther west, where the influence of increased salinity due to strong evaporation extends to the depths. (This means that there is a breakthrough here, as it were, of the oceanic 'troposphere' towards the 'stratosphere'; an exchange of waters between the lesser and greater circulations.)

The injection of salt water at about latitude 35° N. (that of Gibraltar) is very clearly to be seen in Fig. 134, the lengthwise section of salinity distribution in the Atlantic Ocean. This is what makes the Atlantic deep water

farther south so strikingly distinguishable—chiefly by its higher salt content—from both the bottom waters and the layers above (which, by the way,
nevertheless also belong to the 'lower storey' of the ocean).

The deep water penetrates far to the south, taking with it on its way
portions of the bottom waters, which thus return to the Antarctic Ocean. It
goes without saying that these bottom waters must return somewhere,
though not as bottom waters—just as arterial blood leaving the heart must
return to the heart, but no longer as arterial blood. In the course of its long
voyage to the north, the Antarctic current gives off some of its waters to the
Atlantic deep water, with which these are carried back to the south. And
indeed, this deep water itself gradually changes in character.

On the northern side of the region where the Antarctic bottom waters
slant down along the sloping bed, the northern deep water is forced by the
slope of the bottom waters to rise obliquely upwards. This risen water, rich
in nutrients (fertilizers derived from organic waste sinking to the bottom
elsewhere) is all-important to organic life in these regions; hence the
abundance of life in Antarctic waters.

Once it has reached higher levels, the course of the deep water must
eventually turn. Some of the water flows under the surface to the south, to
the source region of the bottom water, whence water can again drain off
downwards. Another body of it turns under the surface towards the north,
in the direction of the *Antarctic convergence*, the source of subantarctic
intermediate water. This is the third type of water which plays an important
part in the greater circulation.

In the observations made at individual oceanographic stations like the two
represented in Fig. 133, this type of water betrays its presence by a minimum
salinity, usually at a depth of roughly 800 metres. It is very clearly visible
in the salinity lines in vertical cross-sections, as a tongue-shaped protrusion
of less saline water; and it is most conspicuous of all in the southern half of
the Atlantic, starting at the surface at about latitude 50° S. The pattern of this
tongue of low salinity immediately suggests a spread of this water northward, between the saltier upper layer and the likewise saltier, deep water.
The area of origin of this water is the belt of sea along the *Antarctic convergence*, which encompasses the whole southern hemisphere at, roughly,
latitude 50° S. This region of the southern oceans is situated within the belt
of depressions travelling from east to west, where there is much rainfall, and
the salinity of the surface water is therefore below average. The motion of
the water tends predominantly eastward, but to the south of the convergence
line (which, of course, is not really a line but a belt) it has, on an average, a
small, northward component which it does not have to the north of that line.
It is precisely this which causes the convergence, the 'driving together' of
surface water. A portion of it, the coldest portion (coming from the south),
must therefore continually be escaping downwards. The components of
motion involved are again small, far smaller than those of the powerful
West Wind Drift. In course of time there is, nevertheless, a displacement of

water towards the depths, down to between 600 and 1000 metres, and at the same time northward. So it is again a creeping current, ambling on well beyond the Equator, just as the bottom current (likewise from the south) and the deep current (in the opposite direction) do. Some of the Antarctic intermediate water mixes with the deep water on the way, and returns southward with it.

Up to about latitude 30° N. the tongue of less saline water is visible under the top layer. Once again, the marked asymmetry between north and south in the Atlantic Ocean becomes apparent. Although some *arctic* intermediate water is formed in the north, it spreads very little. It arises to the east of the Newfoundland Bank, where cold water, of low salinity, of the Labrador Current dives under the Gulf Stream waters. In the salinity chart, it is seen to extend some distance downward and southward, but it reaches no farther than the edge of the highly saline Sargasso Sea area. The boundary between the polar water and the Gulf Stream is called either the Arctic convergence, or the polar front.

This account of the greater circulation of the Atlantic waters is mainly *meridional*; that is to say, it concerns the greater circulation in so far as this can be depicted in a vertical north-to-south plane. The main outlines are represented as a diagram in Fig. 135, borrowed from Wüst, and largely based on the classic explorations of the *Meteor* expedition.

NEW IDEAS

Oceanographic expeditions have also collected useful data relating to the horizontal flow pattern in the depths of the oceans, but in themselves these data do not yet present an altogether complete and consistent picture. Meanwhile, the American oceanographer Stommel has been developing a theory which has led to a bold picture, represented in a somewhat simplified form in Fig. 136. This figure, instead of showing the flow in one level, sums up the total transport beneath the level of 2000 metres.

If we take the Atlantic Ocean first, we shall see that the two main supply currents, or 'arteries' on the western side, not far from the North and South American coasts, carry southward from their source region (the black dot near Greenland) its deep waters, and northward from its source region (the black dot in the Weddell Sea) the Antarctic bottom water. Since the vertically-totalled (*nett*) transport below 2000 metres is represented here, this figure does not show that the Antarctic bottom water also penetrates farther northward under the Atlantic deep water, nor that the latter continues farther southward over the Antarctic bottom waters.

Streams of water, more diffuse and far slower, detach themselves from these main currents in the west, and all swerve off towards the Pole. The postulate is that these slower, outspread streams are gradient currents. Because the gradient current becomes slower towards the Poles for a given pressure gradient, it follows from the theory of gradient currents that

convergence, hence an upward escape of water, occurs in these areas. Therefore, over against the descent of water in the areas of origin, and along the
feed-currents (which are *not* gradient currents), there is a diffuse, very slow
ascent of the water in the other areas of the ocean.

An important part of this bold, grand concept is borne out by the observed
facts. We saw in the preceding chapter that a strong countercurrent, flowing
in a south-westerly direction at velocities of as much as 20 centimetres per
second, had been detected under the Gulf Stream on the western side
of the North Atlantic, at 2800 metres depth.

FIG. 136 Diagram of deep-sea circulation below 2000 metres, after Stommel.

The existence of similar currents in the Middle and South Atlantic, at
great depths on the western side, has also been established (by Wüst),
notably by dynamic calculations based on observations made by the *Meteor*
expedition, already referred to in the preceding chapter. These currents do,
in fact, run about parallel to the coastline of South America; one composed
of Atlantic deep water flowing from north to south, and one consisting of
Antarctic bottom water proceeding northward, partly under and partly
alongside, the former. The computed velocities of both are from 10 to 15
centimetres per second. In the regions to the east of the two feed-currents,
the velocities are incomparably lower, something of the order of millimetres
per second.

As we have already said, the picture shown by recorded observations of
the deep-sea circulation in the Atlantic—the most thoroughly explored of all
the oceans—is, as yet, far from complete and perfect. To some extent,
Stommel's presentation is still hypothetical. Both these comments apply,
with yet greater force, to the other oceans.

PLATE XXIX

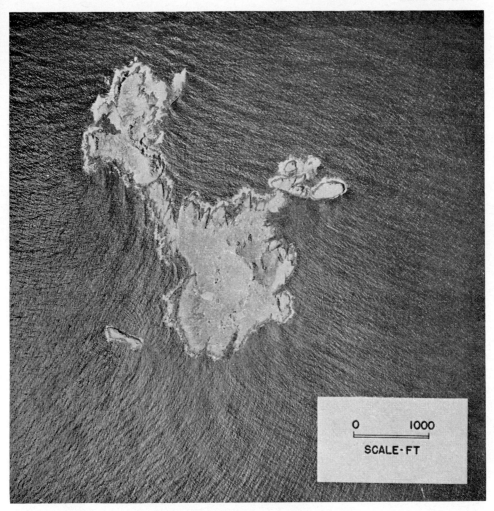

Refraction, reflection and scattering of swell and wind-waves around Farallon Island, California. There are breakers all round the coast, though most marked at the top of the photograph. The swell coming from top right rounds the island both on the left and right, producing a crossed pattern below. The islet on the left below ' radiates' the waves back in all directions. (U.S. Navy photograph.)

PLATE XXX

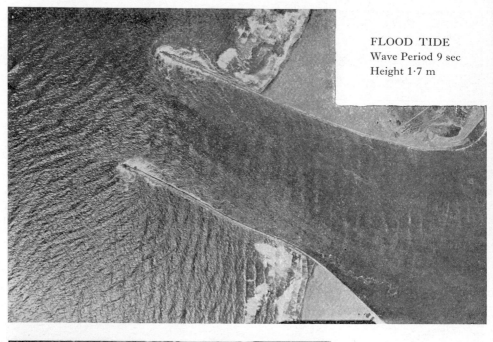

FLOOD TIDE
Wave Period 9 sec
Height 1·7 m

EBB TIDE
Wave Period 12 sec
Height 1·7 m

Waves in the entrance to Humboldt Bay, California. *Above* At flood tide. *Below* At ebb tide, in which the waves become steeper owing to the countercurrent and begin to break in comparatively deep water in several places. (U.S. Navy photographs.)

THE INDIAN OCEAN AND THE PACIFIC

Antarctic bottom water, to some extent at least entering from the Atlantic, is also present in the Indian Ocean; but some of it comes direct from the margin of Antarctica. (This is not apparent from Stommel's highly simplified picture of the deep-sea circulation.) There is also subantarctic, intermediate water in this ocean. At depths of between 700 and 1400 metres, it penetrates from the Antarctic convergence to about the Equator. Sandwiched between these two types of water of southern origin, is the more saline, deep water which, coming from the west, enters the Indian Ocean to the south of the Cape of Good Hope. One pointer to this is furnished by the salinity and oxygen contents, which decrease from west to east. There is no source of cold, deep water in the northern part of the Indian Ocean; but the Red Sea does supply water of high salinity which, because of its density, extends to great depths and spreads southward, mingling with the deep water of Atlantic origin. The contribution of the Red Sea to the circulation in the Indian Ocean is comparable to that of the Mediterranean in the Atlantic, though on a smaller scale. The outflow through the Bab-el-Mandeb Strait is estimated to be one-sixth of that through the Straits of Gibraltar.

Above a depth of 1500 metres in the *Pacific Ocean* (see Fig. 137) 'intermediate' water is again clearly perceptible, notably the subantarctic intermediate water, which flows down and northward from the Antarctic convergence to below the more saline, warmer, upper layer of the southern hemisphere, while, in the northern hemisphere, the subarctic intermediate water spreads southward in the same way. A symmetry with respect to the Equator therefore exists in the Pacific Ocean, so far as the intermediate water is concerned. The main source of the northern intermediate water is to the north-east of the Japanese Islands, along a line (called Arctic convergence line, or the 'polar front') where comparatively cold, but less saline waters from the Oya Shio dive under the warmer, saline waters of the Kuru Shio.

The lowest layers of the Pacific, like those of the other two oceans, consist of Antarctic bottom water.

As to the layers above these bottom waters up to a depth of about 1500 metres, the Pacific Ocean not only lacks an area of origin of cold, deep water worthy of the name, but is also without adjacent seas comparable to the Mediterranean or Red Sea which could bring saline water to the deeps. Accordingly, to a large extent, the deep layers above the Antarctic bottom waters (present here, too) are still of Atlantic and Indian origin. They therefore enter the Pacific from the west, and probably fan out northward and eastward. Meanwhile, however, through mixing with the bottom water below, and with the intermediate water above, these waters have become so 'diluted' that the salinity maximum (by which the deep water in the Atlantic and Indian Oceans is differentiated from the underlying and

11

overlying waters) has vanished. The distant origin of the deep water in the Pacific is inferable not only from its relatively low salinity, but also from its low oxygen content, namely between 4 and 1 c.c. per litre at depths (1500–4000 metres) where in the Atlantic it amounts to between 4 and 6 c.c. per litre.

The decrease in oxygen content from west to east and, especially, from south to north (see Fig. 137, below) indicates the direction in which the deep water flows in the Pacific.

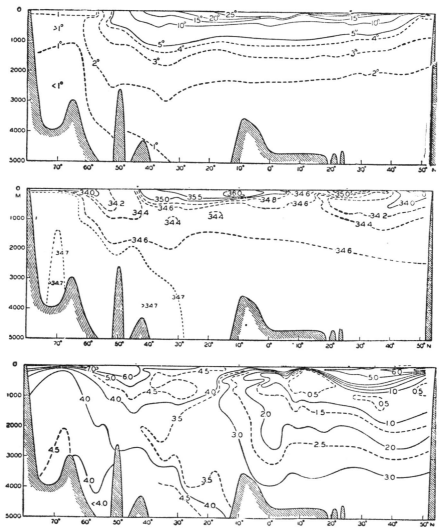

FIG. 137 South–North section through the Pacific Ocean, approximately along the meridian of 170°W. Distribution of temperature (above), salinity (centre) and oxygen (below) according to Sverdrup. The reader should know that the many observations made in the Pacific in recent years were not available when these diagrams were drawn.

The significance of the limited source regions in the Atlantic Ocean—the Weddell Sea for the bottom water, the Irminger Sea, the Labrador Sea and the Mediterranean for the deep water—not only to the great circulation of the Atlantic itself, but to that of all the oceans, is apparent from the foregoing.

CIRCULATION RATE. RADIOACTIVITY

Finally, a word about the oceanic circulation rate. This is by no means a new question. Driven by curiosity and astonishment, the goad to all scientific research, oceanographers approached the problem from various angles. Latterly, however, as in so much scientific work, practical utility and even practical necessity, have added a note of urgency to the investigations. This new driving force which has entered the study of deep-sea circulation is associated with the problems of atomic energy and radioactivity.

Some readers may wonder what the sea has to do with nuclear energy (a better term than 'atomic energy'). It is not as a source of that energy that it claims our attention, but as a dumping-ground for certain injurious by-products and waste products. These are highly radioactive substances which are formed during the process of obtaining nuclear energy from heavy atoms, and which emit rays liable to endanger life. The question now is: How are we to get rid of these radioactive products?

Burning is of no avail; burying in the ground is not safe enough; nor are the oceans vast enough to be a safe repository for all of them. The one redeeming feature of these products is their finite life as emitters of radio-activity, which makes it possible to empty small amounts of them somewhere in the sea; though even so, the utmost care is imperative. Moreover, with or without our consent, some constituents of these radioactive products will eventually enter the sea by way of the atmosphere. That is why we need to know exactly how the oceanic waters circulate; for, once we have this knowledge, we shall be able to make the necessary calculations to show how these products will spread throughout the width and depth of the oceans. On this, again, depends the safety with which such products can be discharged into the sea. As the permissible amounts which may be entrusted to the sea likewise depend on these calculations, it is necessary that we should find out more about these circulatory currents of the oceans, both at the surface and at great depths.

This is now a new target for oceanography; but we are also provided with new tools, and these likewise happen to be linked with radioactivity. Several radioactive substances which reach sea-water from the air, from rivers, or from the sea-bed, in minute quantities, can be measured, and thus, as tracers, serve to teach us something about the history of the mass of water in which they are found.

One of the most 'promising' substances in this respect is radioactive carbon, called radiocarbon or C-fourteen (symbol ^{14}C), which naturally occurs in very small concentrations in the atmosphere and in the sea, mixed with 'common' carbon ^{12}C and, like the latter, built as atoms into the molecules of atmospheric carbon dioxide (CO_2), or carbonic acid (H_2CO_3) and carbonates in sea-water. In the higher layers of the atmosphere, radiocarbon atoms are constantly being formed through the bombardment of nitrogen atoms (^{14}N) by neutrons deriving from cosmic rays. These radiocarbon atoms soon combine with oxygen to form carbonic acid gas, with which they are disseminated throughout the atmosphere. But, as has been said, they are radioactive, which means that each of them tends, after some time, to eject an electron from its nucleus (this is its radioactive emission) and, owing to this loss, itself to become a different kind of atom, an atom of another element—nitrogen again. So radiocarbon atoms have a limited life, the length of which is, however, unpredictable, as one ^{14}C atom (or rather, its *nucleus*) may live for one day, whereas another may live for a hundred thousand years. All we can say is that the average life is a little more than 8000 years. The 'half-life', so-called, provides a better standard. For radiocarbon this is 5570 years; this means that in this number of years, half of a not too small number of ^{14}C atoms disappear, that is, they are converted to nitrogen atoms by the radioactive 'disintegration' described above. Thus radiocarbon is continuously being formed in higher regions on the one hand, while on the other some of it is constantly vanishing, so that a balance is established whereby the ^{14}C content of the atmosphere is maintained at a certain level. This content is most conveniently expressed by the ratio of the ^{14}C content to the total carbon content, which is approximately 1 to 800 thousand million. It can only be determined by measuring the radioactivity of a sample of CO_2.

Now, if atmospheric carbon, in whatever form, becomes imprisoned somehow and somewhere—say taken up by a plant, wood, or sea-water— its radioactivity, compared with that of atmospheric carbon, will gradually decline. From the extent of this decrease it is possible to tell how long ago this carbon (in the form of CO_2) left the atmosphere and was taken up by the tissue of the plant or wood, or by the sea-water; in other words, we can tell the age of that tissue, wood or sea-water. When we say within this context that sea-water is 'of such-and-such an age', we mean that it is that much time since it was in communication with the atmosphere. For example, with a one per cent. decrease in radioactivity the age is taken to be 80 years; a fifty per cent. decrease shows it to be 5570 years, as we have seen (for this is the 'half-life').

As will readily be realized, this means of approach is of inestimable value to students of the great circulation of the waters of the oceans.

Before enumerating some of the discoveries made with the aid of this ^{14}C method, however, we wish to put it on record that we already knew something about the tempo of this great circulation before we had the benefit of [14]C. For instance, an estimate of the transport of deep water in the Atlantic was made long ago, on the basis of serial observations made by the *Meteor* expedition. This was drawn up from calculations of current transport by the dynamic method, described in our previous chapter, and it showed the transport of Atlantic deep water from the northern to the southern hemisphere to be something of the order of ten million cubic metres per second. Apportioning this within the estimated volume in the Atlantic Ocean which is occupied by deep water of northern origin, we find that it would take some five centuries to renew this volume of water, that is to say, this particular portion of the volume of the world's oceans.

The circulation at great depths is certainly slower in the Pacific Ocean, because it derives (branches off) largely from the Atlantic deep-sea circulation by way of the southern part of the Indian Ocean.

We saw earlier in this chapter that a simple estimate showed 300 years to be the ventilation time for a deep-sea basin of moderate size, like the Banda basin.

As to the 'age' of deep-sea waters, in the above sense there can be no doubt but that the waters in the depths of the Pacific are the oldest of all the oceanic waters because they derive, to a large extent, from the Atlantic deep sea by way of the southern part of the Indian Ocean. There are several indicators pointing to this greater age, for example, the oxygen content, which decreases from the Atlantic deep sea to the Pacific deep sea; the phosphate content, which increases along this course (owing to the slow descent of organic remains from the top layers which, as they decompose, increase the phosphate content of the deep-sea water in proportion to the length of its sojourn in the depths); and, last but not least, the ^{14}C content, which, since it decreases with increasing age of the water, provides a very reliable means of determining age, as explained above. Here, finally, a few words about the results so far obtained in this way.

It was found that in the Mid-Atlantic Ocean the Atlantic deep water is approximately 650 years old as compared with the surface water in the northern part of the ocean, the site of the region of origin of this deep water. The deep water in the deepest basins on the eastern side of the Mid-Atlantic Ridge, and Antarctic bottom water in the area explored, were found to be slightly 'older', namely 900 years.

In the Pacific Ocean, at depths of 2000–3500 metres, the ^{14}C method revealed ages ranging from 1300 to 2000 years. These greater ages accord with the conviction that the deep waters in these parts are largely of Atlantic origin. It transpires, moreover, that there is an unmistakable increase in age from south to north; along the meridian of 130° W. this increase amounts to 600 years within a distance of 7000 kilometres. If we take it that the water needs that time to travel that distance, then the average velocity must be 12 kilometres a year, or 0·4 millimetres per second.

11*

We must, nevertheless, beware of over-simplifying our mental picture of the great circulation of the oceans. Great ages have also been found in the southern part of the Pacific, for instance in the Tasman Sea between New Zealand and Australia, where the figure was 2000 years at a depth of 1800 metres. There are also a few places elsewhere with water more or less stagnating; for example, (see p. 295) down below in the Black Sea, and in Kau Bay near Halmahera. Apart from these, however, it seems safe to assume that the deep waters in the northern part of the Pacific Ocean are the oldest of all the waters of the sea.

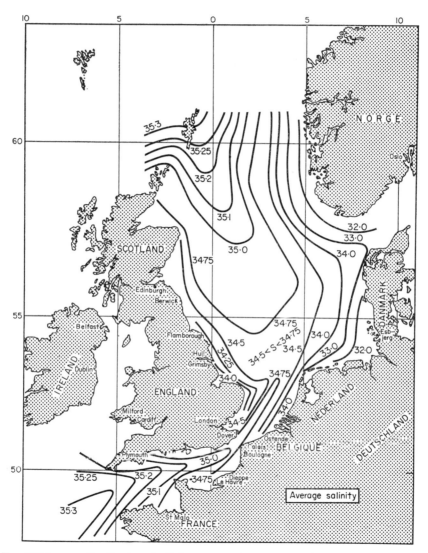

FIG. 138 Average distribution of salinity at the surface of the North Sea and adjacent waters (according to an atlas of the Conseil International pour l'Exploration de la Mer).

FIG. 139 Average distribution of surface temperature in the North Sea and adjacent waters in February (according to charts of the Conseil International pour l'Exploration de la Mer).

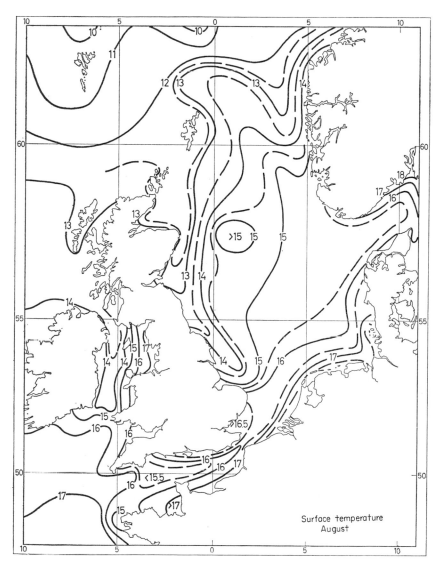

FIG. 140 Average distribution of surface temperature in the North Sea and adjacent waters in August (according to charts of the Conseil International pour l'Exploration de la Mer).

KEY TO CHART 1

Principal basins of the oceans with depths of more than 4000 metres.

Great depths (A–Q).

I	Arabian Basin
II	Somali Basin
III	Mascarenes Basin
IV	Madagascar Basin
V	Indian–Atlantic Antarctic Basin
VI	Indian Australian Basin

    A. Sunda Trench or Java Trench (7450 m)
    B. Wharton Deep (6460 m)

VII	South Australian Basin
VIII	Eastern Indian Antarctic Basin
IX	South China Basin
X	Sulu Basin
XI	Celebes Basin
XII	Banda Basin
XIII	Philippines Basin

    C. Riu-Kiu Trench (7500 m)
    D. Philippines Trench or Mindanao Trench (10,550 m)

XIV	Carolines Basin
XV	Solomon Basin

    E. Bougainville Trench (9140 m)

XVI	Coral Basin
XVII	New Hebrides Basin
XVIII	Fiji Basin
XIX	East Australian Basin
XX	North Pacific Basin

    F. Aleutian Trench (7680 m)
    G. Kuriles Trench (10,500 m)
    H. Japan Trench (10,500 m)
    I. Bonin Trench (9810 m)

XXI	Marianas Basin

    J. Marianas Trench (11,030 m)

XXII	Central Pacific Basin
XXIII	South Pacific Basin

    K. Tonga Trench (10,880 m) Kermadec Trench (10,050 m)
    L. Byrd Deep (8600 m)

XXIV	Guatemala Basin
XXV	Peru Basin

    M. Atacama Trench (8060 m)

XXVI	Pacific Antarctic Basin
XXVII	Labrador Basin
XXVIII	Newfoundland Basin
XXIX	North American Basin
XXX	West Caribbean Basin

    N. Cayman Trench (7240 m)

XXXI	East Caribbean Basin
XXXII	Guyana Basin

    O. Puerto Rico Trench (9220 m)

XXXIII	Brazilian Basin
XXXIV	Argentine Basin
XXXV	South-Antilles Basin
XXXVI	Arctic Basin
XXXVII	West-European Basin
XXXVIII	Iberian Basin
XXXIX	Canaries Basin
XL	Cape Verde Basin
XLI	Sierra Leone Basin

    P. Romanche Trench (7730 m)

XLII	Guinea Basin
XLIII	Angola Basin
XLIV	Cape Basin
XLV	Agulhas Basin
V	Atlantic–Indian Antarctic Basin

    Q. South Sandwich Trench (8260 m)

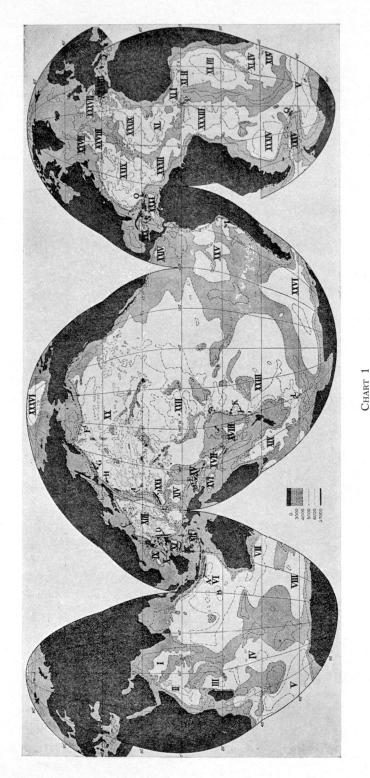

CHART 1

Bathymetric chart of the oceans of the world. The Roman figures and letters refer to the list
of oceanic basins and great depths on facing page. (Chart after Sverdrup, Johnson and Fleming.)

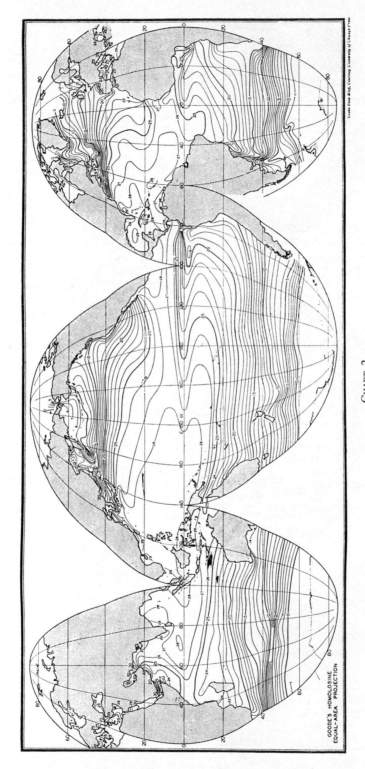

GOODE'S HOMOLOSINE
EQUAL-AREA PROJECTION

CHART 2

Surface temperatures of the oceans in northern summer. (After Sverdrup, Johnson and Fleming.)

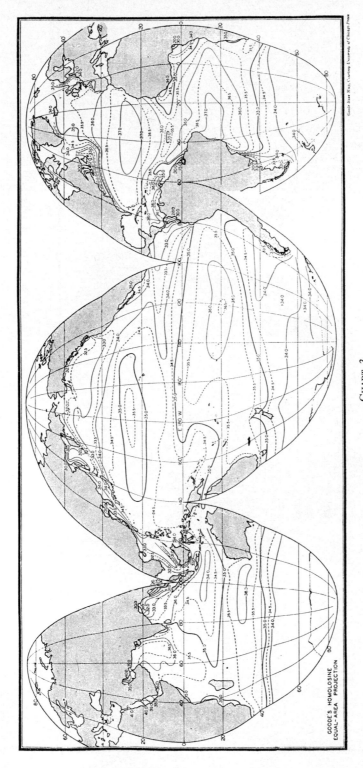

CHART 3

Salinity at the surface of the oceans in northern summer. (After Sverdrup, Johnson and Fleming.)

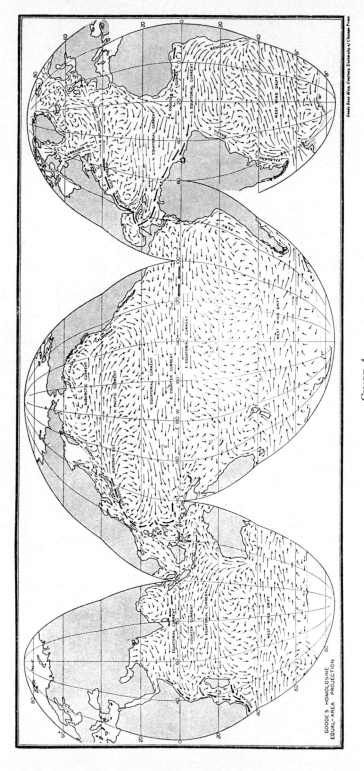

CHART 4

Chart of the surface currents in February–March. (After Sverdrup, Johnson and Fleming.)

BIBLIOGRAPHY

GENERAL

MAURY, M. F. *Physical Geography of the Sea*, Harvard, New York (1855), London (1860). Reprinted, Cambridge, Mass. (1963).

MURRAY, J., HJORT, J. and HELLAND HANSEN, B. *The Depths of the Ocean*, Stechert, London (1912).

KRÜMMEL, O. *Handbuch der Ozeanographie* (2 vols) Stuttgart (1907, 1911).

DEFANT, A. *Dynamische Ozeanographie*, Berlin (1929).

NATIONAL RESEARCH COUNCIL *Oceanography (Physics of the Earth V)* Washington (1932).

ROUCH, J. *Traité d'Oceanographie physique* (3 vols) Paris (1943–48).

SVERDRUP, H. U., JOHNSON, M. W. and FLEMING, R. H. *The Oceans*, Prentice-Hall, New York (1946).

PROUDMAN, J. *Dynamical Oceanography*, Methuen, London (1953).

U.S.S.R. Morskoi Atlas (Oceanographic Atlas, 2 vols) Moscow (1953).

DIETRICH, G. and KALLE, K. *Allgemeine Meereskunde*, Borntraeger, Berlin (1957).

HEDGPETH, J. W. (editor) 'Treatise on marine ecology and paleoecology', Vol. 1, *Memoir No. 67, Bull. geol. Soc.Am.* (1957).

SVERDRUP, H. U. 'Oceanography' in *Handbuch der Physik*, Vol. 48 (1957).

BRUNS, E. *Ozeanologie* Berlin (1958–62).

Climatological and Oceanographic Atlas for Mariners, Vol. I: North Atlantic Ocean, U.S. Weather Bureau, Washington, D.C. (1959).

LACOMBE, H. *Dynamique des Mers*, Paris (1960).

DEFANT, A. *Physical Oceanography*, Pergamon, London (1961).

VON ARX, W. S. *Introduction to Physical Oceanography*, Addison-Wesley, Reading, Mass. (1962).

HILL, M. N. (editor) *The Sea—Ideas and Observations* (3 vols) Wiley, New York (1962/3).

SEARS, M. (editor) *Progress in Oceanography* (ann. vols) Oxford (1963).

PICKARD, G. L. *Descriptive Oceanography*, Pergamon, London (1964).

DIETRICH, G. *General Oceanography*, Wiley, New York (1965).

Oceanographic and Meteorological Atlases, Koninklÿk Ned. Met. Inst., De Bilt (1931–57).

Marine Climatic Atlas of the World (several vols) U.S. Navy Hydrogr. Office, Washington, D.C. (1955).

Climatological and Sea Surface Current Charts of the N. Atlantic Ocean, Met. Office, London (1958).

Climatological and Oceanographic Atlas for Mariners, Vol. I, U.S. Navy Hydrogr. Office, Washington, D.C. (1960).

CHAPTER 1

'Summary of the scientific results of the exploring voyage of H.M.S. *Challenger*' London (1895).

MURRAY, J., HJORT, J. and HELLAND HANSEN, B. *The Depths of the Ocean* (Chapter 1), Stechert, London (1912).
HERDMAN, W. A. *Founders of Oceanography and their Work*, London (1923).
SCHOTT, G. *Geographie des Indischen und des Stillen Ozeans*, Hamburg (1935).
VAN RIEL, P. M. *The Snellius Expedition* (Vol. I), Leiden (1937–38).
MATHEWS, D. J. *Tables of the Velocity of Sound in Pure Water and Sea-Water for use in Echo-Sounding and Sound Ranging* (2nd edn), Hydrographic Dept Admiralty, London (1939).
DALY, R. A. *The Floor of the Ocean*, Chapel Hill, N. C. (1942).
ROUCH, J. *Traité d'Oceanographie Physique*, Vol. 1, 'Les Sondages', Paris (1943).
SCHOTT, G. *Geographie des Atlantischen Ozeans*, Hamburg (1942).
BENCKER, H. 'Chronological list of the main maritime discoveries and explorations' *Hydrogr. Rev.* **XXI**, 130–69 (1944).
SHEPARD, F. P. *Submarine Geology*, Harper, New York (1948).
BOURCART, J. *Geographie du Fond des Mers*, Paris (1949).
KUENEN, PH. H. *Marine Geology*, Wiley, New York and London (1950).
CARSON, R. L. *The Sea Around Us*, New American Library, New York (1951).
PRATJE, O. 'Die Erforschung des Meeresbodens', *Geol. Rdsch.* **39**, 152 (1952).
Symposium on oceanographic instrumentation, Natn Acad. Sci.—National Research Council Pubn 309 (1954).
GUILCHEN, A. *Coastal and Submarine Morphology*, Wiley, New York (1958).
HEEZEN, B. C., THARP, M. and EWING, M. 'The floors of the oceans, I: The North Atlantic', *Bull. geol. Soc. Am. Special Paper* 65 (1959).
SHEPARD, F. P. *The Earth beneath the Sea*, Johns Hopkins, Baltimore (1959).
HILL, M. N. (editor). *The Sea—Ideas and Observations*, (Vol. **III**), Wiley, New York (1963).
Carte generale bathymetrique des Oceans (separate sheets), Int. Hydrogr. Bur., Monaco.

CHAPTER 2

WÜST, G., BÖHNECKE, G. and MEYER, H. H. F. 'Ozeanographische Methoden und Instrumente', *Wiss. Ergebn. dt. atlant. Exped. 'Meteor'* **IV**, 1, Berlin (1932).
BÖHNECKE, G. 'Temperatur, Salzgehalt und Dichte an der Oberfläche des Atlantischen Ozeans', *Wiss. Ergebn dt. atlant. Exped. 'Meteor'* **V**, Berlin (1936).
RUSSELL, F. S. and YONGE, C. M. *The Seas* (Our knowledge of life in the sea and how it is gained), (3rd edn), Warne, London (1963).
WÜST, G. and DEFANT, A. *Wiss. Ergebn. dt. atlant. Exped. 'Meteor'* **VI**, *Atlas*, Berlin (1936).
DORSEY, N. E. *Properties of Ordinary Water Substance*, New York (1940).
HAMAKER, H. C. and HARDON, H. J. '*Snellius'-Expedition*, Vol. **II**, Part 1, 'Methods and Instruments', Leiden (1941).
KALLE, K. *Der Stoffhaushalt des Meeres* (2nd edn), Leipzig (1945).
SVERDRUP, H. U., JOHNSON, M. W. and FLEMING, R. H. *The Oceans*, Chapters 3, 4, 6, 8, 10, Prentice-Hall, New York (1946).
ECKART, C. *Principles of Underwater Sound*, Prentice-Hall, Washington D.C. (1946).
CARSON, R. L. *The Sea Around Us*, New American Library, New York (1951).
EKMAN, S. *Zoogeography of the Sea*, Sidgwick and Jackson, London (1953).

Symposium on oceanographic instrumentation, *Nat. Acad. Sci.—National Research Council Pubn* 309 (1954).

WÜST, G., BROGMUS, W. and NOODT, E. 'Die zonale Verteilung von Salzgehalt, Niederschlag, Verdunstung, Temperatur und Dichte an der Oberfläche der Ozeane', *Kieler Meeresforsch.*, **10**, 137 (1954).

HARVEY, H. W. *The Chemistry and Fertility of Sea Waters*, C.U.P. Cambridge (1957).

RICHARDS, F. A. 'Some current aspects of physical oceanography', *Physics Chem. Earth*, **2**, 77 (1957).

BARNES, H. 'Apparatus and Methods of Oceanography, Part I: Chemical' in *Oceanography and Marine Biology*, Macmillan, London (1963, 1964).

'Physical and chemical properties of sea water', *Natn Acad. Sci.—Natn Res. Council Pubn* 600 (1959).

'Mean monthly Temperature and Salinity of the Surface Layers of the North Sea and adjacent Waters', International Council for the Exploration of the Sea, Charlottenlund (1962).

HILL, M. N. (editor), *The Sea—Ideas and Observations* (Vol. **II**), Wiley Interscience, New York (1962).

BARNES, H. (editor), *Oceanography and Marine Biology* (Vols **1** and **2**), Macmillan, London (1963).

CHAPTER 3

Geography of the Polar Regions, American Geographical Society, New York (1928).

SMITH, E. H. 'Arctic ice with especial reference to its distribution to the North Atlantic Ocean', *The Marion Expedition Scientific Results*, Part 3, Washington (1931).

SVERDRUP, H. U., *et al. Polarbuch*, Berlin (1933).

MAURSTAD, A. 'Atlas of Sea Ice', *Geofysiske Publikasjoner X*, Noll, Oslo (1935).

MACKINTOSH, N. A. and HERDMAN, H. F. P. 'Distribution of pack-ice in the Southern Ocean', *'Discovery' Reports XIX*, 285 *et seq.* (1940).

SVERDRUP, H. U. *et al. The Oceans*, Chapters 3, 6, 15, Prentice-Hall, New York (1946).

Ice Atlas of the Northern Hemisphere, U.S. Hydrographic Office, Washington D.C. (1946).

HERDMAN, H. F. P. 'The Antarctic pack-ice', *Marine Observer XVIII*, 205 (1948).

BÜDEL, J. *Atlas der Eisverhältnisse des Nordatlantischen Ozeans und Übersichtskarten der Eisverhältnisse des Nord- und Sudpolargebietes*, Dt. Hydrogr. Inst. No. 2335 (1950).

KOENIG, L. S., GREENAWAY, K. R., DUNBAR, M. and HATTERSLEY-SMITH, G. 'Arctic ice islands', *Arctic*, **5**, 67 (1952).

AHLMANN, H. W. 'Glacier variations and climatic fluctuations', *Am. Geog. Soc. Bowman Memorial Lectures*, **3**, 1 (1953).

CRARY, A. P. 'Arctic ice island research', *Advances in Geophysics*, **3**, 1 (1956).

ANDERSON, D. L. (editor). 'Arctic sea ice', *U.S. Natn Acad. Sci. Pubn*, 598 (1958).

CRARY, A. P. 'Arctic ice island and ice shelf studies', *Arctic*, **11**, 3 (1958); **13**, 32 (1960).

Supplement Pilot Chart N. Atlantic, 'Arctic ice and its drift in the North Atlantic', U.S. Navy Hydrographic Office (1965).

Oceanographic Atlas of the Polar Seas, U.S. Navy Hydrographic Office Pubn 705, (Part I: Antarctic, Part II: Arctic) (1959).

BAIRD, P. D. *The Polar World*, Wiley, London (1964).

CHAPTER 4

EKMAN, V. W. 'On dead water', *Scient. Results Norw. N. Polar Exped.* 1893–1906, **5**, No. 15 (1904).

KRÜMMEL, O. *Handbuch der Ozeanographie*, Vol. **2**, Stuttgart (1911).

VON LARISCH, F. GRAF, *Sturmsee und Brandung*, Leipzig (1925).

SVERDRUP, H. U., JOHNSON, M. W. and FLEMING, R. H. *The Oceans*, Ch. 14, Prentice-Hall, New York (1946).

MUNK, W. H. and TRAYLOR, M. A. 'Refraction of ocean waves—a process linking underwater topography to beach erosion', *J. Geol.*, **55**, 1 (1947).

BIGELOW, H. B. and EDMONDSON, W. T. 'Wind waves at sea, breakers and surf', *Publ. No.* 602, U.S. Navy Hydrographic Office, Washington, D.C. (1947).

GROEN, P. 'Contribution to the theory of internal waves', *Meded. Verh. K. Ned. met. Inst.*, **11** (1948).

SHEPARD, F. P., MACDONALD, G. A. and COX, D. C. 'The tsunami of April 1, 1946', *Bull. Scripps Inst. Oceanogr.*, **5**, 391 (1950).

U.S. NAVY HYDROGRAPHIC OFFICE, 'Techniques for forecasting wind waves and swell', *U.S. Navy Hydrographic Office Pubn* 604 (1951).

DEFANT, A. 'Über interne Wellen, besonders solche mit Gezeitencharakter', *Dt. hydrogr. Z.* **5**, 231 (1952).

MUNK, W. H. 'Forecasting ocean waves', *Compendium of Meteorology*, 1082, Am. Meteorol. Soc. (1952).

BRETSCHNEIDER, C. L. 'Generation of wind waves in shallow water', *Beach Erosion Board Technical Memorandum No.* 51 (1954).

MICHE, M. R. 'Propriétés des trains d'ondes océaniques et de laboratoire', *Bull. Inf. Com. cent. Océanogr. Étude Côtes* No. 135, Paris (1954).

RUSSELL, R. C. H. and MACMILLAN, D. H. *Waves and Tides* (2nd edn), London (1954).

BRUNS, E. *Handbuch der Wellen der Meere und Ozeane*, Berlin (1955).

PIERSON, W. J. 'Wind-generated gravity waves', *Adv. Geophys.*, **2**, 93 (1955).

PIERSON, W. J., NEUMANN, G. and JAMES, R. W. 'Practical methods for observing and forecasting ocean waves by means of wave spectra and statistics', *U.S. Navy Hydrogr. Office Pubn* 603 (1955).

ROLL, H. U. 'Oberflächen-Wellen des Meeres' in *Handbuch der Physik*, 48 (1957).

BRETSCHNEIDER, C. L. 'Revisions in wave forecasting: deep and shallow water', *Proc. 6th Conf. cst. Engng*, 30 (1958).

GROEN, P. and DORRESTEIN, R. *Zeegolven*, Kon. Ned. Met. Inst. Pubn 111, No. 11 (2nd edn) (1958).

WALDEN, H. 'Die winderzeugten Meereswellen', *Einzelveröff. Seewett-Amt*, **18**, 1 (1958).

WEHAUSEN, J. V. and LAITONE, E. V. 'Surface waves' in *Handbuch der Physik*, Vol. **9**, Berlin (1960).

VARIOUS AUTHORS. 'Waves' in *The Sea—Ideas and Observations* (edited by M. N. Hill) Vol. **I**, Section V, Wiley Interscience, New York (1962).

KINSMAN, B. *Wind Waves, their Generation and Propagation on the Ocean Surface*, Prentice-Hall, Englewood Cliffs, N.J. (1965).

TRICKER, R. A. R. *Bores, Breakers, Waves and Wakes*, Elsevier, New York (1965).

CHAPTER 5

LORENTZ, H. A. *Verslag van de Staatscommissie inzake hogere waterstanden tijdens storm, als gevolg van de afsluiting van de Zuiderzee*, The Hague (1926).

SCHALKWIJK, W. F. 'A contribution to the study of storm surges on the Dutch coast', *Meded. Verh. K. Ned. Met. Inst. B*. No. 7 (1947).

HANSEN, W. 'Gezeiten und Gezeitenströme der halbtägigen Hauptmondtide M_2 in der Nordsee', *Dt. hydrogr. Z.*, Ergänzungsheft **1** (1952).

VILLAIN, C. 'Les lignes cotidales dans les oceans', *Bull. Inf. Com. cent. Oceanogr. Etude Cotes*, **3**, Nos. 4, 5, 7, 9 (1951); **4**, No. 6 (1952).

PROUDMAN, J. *Dynamical Oceanography*, Methuen, London (1953).

RUSSELL, R. C. H. and MACMILLAN, D. H. *Waves and Tides* (2nd edn), London (1954).

WEENINK, M. P. H. 'The "twin" storm surges during 21–24 December 1954', *Dt. hydrogr. Z.*, **9**, 240 (1956).

BARTELS, J. 'Gezeitenkräfte' in *Handbuch der Physik*, Vol. **48** (1957).

DEFANT, A. 'Flutwellen und Gezeiten des Wassers' in *Handbuch der Physik*, Vol. **48** (1957).

DOODSON, A. T. 'Oceanic tides', *Adv. Geophys.*, **5**, 118 (1958).

WEENINK, M. P. H. 'A theory and method of calculation of wind effects on sea levels in a partly-enclosed sea, with special application to the southern coast of the North Sea', *Meded. Verh. K. Ned. Met. Inst.*, **73** (1958).

Koninklijk Nederlands Meteorologisch Instituut and Rijkswaterstaat, 'Contributions on storm surges and tidal movements', *Report of the Delta Committee*, Vols. **2**, **3** and **4**, The Hague (1960).

DEFANT, A. *Physical Oceanography*, Vol. **II**, Pergamon, London (1961).

WELANDER, P. 'Numerical prediction of storm surges', *Adv. Geophys.* **8**, 316–79 (1961).

ROSSITER, J. R. 'Tides' in *Oceanography and Marine Biology* (edited by H. Barnes), Vol. **1**, Macmillan, London (1963).

GROEN, P. and GROVES, G. W. 'Surges' in *The Sea—Ideas and Observations* (edited by M. N. Hill), Chapter 17, Wiley Interscience, New York (1962).

Atlas der Gezeitenströme für die Nordsee, den Kanal und die Britischen Gewässer, Dt. Hydrogr. Inst., Hamburg (1963).

DRONKERS, J. J. *Tidal Computations for Rivers and Coastal Waters*, Amsterdam (1964).

CHAPTER 6

KRÜMMEL, O. *Handbuch der Ozeanographie*, Vol. **2**, Stuttgart (1911).

WÜST, G. 'Florida und Antillenstrom', *Veröff. Inst. Meeresk. Univ. Berlin* A.12, (1924).

SCHOTT, G. *Geographie des Indischen und des Stillen Ozeans*, Hamburg (1935).

DEFANT, A. 'Die absolute Topographie des physikalischen Meeresniveaus und der Druckflächen, sowie die Wasserbewegungen im Atlantischen Ozean', *Wiss. Ergebn. dt. atlant. Exped.* '*Meteor*', Vol. **VI**, Part 2, Chapter 5 (1941).

MEARS, E. G. 'The ocean current called "The Child"', *Smithsonian Report*, 245 (1943).

SANDSTRÖM, J. W. 'The Gulf Stream and the weather', *Ark. Mat. Astr. Fys.*, **30**, 1 (1944).

SCHOTT, G. *Geographie des Atlantischen Ozeans*, Hamburg (1942).

SVERDRUP, H. U., JOHNSON, M. W. and FLEMING, R. H. *The Oceans*, Chapters 10–13 and 15, Prentice-Hall, New York (1946).

ISELIN, C. O'D. and FUGLISTER, F. C. 'Some recent developments in the study of the Gulf Stream', *J. mar. Res.*, **VII**, 317 (1948).

RODEWALD, M. 'Golfstrom und Wetter', *Annln Met. Hamburg*, **1**, 65 (1948).

MODEL, F. 'Warmwasserheizung Europas', *Ber. dt. Wetterd. US-Zone* Nr. 12 (1950).

MUNK, W. H. 'On the wind-driven ocean circulation', *J. Met.*, **7**, 79 (1950).

FUGLISTER, F. C. and WORTHINGTON, L. V. 'Some results of a multiple ship survey of the Gulf Stream', *Tellus*, **3**, 1 (1951).

SCHOTT, G. 'Der Peru-Strom', *Erdkunde*, **5** (1951).

CHAPIN, H. and WALTON-SMITH, F. G. *The Ocean River, The Story of the Gulf Stream*, New York (1952).

CROMWELL, T. 'Circulation in a meridional plane in the Central Equatorial Pacific', *J. mar. Res.*, **12**, 196 (1953).

WORTHINGTON, L. V. 'Three detailed cross-sections of the Gulf Stream', *Tellus*, **6**, 116 (1954).

BÖHNECKE, G. 'Principles of measuring currents', *Publs scient. Ass. Oceanogr. phys.*, No. 14 (1955).

STOMMEL, H. 'A survey of ocean current theory', *Deep Sea Res.* **4**, 149 (1957).

WÜST, G. 'Stromgeschwindigkeiten und Strommengen in den Tiefen des Atlantischen Ozeans', *Wiss. Ergebn. dt. atlant. Exped.* '*Meteor*', **VI**, 2, 6 (1957).

STOMMEL, H. *The Gulf Stream*, C.U.P., London (1958).

HART, T. J. and CURRIE, R. J. 'The Benguela Current', *Discovery Reports*, **31**, 123–298 (1960).

VARIOUS AUTHORS, *The Cromwell Current*, *Deep Sea Research*, Vol. **6**, No. 4 (1960).

DEFANT, A. *Physical Oceanography*, Vol. **I**, Pergamon, London (1961).

ROBINSON, A. R. *Wind-driven Ocean Circulation*, Blaisdell, New York (1963).

VARIOUS AUTHORS, 'Currents' in *The Sea* (edited by M. N. Hill), Vol. **II**, Section III, Wiley, New York (1963).

CHAPTER 7

MURRAY, J., HJORT, J. and HELLAND HANSEN, B. 'Physical oceanography' in *The Depths of the Ocean*, Stechert, London (1912).

VAN RIEL, P. M. 'The bottom configuration in relation to the flow of the bottom water', '*Snellius' Expedition*, **II**, 2, Leiden (1934).

WÜST, G. and DEFANT, A. *Wiss. Ergebn dt. atlant. Exped.* '*Meteor*', Vol. **VI** (1935–6).

DEACON, G. E. R. 'The hydrology of the Southern Ocean', '*Discovery' Reports*, Vol. **XV** (1937).

VAN RIEL, P. M. 'The bottom water', '*Snellius' Expedition*, Vol. **II**, Part 5, Chapter 1, Leiden (1943).

SVERDRUP, H. U. 'The water masses and currents of the oceans' in *The Oceans*, Prentice-Hall, New York (1946).

MACKINTOSH, N. A. 'The Antarctic convergence and the distribution of surface temperatures in Antarctic waters', '*Discovery' Reports*, **XXIII**, 177 (1946).

WÜST, G., BROGMUS, W. and NOODT, E. 'Die zonale Verteilung von Salzgehalt, Niederschlag, Verdunstung, Temperatur und Dichte an der Oberfläche der Ozeane', *Kieler Meeresforsch.*, **10**, 137 (1954).

DIETRICH, G. 'Beitrag zu einer vergleichenden Ozeanographie des Weltmeeres', *Kieler Meeresforsch.*, **12**, 3 (1956).

VAN RIEL, P. M. 'The bottom water—temperature', '*Snellius' Expedition*, **II**, Part 5, Chapter 2, Leiden (1956).

STOMMEL, H. 'A survey of ocean current theory', *Deep Sea Res.* **4**, 149 (1957).

WÜST, G. 'Stromgeschwindigkeiten und Strommengen in den Tiefen des Atlantischen Ozeans', *Wiss. Ergebn. dt. atlant. Exped. 'Meteor'*, **VI**, Part 2, p. 6 (1957).

BOWDEN, K. F. 'Some recent studies of oceanic circulation', *J. Cons. perm. int. Explor. Mer*, **23**, 453 (1958).

POSTMA, H. 'Chemical results and a survey of water masses', '*Snellius' Expedition*, **II**, Part 8, Leiden (1958).

FUGLISTER, F. C. *Atlantic Ocean Atlas*, Woods Hole Oceanogr. Inst., Woods Hole, Mass. (1960).

STOMMEL, H., ARONS, A. B. and BOLIN, B. 'On the abyssal circulation of the world ocean', Parts I–IV, *Deep Sea Res.*, **6**, 2 (1960); **8**, 2 (1961).

HILL, M. N. (editor), *The Sea—Ideas and Observations* (Vol. **II**), Wiley, New York (1963).

INDEX